FUNDAMENTALS OF
PLANT PHYSIOLOGY

FUNDAMENTALS OF
PLANT PHYSIOLOGY

JAMES F. FERRY, Ph.D.
LIFE SCIENCES EDITOR, *ENCYCLOPEDIA OF SCIENCE AND TECHNOLOGY.*
FORMERLY, PROFESSOR OF BOTANY, ALABAMA POLYTECHNIC INSTITUTE

HENRY S. WARD, Ph.D.
PROFESSOR OF BOTANY, ALABAMA POLYTECHNIC INSTITUTE

THE MACMILLAN COMPANY · NEW YORK

SECOND PRINTING, 1966

LIBRARY OF CONGRESS CATALOG CARD NUMBER: 59-5100

THE MACMILLAN COMPANY, NEW YORK

COLLIER-MACMILLAN CANADA, LTD., TORONTO, ONTARIO

PRINTED IN THE UNITED STATES OF AMERICA

Respectfully dedicated to two men who constantly
inspired and encouraged us along the way

Dr. JOHN M. AIKMAN and Dr. P. D. STRAUSBAUGH

PREFACE

Increasing numbers of students in the liberal arts, in agriculture, and those preparing to teach are finding it desirable to know more about how plants grow, develop, and reproduce than they learn in a general introductory course in biology or botany. These students elect or are required to take additional training in plant science. A course in elementary plant physiology appears to serve this purpose better than any other.

The authors, like their colleagues in many institutions throughout the nation, have been called upon to develop a one-term undergraduate course in plant physiology suitable for students in various fields of learning. This textbook has grown out of the efforts to meet this need.

It is realized that many of the students for which such a course is intended have not taken organic chemistry, biochemistry, advanced physics, or higher mathematics. Therefore, it becomes mandatory to pitch the subject matter at a level which can be understood and used by students who do not have the benefit of advanced undergraduate training.

These and other considerations have imposed the necessity for brevity without sacrificing accuracy, for the selection of one or two logical and accepted explanations of certain plant phenomena from several possibilities, and, to a limited extent, for the review of plant processes usually covered in general biology or botany. For students who later decide to progress further into the study of plant physiology, this book serves to bridge the gap between the introductory studies and the more advanced courses either at the undergraduate or graduate level.

Many figures, graphs, and tables have been borrowed from plant science literature to illustrate how scientists go about obtaining answers to cause and effect relationships involved in plant processes, to emphasize how the separate findings of individual scientists can be blended together in developing better explanations of plant activities, and to supplement the written portions of the text.

When the authors undertook the preparation of this textbook, they were aware of the difficulty of assimilating pertinent facts of plant physiology from the rapidly changing literature and from the several divergent points of view. Nevertheless, it was decided that the most up-to-date and acceptable concepts would be presented. Should these become at variance with later and better concepts, it is expected that the subject matter of the book will be modified to incorporate any basic advancements made in the field.

ACKNOWLEDGMENT

Grateful acknowledgment is made to Dr. E. N. Transeau, Professor Emeritus of Botany, The Ohio State University, for advice regarding the organization of the subject matter, the sequence of topics, and other valuable suggestions; to Dr. P. D. Strausbaugh, Professor Emeritus of Botany, West Virginia University, for editing and criticizing several of the chapters and for helpful counsel regarding the level at which the subject matter is written and presented; to Dr. William B. Bunger, Professor of Chemistry, Alabama Polytechnic Institute, for reading and making suggestions on Chapter 3; to Dr. Howard E. Carr, Head of the Department of Physics, Alabama Polytechnic Institute, for technical advice on parts of Chapter 9; and to the several authors and publishers who granted permission to use certain quotations and illustrations.

Especially do we wish to express our gratitude to Dr. Harry J. Fuller, Professor of Botany, the University of Illinois, for his invaluable advice and assistance in putting the manuscript into its final form. Dr. Fuller not only suggested important modifications and additions, but he also edited every page for accuracy and readability. His broad understanding of the problem of teaching plant physiology to undergraduate students with limited background training provided us with sound guidance in our efforts.

CONTENTS

PREFACE   vii

1   THE IMPORTANCE OF PLANT PHYSIOLOGY IN PLANT SCI-
ENCE   1

2   GROWTH AND DEVELOPMENT—THE PRODUCT OF PHYSI-
OLOGY   6

3   SOME BASIC FACTS OF CHEMISTRY AND PHYSICS REQUIRED
IN THE STUDY OF PLANT PHYSIOLOGY   9

4   THE PLANT CELL   24

5   WATER RELATIONS OF PLANTS   37

6   MINERAL NUTRITION   62

7   PHYSIOLOGICAL SIGNIFICANCE OF SOILS AND SOIL MOIS-
TURE   82

8   SOIL-ROOT RELATIONS   98

9   RADIANT ENERGY AND THE CHLOROPLAST PIGMENTS   117

10   PHOTOSYNTHESIS   125

11   RESPIRATION   144

12   PLANT BIOSYNTHESES   160

13   DYNAMICS OF GROWTH   184

14   ENVIRONMENTAL FACTORS AND PLANT DEVELOPMENT   228

15   PLANT REACTIONS TO STIMULI   267

REFERENCES   273

INDEX   277

FUNDAMENTALS OF
PLANT PHYSIOLOGY

1.
THE IMPORTANCE OF PLANT PHYSIOLOGY IN PLANT SCIENCE

Students occasionally ask, "Why should I study plant physiology?" Trained agriculturists and others have realized for many years, however, that profitable production of field and forest crops is materially aided by a scientific knowledge of plant behavior. Fundamental investigations in plant physiology have contributed in many ways to improved methods of propagating, cultivating, and harvesting economically important plants, and to methods of handling and storing many plant products. Furthermore, control of fungous diseases and insect predators of plants often requires application of the principles of plant physiology. Much of the investigational work carried on by scientific agronomists, horticulturists, floriculturists, and foresters actually lies in the field of pure or applied plant physiology, although often it is not formally recognized as such (1).*

By way of illustration, it has been pointed out that the value of correlating facts in developing an understanding of the complexities of plant behavior may be seen when one considers the important problem of lodging of small grains. From a purely factual point of view, the following practices can be used effectively to reduce or minimize the danger of lodging of small grains: 1. reducing the rate of planting; 2. planting early in the spring; 3. using short growing, stiff strawed varieties; 4. using winter varieties wherever possible rather than spring varieties; 5. using early maturing varieties; and 6. restricting planting to soils less favorably situated with respect to available moisture and fertility.

---

* References indicated by the numbers in the parentheses are found in the References section on page 273.

Each of these control measures may be characterized as representing a single fact. Singly or in various combinations they can be effectively applied to reduce lodging. Here are six seemingly unrelated practices which are admittedly effective in solving the problem without providing an understanding as to why they are effective. In making use of fundamental principles in solving the problem of lodging of small grains, we first must familiarize ourselves with studies in plant physiology concerned with growth behavior of plants. Thus we learn that two kinds of growth characterize plant development, namely, growth in weight and growth by expansion. Available information indicates that growth in weight is favored by the following widely different conditions: 1. cool weather, especially cool nights; 2. abundant sunshine; 3. some limitations in available soil moisture and fertility; and 4. age or maturity of the plants. In general when these conditions prevail, growth is characterized by maximum accumulation of plant foods and good seed development. On the contrary growth by expansion is accelerated by: 1. warm weather, especially warm nights; 2. cloudy weather; 3. an abundance of available soil moisture and fertility; and 4. youth, or young vegetative stages of growth. When these conditions prevail, growth is frequently characterized by heavy or excessive vegetative development. Accumulation of food and seed development are much more limited under these conditions.

It is evident, therefore, that when conditions favor growth by expansion, small grains may grow so rank as to lodge. In the light of the conditions which favor growth by expansion, practical procedures become apparent which might be effectively applied to reduce lodging of small grains, namely: 1. plant as early in the spring as a good seedbed can be prepared to make the fullest possible use of the cooler spring weather; 2. reduce the rate of planting, a practice which opens the stand, thus permitting the entry of more light which in turn favors growth in weight rather than expansive growth; 3. plant early maturing varieties which will complete as much of their total seasonal growth as possible during the cooler part of the growing period; 4. plant fall varieties (when possible) rather than spring varieties because of their greater ability to make maximum use of the cool weather which prevails in late winter and early spring; 5. restrict insofar as possible the planting of small grains to soils which are less favorably situated with respect to available moisture and fertility.

Thus by applying known physiological facts to an important agronomic problem, it is possible to understand the reason for at least five of the six practices for reducing the hazard of lodging. Furthermore, and perhaps equally important, when the problem is approached in this manner, the practices which are effective in reducing lodging are not unrelated. It becomes readily apparent that each practice in turn is effective because it provides some measure of control of lodging of grain by reducing excessive growth by expansion.

Another example may be found in the fact that fields of canning peas and common beans are occasionally frozen back to the soil level when they are 2 to 3 inches tall. Will the plants die following such treatment or will they recover? Studies have been conducted which make it possible to predict with reasonable certainty that the canning peas will recover sufficiently to produce a fair to good crop, but that common beans will not and will have to be replanted. Or a somewhat more fundamental approach may be chosen in arriving at an explanation of this behavior. An important morphological difference in the emergence of peas and common beans from the soil can be applied directly to the solution of the problem. The seed leaves (cotyledons) of common beans are brought above the soil surface during germination (Figure 1), whereas in peas the seed leaves remain below ground in the soil. Emergence from the soil in common beans is accomplished by the elongation of the upper portion of the hypocotyl; whereas in the canning peas, stems emerge by elongation of the epicotyl. Consequently, buds capable of producing new stems remain alive on the portion of the primary stem of peas in the axils of the incomplete leaves below ground. Usually these buds are dormant, but in the event of injury to the portion of the primary stem above ground, the buds may become functional and produce new stems. In bean plants there are no buds remaining below the surface of the soil. In addition, the seed leaves which were raised above the soil surface during emergence and in which the major portion of the food supply is accumulated, were among the above ground parts destroyed. Thus, by making use of fundamental differences in the early growth and development of these two plants, one may predict with considerable assurance that the peas will recover, whereas the beans will not.

In another case the question is frequently asked whether growing properly inoculated alfalfa, sweet clover, or other clovers on relatively infertile to moderately fertile soils is an effective means of increasing the nitrogen content of the soil. Research results indicate clearly that the nitrogen content of the soil is not increased appreciably, if at all, by growing these legumes even though they are inoculated unless the

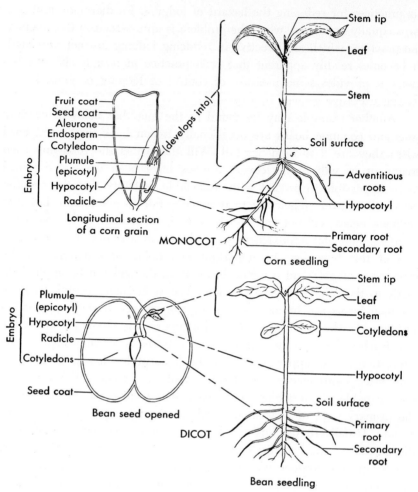

Figure 1 Angiosperm seeds and seedlings.

top growth is returned to the soil. About ⅔ of the total nitrogen in the plants is found in their top growth, and the remaining ⅓ in the roots. Likewise, when these legumes are inoculated, about ⅔ of the nitrogen fixed is obtained from nitrogen gas in the air, ⅓ from available nitrogen compounds in the soil. With this information at hand, it is readily apparent that if the top growth is removed as hay or grass silage and not returned to the land as "green manure," there will be no appreciable change in the nitrogen content of the soil (2).

Scientific investigations usually uncover new problems as they solve other problems. Consequently one experiment leads to others, more information is gathered, new theories are advanced, old ones are found unsatisfactory and are rejected or modified. Interpretations which seemed sufficient a few years ago may now be wholly inadequate. Lines of thinking are constantly subject to revision, and the search for truth goes on constantly. Although vast gaps still exist in our understanding of the physiology of plants, much more has been learned than is being used by many growers of crops. Failure to apply proven principles of plant physiology to crop production increases costs and retards progress. The fact that many questions remain unanswered is to be desired rather than regretted. Lack of knowledge creates the challenge, and the drive of curiosity constitutes the stimulus to push on toward ever better research and resulting explanations.

2.
GROWTH AND DEVELOPMENT—
THE PRODUCT OF PHYSIOLOGY

Practically everything we shall study in this course is in some way related to the growth of plants.

A preview of the study which lies ahead may be had by quickly reviewing some of the major features involved in the growth of a higher plant from a seed to maturity and the production of more seed. A seed contains accumulated food and usually a single embryo which developed from a fertilized egg by the processes of cell division, cell elongation, and cell differentiation (Figure 1). In many plant species the development of the embryo in a seed is arrested during a period of dormancy, at which time most of the physiological processes essential for life are slowed to a minimum. When dormancy is completed or broken, a seed will germinate if it has retained viability through the dormant period and if it is planted in or otherwise reaches a favorable environment. Germination involves a combination of many processes. When a seed is placed in a moist environment, external water molecules will start diffusing into the seed. As they pass through the seed coat, some of them will be adsorbed and cause the seed to swell by imbibition. Other water molecules will move by osmosis through the differentially permeable cytoplasmic membranes into the vacuoles of the living cells of the seed. The net increase in water content will also add to the internal pressure (turgor) but more importantly, the increased water is primarily responsible for the reactivation of the various controlling (enzyme) systems in the cells which, in turn, will step up all physiological processes in the seed. Respiration will be accelerated and the hydrolysis (digestion) of some of the accumulated foods to soluble forms will begin. The soluble foods will become translocated to the epicotyl tip (plumule) and

6

hypocotyl tip (radicle) or growing points of the embryo where the foods will supply energy and sustenance for growth. The seed will then resume active growth (germinate), and the epicotyl tip will develop into the shoot of the seedling, while the hypocotyl tip will give rise to the primary root. Once more by the combined processes of cell division, elongation, and differentiation, the primary root will produce secondary roots and these tertiary roots. The epicotyl will likewise ultimately produce the stem, branches, buds, and leaves, and eventually by reproductive development, the flowers, fruits, and seeds.

For a time the growth of the seedling will be dependent primarily upon moisture, enzymes, hormones, vitamins, and the accumulated food in the seed (endosperm or cotyledons). Soon, if everything goes well, chlorophyll synthesis will begin and the leaves of the young seedling will become green. Carbon dioxide will diffuse from the atmosphere into the chloroplasts of the chlorenchyma, and water will enter the roots by osmosis or as a result of transpiration. A large part of the water will then move to the leaves where much of it will be lost to the atmosphere by evaporation (transpiration). However, some of the water will enter the chloroplasts and react with carbon dioxide in the production of sugar by the process of photosynthesis. Minerals and gases dissolved in the soil solution and on the surface of soil particles will enter and move within the plant. Photosynthesis will usually be followed by the several other processes of food production such as starch, fat, and protein synthesis. The products of these syntheses may then be digested, translocated, and resynthesized; or they may be used in respiration and assimilation; or if in excess, they may accumulate in one or more tissues according to the hereditary constitution of the plant.

In time pollen will be produced in the anthers (male parts) of a flower, and it will be transferred in one or more ways (pollination) to the stigma (tip of the pistil or female part) of the flower. There the pollen will germinate and develop a pollen tube which will literally eat its way by enzymatic digestion through the stigma, style, and ovary, eventually reaching and penetrating the embryo sac where the egg has been formed. One of the sperms produced by the generative nucleus in the pollen tube will unite with and fertilize the egg forming a single cell (zygote) possessing hereditary characteristics of both the male and female. The zygote will begin the processes of cell division, elongation, and differentiation which will result in an embryo in some stage of development in the seed depending chiefly upon the species. In many species this initial growth of the embryo is temporarily retarded by a period of dormancy. When dormancy is completed or broken, this developmental cycle is repeated.

Thus it is seen that diffusion, imbibition, osmosis, active or passive absorption, mineral absorption, transpiration, chlorophyll synthesis, photosynthesis, starch synthesis (in most species), fat synthesis, protein synthesis, digestion, translocation, respiration, assimilation, and reproduction are all intimately involved in growth under the influence of environmental factors, enzymes, hormones, and vitamins. Let us turn now to developing a broader understanding of these and other closely related phenomena which influence plant behavior.

3.

SOME BASIC FACTS OF CHEMISTRY AND PHYSICS REQUIRED IN THE STUDY OF PLANT PHYSIOLOGY

The physical sciences are widely used in experimental work on plants. A knowledge of certain fundamental facts of physics and chemistry is essential for a broad understanding of physiological processes. More and more the laws of chemistry and physics make possible logical interpretations of plant activities. Inorganic chemistry, organic chemistry, physical chemistry, colloidal chemistry, and biochemistry,—all are indispensable tools for the student of plant behavior. Nuclear physics, which has given and continues to give us a better understanding of atomic structure and properties, now supplies information necessary for the development of sound explanations which only a few years ago were impossible.

One does not progress far with a study of plant structure and function until he is confronted with considerations which reach beyond the grosser features and activities of plants. A knowledge of the composition and nature of protoplasm, cell walls, tissues, organs—indeed the plant as a whole—involves phenomena in addition to those which may readily be observed. To understand the macroscopic or microscopic structures of plants and the processes responsible for the formation, modification, or destruction of these structures, it is necessary to consider the nature and properties of those invisible particles of which all matter is composed.

Plants are made up of numerous compounds each of which is composed of molecules of specific chemical composition. A molecule may be defined as the smallest particle into which a compound can be divided without changing the properties of that compound. Plant parts such as the protoplasmic structures and cell walls owe their properties both to the kinds of molecules of which they are composed and to the arrangement of these molecules. Each molecule, moreover, is made up of smaller units of matter called atoms which are definite in kind and in structural arrangement. The characteristic properties and reactions of the molecules of substances such as water, mineral salts, and organic compounds depend upon the organization and arrangement of these smaller units, the atoms. The properties of atoms likewise are determined by the still smaller units of which they are composed,—electrons, protons, and neutrons.

Atoms, Nuclei, Electrons, Protons, Neutrons and Isotopes.

Each atom is now known to consist of an extremely minute core called the nucleus which carries a positive electric charge. Associated with each nucleus there are negatively charged electrons, sufficient in number to balance the positive charge on the nucleus. If the nucleus has a positive (+) charge of 12, then there will be grouped around it 12 electrons, with a total of 12 negative (−) charges. The atom may be compared to our solar system in which the sun at the center corresponds to the nucleus of the atom and the planets moving about the sun in their respective orbits represent the electrons of the atom. The relative distances between the nucleus and its different electrons are of the same proportion as those lying between the sun and its several planets. For example, if all its atoms could be squeezed until the nuclei and the electrons were in actual contact, then the earth would occupy approximately the space of a large grapefruit. An atom, therefore, consists essentially of a nucleus, extremely minute dimensionally, surrounded by vast space in which are located the electrons that balance the charge of the nucleus.

The properties of an element are determined by its positive nuclear charge, and this is the atomic number of the element. Thus hydrogen with a nuclear charge of one has an atomic number of 1; helium with a nuclear charge of two has the atomic number 2; and lead with a nuclear charge of eighty-two has the atomic number 82 (Figure 2 and Table 1).

As previously stated, the atom as a whole is electrically neutral. The negatively charged electrons balance the positive charge of the nucleus. Thus, hydrogen has 1 electron, helium 2, and lead 82. The weight of the atom is concentrated in the nucleus which contains more than 99.9 per cent of the total weight of the atom. Thus we can see

Table 1 International atomic weights—1955. (*Journal of the American Chemical Society.*)

	SYMBOL	ATOMIC NUMBER	ATOMIC WEIGHT*		SYMBOL	ATOMIC NUMBER	ATOMIC WEIGHT*
Actinium	AC	89	227	Molybdenum	Mo	42	95.95
Aluminum	Al	13	26.98	Neodymium	Nd	60	144.27
Americium	Am	95	(243)	Neon	Ne	10	20.183
Antimony	Sb	51	121.76	Neptunium	Np	93	(237)
Argon	A	18	39.944	Nickel	Ni	28	58.71
Arsenic	As	33	74.91	Niobium			
Astatine	At	85	(210)	(Columbium)	Nb	41	92.91
Barium	Ba	56	137.36	Nitrogen	N	7	14.008
Berkelium	Bk	97	(249)	Osmium	Os	76	190.2
Beryllium	Be	4	9.013	Oxygen	O	8	16.00
Bismuth	Bi	83	209.00	Palladium	Pd	46	106.4
Boron	B	5	10.82	Phosphorus	P	15	30.975
Bromine	Br	35	79.916	Platinum	Pt	78	195.09
Cadmium	Cd	48	112.41	Plutonium	Pu	94	(242)
Calcium	Ca	20	40.08	Polonium	Po	84	210
Californium	Cf	98	(249)	Potassium	K	19	30.100
Carbon	C	6	12.011	Praseodymium	Pr	59	140.92
Cerium	Ce	58	140.13	Promethium	Pm	61	(145)
Cesium	Cs	55	132.91	Protactinium	Pa	91	231
Chlorine	Cl	17	35.457	Radium	Ra	88	226.05
Chromium	Cr	24	52.01	Radon	Rn	86	222
Cobalt	Co	27	58.94	Rhenium	Re	75	186.22
Copper	Cu	29	63.54	Rhodium	Rh	45	102.91
Curium	Cm	96	(245)	Rubidium	Rb	37	85.48
Dysprosium	Dy	66	162.51	Ruthenium	Ru	44	101.1
Erbium	Er	68	167.27	Samarium	Sm	62	150.35
Europium	Eu	63	152.0	Scandium	Sc	21	44.96
Fluorine	F	9	19.00	Selenium	Se	34	78.96
Francium	Fr	87	(223)	Silicon	Si	14	28.09
Gadolinium	Gd	64	157.26	Silver	Ag	47	107.880
Gallium	Ga	31	69.72	Sodium	Na	11	22.991
Germanium	Ge	32	72.60	Strontium	Sr	38	87.63
Gold	Au	79	197.0	Sulfur	S	16	32.066
Hafnium	Hf	72	178.50	Tantalum	Ta	73	180.95
Helium	He	2	4.003	Technetium	Tc	43	(99)
Holmium	Ho	67	164.94	Tellurium	Te	52	127.61
Hydrogen	H	1	1.0080	Terbium	Tb	65	158.93
Indium	In	49	114.82	Thallium	Tl	81	204.39
Iodine	I	53	126.91	Thorium	Th	90	232.05
Iridium	Ir	77	192.2	Thulium	Tm	69	168.94
Iron	Fe	26	55.85	Tin	Sn	50	118.70
Krypton	Kr	36	83.80	Titanium	Ti	22	47.90
Lanthanum	La	57	138.92	Uranium	U	92	238.07
Lead	Pb	82	207.21	Vanadium	V	23	50.95
Lithium	Li	3	6.940	Wolfram			
Lutetium	Lu	71	174.99	(Tungsten)	W	74	183.86
Magnesium	Mg	12	24.32	Xenon	Xe	54	131.30
Manganese	Mn	25	54.94	Ytterbium	Yb	70	173.04
Mendelevium	Mv	101	(256)	Yttrium	Y	39	88.92
Mercury	Hg	80	200.61	Zinc	Zn	30	65.38
				Zirconium	Zr	40	91.22

* A value given in brackets denotes the mass number of the isotope of longest known half-life.

that the weight of an electron is relatively very little, and that the weight of the atom, commonly called the atomic weight, is essentially the weight of its nucleus.

The real weight of an oxygen atom is exceedingly small (0.000,000,-000,000,000,000,000,000,059 pounds), as are the weights of all other atoms. To eliminate the necessity of using cumbersome fractions such as this, an atomic weight of 16 was assigned to oxygen, and the atomic weights of all other atoms are computed on this basis. Therefore, atomic weights are relative and vary from the lightest atom, hydrogen, to the heaviest naturally occurring element, uranium, that is, from 1 to 238.1 respectively. A few intermediate examples are carbon 12, oxygen 16, iron 55.8, silver 107.9, and mercury 200.6.

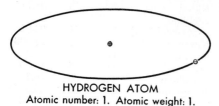

HYDROGEN ATOM
Atomic number: 1. Atomic weight: 1.

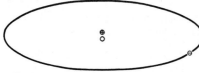

DEUTERIUM (Heavy Hydrogen) ATOM
Atomic number: 1. Atomic weight: 2.

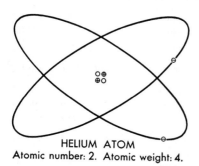

HELIUM ATOM
Atomic number: 2. Atomic weight: 4.

e = Electron   ⊕ = Proton   o = Neutron

Figure 2   Examples of atomic structure.

Inside the nucleus there are protons and neutrons, one or more of each. These differ in that the protons have a (+) charge, whereas neutrons have no charge at all. For example, hydrogen has an atomic number of 1, and an atomic weight of 1. In view of the foregoing, the conclusion must be drawn that the hydrogen atom has a nucleus which consists of a single proton and nothing else. On the other hand helium has an atomic number of 2 and an atomic weight of 4. This indicates that the nucleus has a (+) charge of 2 and therefore consists of 2 protons. However, helium has an atomic weight of 4 and hence in addition to the 2 protons, there must be 2 neutrons to make the atomic weight 4. Uranium has an atomic weight of 238 and an atomic number of 92. Uranium must therefore have 92 protons, and the remainder of its weight must be made up of neutrons, giving 238 minus 92, or 146 neutrons. The mass of the proton is approximately the same as that of the neutron.

To summarize: For each electron in the space surrounding the nucleus, the nucleus itself has a proton with an opposite charge. The weight of the nucleus, which is approximately the atomic weight of the atom, is the sum of the weights of its protons and neutrons, the weight of the electrons being negligible. The number of protons in the nucleus is the atomic number of the element.

It has been discovered that two atoms may have identical nuclear charges (therefore identical atomic numbers) and yet have different atomic weights. Such atoms are called isotopes. For example, about 28 years ago, a heavy isotope of hydrogen was discovered. Its atomic number is 1, but its atomic weight is 2. That means it consists of 1 proton and 1 neutron. This is considerably at variance with conventional hydrogen which has 1 proton and nothing else in the nucleus. The heavy isotoype of hydrogen is called deuterium. Only 1 deuterium atom occurs in 5000 atoms of ordinary hydrogen. Hence, it has practically no effect on the average atomic weight of hydrogen. On the other hand, 75 per cent of ordinary chlorine gas atoms have a weight of 35, and 25 per cent have a weight of 37. Thus the average atomic weight of chlorine is 35.46,—by no means a whole number in itself, but made up of isotope atoms with a different whole number of neutrons in the nucleus. Were it not for these isotopes, all atomic weights would consist of whole numbers since they represent an accumulation of weights of protons and neutrons each of which has a relative weight of approximate unity.

This brief discussion of the nucleus indicates the essential ground work on which rest the transmutations and the release of enormous energy beyond anything obtainable by ordinary chemical reactions. It is the core of the atom, namely the nucleus, which forms the basis of radioactive isotopes for both tracer work and therapy, for radioactive iodine used in the treatment of thyroid cancers, for autoradiography, for the probing of the biologists into the fundamentals of life by creating mutations, and for the selective killing of harmful bacteria. The nucleus of the atom is the basis of attack for the chemist and the industrial scientist in improving the properties of materials and alloys.

A knowledge of the different states of matter and their interrelationships is of material assistance in the understanding and interpretation of plant behavior. To appreciate protoplasm as the medium in which the varied and complex chemical and physical processes of the living cell occur, we find it necessary to consider certain properties of matter. In addition to the familiar solid, liquid, and gaseous states, we must learn about three others of particular importance to living organisms:

1. solutions; 2. emulsions; and 3. colloidal suspensions. By careful manipulation of these physical and chemical systems, man has been able to reproduce artificially many of the processes of plants and animals and to discover phenomena characteristic of life.

SOLUTIONS

The molecules of salts, acids, and bases are to some extent further separated or dissociated into ions (electrically charged atoms or groups of atoms called radicals). An ion bearing one or more positive charges of electricity is called a cation, for example, K^+, H^+, NH_4^+, Ca^{++}. An ion bearing one or more negative charges of electricity is known as an anion, for example, Cl^-, OH^-, NO_3^-, SO_4^{--}. When two kinds of atoms remain joined together and behave in a chemical reaction as though they were a single ion, the atomic partnership or group is called a radical.

If a soluble substance such as ordinary table salt (NaCl) is dissolved in water, some of its particles become subdivided and separated as molecules and ions. The water is designated as the solvent; the substance dissolved and distributed in the solvent is the solute. Thus a simple solution may be defined as a system in which one component (the solute) is uniformly dispersed throughout a second component (the solvent) in the form of molecules only or of molecules and ions. Many organic substances, however, are insoluble or only slightly soluble in water.

Therefore, particles in true solutions are molecules or molecules and ions. Since they are usually less than 0.001 of a micron (μ) in diameter (a micron $= 1/1000$ of a millimeter), molecules and ions are sub-ultramicroscopic in visibility. Solutions will absorb but not diffract (scatter) light waves. Moreover, true solutions are essentially homogeneous and once formed, they will never settle out unless conditions are changed in such a way as to alter solubility of the solute. (Some substances will dissolve readily in hot water, but when the water is cooled, the solute, or a part of it, settles out.)

Solutions in living plants provide the media in which the major movement of materials from cell to cell takes place. Solutions occur in the cell walls, cytoplasm, plastids, nucleus, and vacuole. Solutions constitute important systems within all living protoplasm and may be either aqueous or non-aqueous, although the latter are relatively unimportant in plants. Plant solutions may contain acids, bases, salts, and soluble organic substances, and thus their properties vary.

Soil solutions are extremely important to living plants. Soil water accelerates the ionization of minerals. The soil water does not carry the minerals into the roots, but the water serves rather as a solvent in which the minerals separate into molecules and ions. As ions, the minerals may move into or out of the roots independently of the water molecules.

Methods of Stating The Concentration Of Solutions.

Based on concentration, at least six kinds of solutions are important in the study of plant physiology. Volume molar solutions are made by adding water to the molecular weight in grams of any soluble substance until the total volume is one liter. This kind of solution is frequently referred to as a molar solution and is often designated with the symbol M. A millimole is $1/1000$ of an M. Weight molar solutions are made by dissolving the molecular weight in grams of the substance in 1000 grams of water. This type of solution is sometimes called a molal solution. A weight percentage solution may be prepared by taking the percentage of the desired substance in grams and adding the required amount of water in grams. Thus, for most practical purposes, a 10 per cent sodium chloride solution may be prepared by dissolving 10 grams of NaCl in 90 grams (approximately 90 cc.) of water. Solutions of solids in water or other solvents are often made on a weight percentage basis. A volume percentage solution is made by taking the percentage of the substance required in cubic centimeters (milliliters) and diluting to 100 cc. Hence, for general usage, a 10 per cent solution of alcohol may be prepared by adding 10 cc. of alcohol to 90 cc. of water. A normal solution contains one gram–equivalent of the solute in one liter of solution (not one liter of the solvent). An equivalent weight of a compound is that amount of it which will interact with one equivalent weight of an element. For example, the formula–weight of HCl (36.47 g.) is also an equivalent weight, for it contains 1.008 g. of hydrogen and this amount of hydrogen is displaceable by one equivalent weight of a metal. On the other hand H_2SO_4 (98.08 g.) contains two equivalents. Therefore, $1N$. H_2SO_4 equals $98.08 \div 2$ or 49.04 g. per liter of solution. $AlCl_3$ (133.3 g.) contains three equivalents, hence $1N$. $AlCl_3$ equals $133.3 \div 3$ or 44.4 g. per liter of solution. A milliequivalent is $1/1000$ of an equivalent. A solution containing 1 part per million of solute is made by dissolving 1 milligram of the solute in 1 liter of solvent. A saturated solution is one in which the maximum amount of the solute is uniformly dispersed throughout the solvent at any given temperature and pressure. In studying the mechanisms of mineral absorption by plant cells, the plant physiologist often uses three methods of expressing the concentrations of the nutrient elements in water solution: milliequivalents per liter, parts per million per liter, and millimoles per liter.

Types Of Solutions.

There are six possible combinations: gas in gas; gas in solid; solid in solid; gas in liquid; liquid in liquid; and solid in liquid. Of these, the last three are most important in plants.

INTERFACIAL PHENOMENA

At this point it is appropriate to consider some other properties of molecules. The molecules of any substance are constantly in motion due to their intrinsic molecular energy. The energy of molecular motion is correlated with heat and is directly proportional to the absolute temperature. Apparently at minus 273°C. (absolute zero) there is no molecular motion. The heat energy of the environment is therefore the primary source of energy of the movement of molecules of various kinds. The radiation of energy from the sun is the principal source of the heat energy of the earth's surface, and this, in turn, becomes the source of the energy of molecular motion in plants and all other objects on the earth. Other factors remaining constant, increase in temperature will result in an increase in molecular motion or vice versa as demonstrated by the rise and fall of the mercury in a thermometer when the temperature fluctuates. Molecules are very small with relatively tremendous spaces separating them. Some appreciation of these facts may be had when it is recalled that if it were possible to compress the earth until all the molecules, atoms, electrons and protons were squeezed together, the world would be about the size of a large grapefruit; or it has been stated that if each individual molecule in a glass of water could be increased to approximately the size of a pea seed, the distance between any two molecules would be about thirty miles. If other conditions remain unchanged, molecular activity (that is, pressure) becomes greater with increase in concentration of any particular kind of molecule per unit volume. In other words, the greater the number of molecules of a substance which are crowded into any given space, the greater the molecular activity.

Molecular activity may also be influenced by what has been called freedom of movement; the latter involves the forces of cohesion and adhesion. Cohesion may be defined as the mutual attraction of like molecules, for example, water for water. On the other hand adhesion is the attraction of unlike particles, for example, cell wall materials or protoplasm for water. Referring to the effects of temperature on molecular motion, it was pointed out that the higher the temperature the greater the movement of the molecules involved. Likewise the faster the motion of any particular kind of molecule, the less the cohesive force or lines of attraction between such molecules. In ice the temperature is relatively low, the activity of the water molecules is reduced, and the force of cohesion is increased. If heat is applied, the temperature is raised, the activity of the water molecules is increased, the force of cohesion is reduced, and the ice melts or changes to liquid water. If still more heat is applied, the motion of the water molecules may be increased to the point where cohesion is no longer effective and the water molecules pass off as a gas or vapor. These phenomena are reversible. Thus in solids cohesive forces reduce the freedom of dispersal of molecules, whereas in gases the motion of the molecules under ordinary temperatures and pressure is sufficient to offset lines of attraction. When the molecules of one substance are held close to the surface of another substance due to adhesion, the phenomenon is known as adsorption. If the adsorption is simply a physical "holding" of one kind of molecule by another kind, it is referred to as interfacial or mechanical adsorption, for example, water on glass. If in addition to the physical attraction between two unlike kinds of molecules a chemical reaction occurs, it is called chemical adsorption; for example, the familiar reaction of iodine solution with starch in which the starch stains blue-black is often considered to be a kind of chemical adsorption. Most surfaces when wet bear an electrical charge. Cellulose, in common with many other substances, acquires a negative charge when immersed in water. If a strip of cellulose paper is dipped in an aqueous solution of a dye the particles of which bear positive charges, the dye particles will be electrically adsorbed on the negatively charged cellulose surfaces, that is, they are held to the surface of the cellulose by the forces of electrical attraction. If on the other hand the dye particles in solution bear negative charges, they will be repelled by the cellulose. If the movement of a liquid into small spaces or through extremely minute tubes is brought about by the interaction of the forces of cohesion and adhesion, the phenomenon is known as capillarity. The movement of molecules between two dry glass slides when dipped in water, the slow movement of water through the capillary pore spaces (micropores) of a soil, and the limited rise of water in the xylem vessels of some plants are examples of capillarity. A state known as dynamic equilibrium is reached when equal numbers of molecules of any substance are moving in all directions simultaneously. As an example, when equal numbers of water molecules are passing across a membrane in both directions per unit of time, the system is said to be in a state of dynamic equilibrium. Mass movement is the bodily movement of groups of molecules occasioned by extrinsic energy or forces originating outside those molecules, that is, energy other than their own intrinsic energy. A log carried along by the flow of a river, a landslide, or the movement of bodies of air due to convection currents are examples of mass movement. Unless it affects temperature or pressure, mass movement will neither accelerate nor decrease the molecular movement of the individual molecules.

The last type of molecular behavior which will be considered at this time is that which is commonly referred to as surface tension. When a liquid like water forms an interface with a gas or mixture of gases such as air, the molecules of the liquid become both definitely arranged and more concentrated in the surface layer than they are in the body of the liquid. This contributes to the tenacity of the surface layer or film. Every molecule in the surface layer of the liquid is strongly pulled toward the interior by the molecules beneath it. Since there is no outward pull which equals these internally directed forces, the surface layer of molecules in the liquid is constantly under tension. This can be demonstrated by horizontally lowering a clean needle on a water surface. The surface film of water will support the needle even though the needle has a much greater specific gravity than the water. Although the term surface tension is sometimes restricted to tensions developed at the surface of a liquid when in contact with a gas, such tensions are not confined to boundaries between liquids and gases. When a solid and a liquid or two immiscible liquids form an interface, the abutting layers of molecules are subject to strain, and the tensions developed are called interfacial tensions. Surface tension is merely one variety of interfacial tension. Since rise in temperature increases the kinetic energy of molecules which in turn acclerates molecular motion and reduces cohesion, it follows that as temperature is increased, surface tension decreases. Furthermore as regards water, most organic compounds reduce surface tension, whereas most inorganic salts when dissolved in water increase its surface tension. For example, the attraction between an alcohol molecule and a water molecule is less than that between two water molecules. On the other hand the molecules of most inorganic salts attract water molecules more strongly than the water molecules attract each other. Thus in the latter surface tension is increased in the liquid.

EMULSIONS AND COLLOIDAL SUSPENSIONS

If 10 grams of coarse sand free from dust are placed in a flask containing 100 cc. of water and shaken vigorously, it will be observed that the sand will settle out immediately when no longer agitated. If the sand is then pulverized and again shaken in 100 cc. of water, a murky mixture designated as an ordinary suspension will result which will not settle out for hours or even days. If it were possible to grind the sand into molecules and these were then added to water, a true solution would result in which the sand molecules would remain dispersed indefinitely. However, before the grains of sand could be ground or subdivided into individual molecules, particles so small would occur that, if shaken with water, there would result a mixture possessing characteristics different from those either of an ordinary suspension or of a a true solution. Such a heterogeneous mixture, intermediate between a suspension and a solution, is called a colloidal suspension. The solid particles (molecular aggregates or micelles) so scattered form the dispersed or discontinuous phase, and the medium in which they are distributed or suspended is called the dispersion medium or continuous phase. Organizations of matter of this kind are known as colloidal systems and these are very important in plants.

A colloidal suspension is a system in which the particles of the dispersed or discontinuous phase are entirely separated by the particles of the intervening dispersion medium or continuous phase, for example, very fine sulfur particles in water. (In colloidal suspensions, the dispersed phase is composed of micelles, or rarely very large molecules such as those of certain proteins and organic dyes which are more than 0.001 μ in diameter.) Emulsions are systems in which one liquid is dispersed throughout another with which it is virtually immiscible, the particles of the dispersed liquid exceeding 0.1 μ in diameter, for example, milk. A sol is a colloidal system which possesses the property of fluidity at room temperature (20° C.). A gel is a colloidal system which is a "liquid solid" at room temperature, being more or less elastic, for example, gelatin, jellies, and agar. Gelation is the change of a sol to a gel; solation is the change of a gel to a sol. Hydrophilic (water-loving) sols are systems in which one or more molecules of water become associated with (hydration) each of the particles of the dispersed phase, for example, agar, gelatin, starch, and gum acacia. Hydrophobic (water-fearing) sols do not involve water of hydration, that is, water molecules do not become associated with the dispersed particles of the system.

Most colloidal systems composed of metallic molecular aggregates dispersed in water are examples of hydrophobic sols.

As previously explained, the particles in colloidal suspensions are micelles or molecular aggregates, more rarely very large molecules, and they range in diameter from 0.001μ to 0.1μ. These particles can be detected under the ultra-microscope by light diffraction. Colloidal suspensions are very dilute; they possess electrical conductivity; they are not viscous; they display Brownian movement; and they are readily precipitated by electrolytes (very small amounts being required) or by suspensions of opposite charge. Particles of suspension size are very common in many soils, and because of their effect upon water retention, play an important role in the environment of roots.

The particles in emulsions are also molecular aggregates, the particles of the dispersed liquid exceeding 0.1μ in diameter. These particles likewise are visible under the microscope. Emulsions possess electrical conductivity. They may be precipitated by large amounts of salts of alkalies (salts of Na, K, and others which occur as soaps in plant cells). Precipitation is reversible. A reversible emulsion added to a suspension makes precipitation of the suspension difficult or impossible. Emulsions gelate at low temperatures and solate at higher temperatures. Protein emulsions may be coagulated by removal of water by heat, 95 per cent ethyl alcohol, freezing, acids, and certain enzymes. Examples of oil-in-water emulsions are milk, cream, mayonnaise, and latex. Butter is an example of a water-in-oil emulsion.

Emulsions generally lack stability unless there is also present in the system an emulsifier or emulsifying agent. In the absence of an emulsifier, the two components of an emulsion, such as milk, rapidly separate, and the oil, being the component of lower specific gravity, rises to the top. Some emulsifying agents commonly used are soaps, saponins, gelatin, proteins, and gum acacia which is employed to stabilize many pharmaceutical preparations. Emulsions are not generally considered to be true colloidal systems, but like suspensions they approach colloidal systems in properties.

Colloidal systems in living plants may be present in the cell walls, cytoplasm, plastids, nucleus, and vacuoles. They may occur either as sols or gels in protoplasm and are intimately associated with true solutions.

Of all the features of colloidal systems, the tremendous surface exposed is perhaps the most important because of the significant increase in energy relations and associated phenomena. For example, a one-centimeter cube has a surface of 6 square centimeters, but when disintegrated into particles of colloidal size, the combined surfaces of all the resulting particles are approximately equal to 1.5 acres. Appreciation of this fact enables us to understand better how so many dynamic life processes can occur simultaneously in the extremely minute droplet of protoplasm in each individual living cell.

Types of Colloidal Systems.
The following table lists some general types of colloidal systems.

Table 2 General types of colloidal systems

TYPES	EXAMPLES
1. Solid-in-solid	Some alloys, certain types of colored glass, some precious stones (e.g. black diamond).
2. Solid-in-liquid	Many sols (e.g. sulfur in water).
3. Solid-in-gas	Smoke, fine dust clouds, certain fumes.
4. Liquid-in-solid	Certain minerals and gems (e.g. pearls).
5. Liquid-in-liquid	Many sols (e.g. kerosene in water).
6. Liquid-in-gas	Clouds, fogs, mists.
7. Gas-in-solid	Some minerals. An uncommon type of colloidal system.
8. Gas-in-liquid	Some foams. An uncommon type of colloidal system.

Gas-in-gas systems do not exist, since gases do not form molecular aggregates. Of the eight types listed, the solid-in-liquid and liquid-in-liquid systems have by far the greatest importance from the standpoint of living organisms. Examples of emulsions and colloidal suspensions in addition to those listed above are milk, cream, butter, mayonnaise, egg albumin, enzymes, gelatin, agar, latex, and pectic compounds.

Tyndall Phenomenon.
If pure water or a true solution is placed in a clean bottle having parallel sides and an intense beam of light is passed through the bottle, observation at right angles to the path of the light will disclose no trace of the light. Such a liquid is said to be optically empty. If on the other hand the bottle is filled with a hydrophobic sol and again observed in the manner described, the path of the light through the sol will be clearly delineated by a murky cone. The broader the base of the cone, the more prominent the effect. The intensity of the effect varies with the density and/or size of the dispersed molecular aggregates. This phenomenon, known as the Tyndall phenomenon, is due to the scattering or diffraction of light from the surface of colloidal particles, and was named for the man who discovered it. Hydrophilic sols also exhibit the Tyndall effect, but usually much less prominently than hydrophobic sols.

The ultramicroscope utilizes the principle of the Tyndall phenomenon. Colloidal particles cannot be observed directly by means of the ultramicroscope, but the number or density of particles in a given volume of sol may be determined since the light diffracted from their surfaces can be seen. Although it reveals little regarding the actual size and shape of the dispersed particles, the Tyndall phenomenon can be used to distinguish colloidal systems from solutions, and therefore it is useful in the study of protoplasm and other complex systems.

Brownian Movement.

If a drop of a hydrophobic sol, such as the sulfur suspension previously described, is placed in the concavity of a clean, hollow-ground, hanging drop slide and observed with the high power of a microscope, the dispersed particles will be seen to be undergoing a jostling, zig-zag movement. Such particles suspended in a liquid like water are continually bombarded by the molecules of the liquid. The impact of the molecules is not equal on all sides of a particle at any given moment. Thus the particle is driven back and forth. Brownian movement is caused by the kinetic activity of the molecules of the solvent and is the nearest approach we have to actual visible evidence of the validity of the kinetic theory of matter. It almost brings before our eyes the so-called "dance of the molecules." Increase in temperature accelerates the rate of Brownian movement because of an increase in the kinetic energy of the solvent molecules.

Brownian movement is evidenced by smaller bacteria when suspended in water, by solid-in-gas colloids such as smoke, and in the protoplasm of many plant species. The smaller the volume and/or mass of the suspended particles, the more vigorous the movement. Likewise the less viscous the liquid, the more vigorous is the molecular bombardment and hence the more rapid the movement of the particles.

Coagulation, Flocculation, and Precipitation.

If egg albumin is heated in a water bath to approximately 60° C., or if it is mixed with equal parts of 95 per cent ethyl alcohol, the albumin becomes a white semi-solid; the resulting physical change is commonly referred to as coagulation. The large protein molecules of the albumin are enclosed in one or more layers or shells of water molecules, the latter often referred to as water of hydration. In the first instance mentioned above the increased temperature increases the kinetic energy of the water molecules to the extent that their molecular activity offsets the lines of force holding them to the protein molecules and the water moves away. This enables the protein molecules to agglomerate or coagulate. In the second case the alcohol has a greater affinity for the water molecules than the protein, thus the water again leaves the protein molecules and coagulation occurs. Physiologically active protoplasm has a high protein content. When exposed to very high or low temperatures, to high concentrations of salts, or to various other factors, protoplasm may be irreversibly coagulated. Clay soils under certain conditions exhibit the properties of hydrophilic sols and therefore may manifest flocculation, a kind of behavior similar to coagulation. There is a close analogy between the coagulation or flocculation of a hydrophobic sol by an electrolyte and a precipitation reaction between one electrolyte and another.

The attributes which collectively we recognize as life reside in the protoplasm, which is a complex colloidal system of proteins, carbohydrates, fats, and lipoids permeated by a water solution of soluble organic and inorganic molecules and ions, many of which are highly reactive. It is apparent, then, that protoplasm is a complex of chemical and physical systems, no one constituent of which is living. The qualities that distinguish protoplasm from non-living systems result from the unique organization of atoms, ions, molecules, and colloidal particles with their associated chemical, electrical, and surface energies. Thereforce, it should be evident that successful propagation, intelligent management, and profitable production of field and forest crops may be materially aided by a knowledge of living protoplasm.

4.
THE PLANT CELL

A microscopic examination of any plant will reveal that it is composed of one or more structural and functional units called cells. Robert Hooke in about 1665 used the term cell to describe the small compartments or units which he observed in thin sections of commercial cork. As originally introduced, the term was restricted to the tiny "rooms" surrounded by non-living cell walls. Subseqent studies revealed that within the walls of many cells there is a complex substance which came to be known as protoplasm. Still later researches disclosed that this substance is made up of many important parts and materials, and that it is the delicate interrelationships or organization of these various individually non-living constituents that is physically and chemically responsible for the collective attributes which we recognize as life. As generally used today, the term cell includes the wall and everything enclosed within it as shown in Figures 3 and 4.

The size and shape of a plant are due in a large measure to the development and arrangement of its individual cells. Furthermore, the activities of an organism are the results of the combined and interrelated physical and chemical processes which occur in its cells. It is the growth and differentiation of the cells in plants which bring about the formation of various organs such as leaves, stems, and roots. Therefore, if we are to understand plants and be able to utilize them and their products more effectively, we must have a working knowledge of the physical and chemical nature of the units of which they are composed and the processes which take place in these units.

The Physicochemical Nature of Protoplasm

It is well established that most biological problems lead ultimately to a consideration of one phase or another of the more fundamental

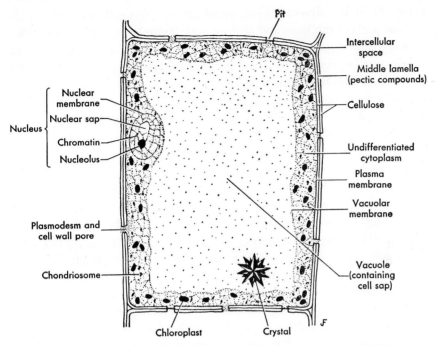

Pit
Intercellular space
Middle lamella (pectic compounds)
Nuclear membrane
Cellulose
Nuclear sap
Nucleus
Chromatin
Nucleolus
Undifferentiated cytoplasm
Plasma membrane
Vacuolar membrane
Plasmodesm and cell wall pore
Chondriosome
Vacuole (containing cell sap)
Chloroplast   Crystal

Figure 3 Diagram of a living plant cell exaggerated to show important parts.

aspects of the structure, constitution, and physicochemical properties of protoplasm. Protoplasm has been variously defined as the living substance of which all organisms are composed, as the physical and

chemical basis of all life phenomena, and as a living system composed of individually non-living materials. Such definitions are interesting but too general to convey much specific information. What, then, is known about this complex of chemical and physical systems which is so widely regarded as the seat of all life activity?

It can be said that the protoplasm of a cell as a whole can carry

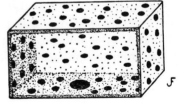

Figure 4 Three-dimentional diagram of a plant cell with front face removed. In general, plant cells have length, width, and depth, but may have as many as fourteen sides or faces when young.

on all the processes essential for life, and further that it can carry on several of these processes simultaneously. Living matter (protoplasm) is distinguished by complexity of function and variability of structure, and also by its ability to manufacture more of itself from non-living materials. It is different, either chemically or physically or both, in the various parts of the same cell (for example, cytoplasm, nucleus, plastids). Moreover, protoplasm is not the same in all cells of the same plant. While it is somewhat different in various species, particularly in the make-up of chromosomes and genes, nevertheless protoplasm is fundamentally the same in all living organisms.

Protoplasm is extremely reactive, having the ability to change rapidly in chemical composition and physical structure from moment to moment. A complex of dynamic, unstable systems of many non-living substances, exact chemical analyses of protoplasm precisely as it exists in living cells are not possible, for when living protoplasm is subjected to analysis, it becomes disorganized and its properties undergo marked changes. Various techniques have been utilized to investigate the substances present after the protoplasmic system has been disturbed. These studies show that water is the chief inorganic component of all physiologically active plant protoplasm, frequently making up 90 per cent or more of the system; that proteins and other nitrogen-containing compounds constitute the bulk of the organic matter present, amounting to as much as 65 per cent of the dry weight; that lipids (fatty substances) are likewise present but in smaller amounts; and that protoplasm also contains carbohydrates, organic acids, and minerals, many of which are soluble in water.

Protoplasm, instead of being a simple substance, is a highly organized system of complex substances capable of growth, motility, reproduction, and other remarkable powers characteristic of life. It should be emphasized, however, that life exists only so long as the organization of the protoplasmic system is maintained. Therefore, the properties of protoplasm result not only from the kinds of substances present in it, but also from the physical and chemical interrelationships which occur among these substances.

THE PROTOPLAST

The term protoplast is used here in its broadest sense to designate all the contents of a living plant cell, exclusive of the wall (Figure 3).

Cytoplasm.

Although that part of the protoplasm known as cytoplasm is frequently semitransparent and granular in appearance due to the presence of food particles and other substances, it may assume various colors and aspects. The cytoplasm of active cells is miscible in water if not enclosed in a membrane, and it is somewhat elastic. Cells which are physiologically active have cytoplasm of low viscosity (4 or 5 times that of water), while in dormant cells the cytoplasm may become almost rigid. The cytoplasm in living cells may change rapidly in response to variations in temperature, differences in acidity, dehydration, mechanical injury, electric shock, and exposure to various chemical compounds. Cytoplasm may therefore range in physical state from a fluid (sol) to a jelly-like consistency (gel) and vice versa. Such changes are frequently referred to as solation and gelation and are reversible within certain limits without apparent injury to the living matter. However, if the water surrounding the proteinaceous constituents of the cytoplasm is removed, coagulation occurs. Coagulation may be brought about by temperatures of 60 degrees centigrade or above, alcohols, various electrolytes, electric currents, freezing, mechanical pressure, and by certain wave lengths of light or radiant energy, especially ultraviolet radiation, X-rays, and radium radiations. Coagulation is usually irreversible, and it generally results in death. Although cytoplasm has electrical properties, its electrical conductivity appears to be low. The cytoplasm at one end of a cell may have an electrical charge different from that at the other end, a condition frequently referred to as polarization. Under usual growing conditions, the cytoplasm of a living cell may undergo a type of movement called streaming or cyclosis. It is not known definitely why such movement occurs, although it is believed to be influenced by polarity within the cells. Cyclosis may be accelerated by increases in temperature (up to the point of injury), by dilute concentrations of toxic substances (for example, a 1 per cent solution of $CuSO_4$), by narcotics, by thiamine hydrochloride (vitamin B_1), and by light perhaps as it affects temperature. It may be inhibited by low temperatures, absence of oxygen, or anesthetics in relatively high concentrations.

Water is the chief inorganic component of all physiologically active cytoplasm ranging from more than 90 per cent in some cells to as low as 4 or 5 per cent in the cells of stored seeds. The water content constantly changes with the degree of activity of the cytoplasm and with the growth and maturation of cells. Nevertheless, a highly aqueous medium is essential for the rapid and varied chemical and physical processes which are constantly taking place in active living cytoplasm. In addition to water, cytoplasm contains, as already stated, a multitude of other substances such as carbohydrates, fats and oils, proteins and other nitrogenous materials, organic acids, pigments, and minerals. Of these various materials, proteins and other nitrogen-containing compounds constitute the bulk of the organic matter present.

Where the cytoplasm is in contact with the cell wall, with a vacuole, or with the nucleus interfacial tensions occur and there is formed a surface layer which differs considerably in its properties from the undifferentiated cytoplasm. Such layers, which are too thin to be visible under the microscope, are called membranes. That part of the cytoplasm adjoining the cell wall is often designated the plasma membrane, while that adjoining a vacuole is called a vacuolar membrane. That these membranes are differentially permeable is a generally accepted fact. Differentially permeable membranes are membranes through which the particles of certain substances may move readily, but through which the movement of the particles of other substances is either retarded or prevented entirely. The accumulation of lipoidal substances in the cytoplasmic membranes apparently contributes to their differential permeability.

Plasmodesms.

The cell walls in many tissues possess minute pores or openings through which extend exceedingly fine threads of cytoplasm called plasmodesms. These form a system of protoplasmic connections which may provide a means for the interchange of materials among and for coordination of activities of adjoining cells (Figures 3 and 5 G).

Plastids.

Most plastids are spherical, ovoid, or ellipsoid in shape, but ribbonlike or collar-shaped plastids are not uncommon, especially in some lower plants. In higher plants plastids are usually small, differentiated organizations of living protoplasm suspended in the cytoplasm. Specific processes occur in them which result in the formation of sugars, starch, fats, proteins, cellulose, the chlorophylls and other pigments. As the cells multiply by division, the plastids likewise increase in number by the division and growth of very small globules or rodlets called proplastids which occur in the cytoplasm. There is evidence also that division of plastids by constriction (fission) may occur, at least in some cells, even after plastids are fully differentiated (Figure 3). The various types of plastids are frequently named or classified on the basis of the major substances found in them. Five types of plastids are usually recognized:
1. Leucoplasts are colorless plastids commonly found in young cells

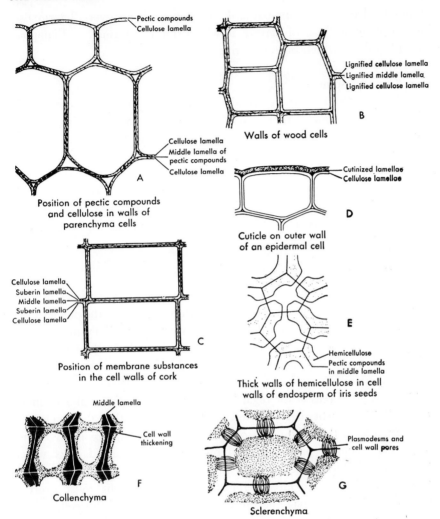

Figure 5   Cell types and cell wall materials. (*A-E from Sampson, H.C.* Work Book In General Botany. *Harper & Brothers.*)

and tissues not exposed to light. These plastids may develop into other types of plastids in response to external and/or internal conditions. They may also serve as centers around which starch grains are formed. 2. Chloroplasts are green. The fundamentally important process of sugar synthesis takes place in these plastids and starch grains may temporarily accumulate in them. 3. Chromoplasts are plastids which are some color other than green, frequently yellow, orange, or red. These plastids sometimes lend color to plant parts. 4. Amyloplast is an over-all term used to designate all types of plastids in which starch is formed. 5. Elaioplasts are plastids in which oils are formed.

Chondriosomes.

In the cytoplasm there are also small bodies of varied form, smaller than plastids, which are called chondriosomes (mitochondria). These are often spoken of as the "power plants" of the cell. Metabolic functions associated with the chondriosomes include the oxidation of various metabolites such as carbohydrates, fatty acids, and amino acids; transfer of electrons to oxygen; oxidative phosphorylation; and the synthesis of proteins. There is also evidence that the chondriosomes in young cells, at least in some plants, may give rise to the plastids of the mature cells (Figure 3).

The Nucleus.

The protoplasm of the nucleus is usually denser than the cytoplasm; however, in some cells it appears as a thin liquid. In the nucleus the proportion of proteins is less than in the cytoplasm, but the nuclear proteins are more complex. The nuclear proteins are relatively high in phosphorus, and possibly this accounts for the fact that they are more reactive.

There is good reason for regarding the nucleus as the center of many cell activities, particularly in view of the evidence that the nucleus is concerned with the production of enzymes which catalyze many, if not most, physiological processes. Moreover, the hereditary factors which influence the development of the plant exist mainly in the nucleus. It is reasonable to conclude, therefore, that the nucleus must exert a controlling influence over the physiological activities of the cell.

The nuclear membrane separates the nucleus and the cytoplasm. The nucleus is filled with a liquid called nuclear sap which varies in density. The nuclear sap apparently is richer in food materials and has a lower water content than the cell sap of the vacuole. Sharp states that embedded in the nuclear sap is a substance in the form of numerous crooked threads, the chromonemata (color threads). These are so named because they contain a substance (chromatin) which is strongly stainable with certain dyes (4). During cell division, the chromonemata give rise to the chromosomes by means of which characteristics are transmitted from parents to offspring. One or more small spherical bodies known as nucleoli (sing. nucleolus) may also be present in the nuclear sap.

The nucleolus has at least two main constituents: a protein, and a sulphuric sugar derivative. At certain stages a form of nucleic acid can be detected in the nucleolus. The significance of the nucleolus is not completely understood.

Vacuole.

In young, rapidly dividing cells, such as those found in root and stem tips and other meristematic regions, almost the entire cell cavity is filled with dense cytoplasm. Numerous small, scattered clear spots resembling bubbles may also be observed. These are watery droplets called vacuoles, so named because early observers erroneously thought them to be "little vacuums." A vacuole is a localized accumulation within the cytoplasm of water containing sugars, salts, acids, gases, pigments, and other inorganic and organic substances in solution or suspension. The contents of a vacuole are known collectively as cell sap. As cells grow older, many of their small vacuoles enlarge and coalesce, forming one or a few large vacuoles. Mature living plant cells characteristically possess a single large central vacuole (Figure 3). A pressure (turgor) created by the inward movement of water into vacuoles forces the cytoplasm and its contents against the inner faces of the cell walls as the cell matures.

Inclusions.

Within the cell may be found other structures and substances generally referred to as inclusions. Structurally these non-living bodies may be liquids, crystals, or solid bodies of various non-crystalline form. These inclusions may represent raw materials, foods, or metabolic by-products. They may be permanent features consisting of waste materials such as calcium oxalate crystals (Figure 3), resins, tannins, and gums. Or they may be starch grains, oil droplets, and aleurone bodies which are inclusions of a temporary nature, which may later be converted into simpler transportable food materials. Although relatively scarce in young cells, inclusions appear in greater amounts as the cells mature, and are generally abundant in cells in which food accumulates.

THE CELL WALL

The cell wall is a product of the protoplast, that is, the materials which become organized into the cell wall are assimilated from foods by the living protoplasm in the cell. Heredity and frequently environment determine the kinds and amounts of cell wall substances formed in various cell types (Figure 5). For example, in the softer tissues of roots, stems, leaves and other plant organs, the cell walls usually contain only pectic compounds and cellulose. Such cell walls, which frequently manifest considerable flexibility and exhibit reversible changes in thickness or other physical properties, are generally referred to as primary walls. In the woody or fibrous parts of plants, the walls of many of the cells become infiltrated with a complex of hardening substances called lignin. The walls of cork cells, characteristic of bark, contain a mixture of fatty, wax-like substances called suberin; while the walls of epidermal cells contain similar water-repellent substances known as cutin. Once a cell wall becomes lignified or suberized, it is generally classed as a secondary wall inasmuch as such cell walls become practically inelastic and do not undergo reversible changes in thickness. Other substances such as hemicellulose, callose, tannins, and minerals may also be found in the walls of certain cells. Each of these cell wall substances will be discussed separately.

THE FORMATION AND NATURE OF THE FIRST CELL WALL—THE MIDDLE LAMELLA

Pectic Compounds.

During cell division, the first wall formed between the daughter cells is composed of pectic compounds (Figure 5). These compounds are formed mainly from sugars. Three types of pectic compounds are generally recognized: pectic acid, pectin, and protopectin. The first of these, pectic acid, does not occur separately in plants, but one of its salts, calcium pectate, is an important constituent of the middle lamella and serves as a binding material between adjoining cells. It is the decomposition of the middle lamella and the resulting partial separation of the cells that accounts in large measure for the mellowing of fruits and vegetables as they ripen under natural conditions or in storage. Cooking brings about a similar breakdown of the middle lamella. The fall of leaves, the abscission of flowers, and the dropping of immature fruits are, in part, occasioned by the disintegration of the middle lamellas in the structures which support these organs. Parasitic fungi often digest and use pectic compounds as food thus causing disintegration of the tissues attacked. Flax and other fibers are obtained from plants by the action of microorganisms in destroying the pectic compounds which hold such cells together, a process called retting.

Pectin is perhaps the best known of the pectic compounds because of its use in the manufacture of jelly and other foods. Each year large quantities of pectin are extracted from plants and sold either as a gelling agent for homemade products or used in the commercial preparation of jellies, creams, salad dressings, or emulsions utilized in foods or drugs. Pectin is obtained principally from apple pomace, cull lemons, orange pulp, sugar beets, and certain species of kelps (algae).

Protopectin is found abundantly in apples and other fleshy fruits. As the fruits ripen in storage, protopectins may be converted to pectins. If the fruit is not used soon thereafter, the process may continue and eventually result in the formation of undesirable products associated with overripening.

All three of these pectic compounds appear to be intimately associated and constitute important ingredients of the middle lamella and the primary cell wall.

FORMATION AND NATURE OF LATER-FORMED CELL WALL LAYERS

Cellulose.

As previously pointed out, during cell division the daughter cells are separated by a first wall, or middle lamella, composed of pectic compounds. Each daughter cell then deposits one or more layers of cellulose on its side of the middle lamella (Figure 5 A). Thus in time each daughter cell becomes enclosed with a wall similar on all sides to that of the mother cell.

Although it is also formed from sugars, cellulose differs structurally from pectic compounds. The cellulose "molecule" is not a molecule in the usual sense, but rather appears to be a chain of carbohydrate molecules. X-ray studies indicate that in cellulose walls, the "molecules" of cellulose become aggregated into bundles called micelles. The micelles, in turn, become joined into a loose network with cavities, called intermicellar spaces, formed between the connecting micelles. In primary cell walls, the intermicellar spaces are filled with pectic compounds. The smallest visible units of cellulose walls are delicate threadlike strands of fibrils which are made up of numerous micellar aggregates. The fibrils apparently wind around the cell in a spiral pattern. The angle and direction of the spiral may vary from layer to layer of cellulose.

In some plant tissues the later-formed cell wall layers are made up almost entirely of cellulose. More than one-third of the food made by herbaceous and young woody plants is converted into cellulose. Cellulose is formed in the cells of all plants, except certain algae and some bacteria. Cotton fibers are almost pure cellulose.

It has been stated that cellulose is a substance which is probably of greater economic importance than any other organic material not used as food by man. Annually millions of dollars are spent and thousands of people are employed in the production and processing of cellulose products. After undergoing various chemical treatments, cellulose from wood and plant fibers is manufactured into paper, cloth, cellophane, collodion, celluloid and other plastics. Cellulose is also utilized industrially in the production of explosives, artificial rubber, acetic acid, charcoal and a multitude of other economically important products.

Cattle and other herbivorous animals are able to digest and utilize cellulose as food whereas man so far has had little success in using cellulose as human food. The digestion of cellulose in the alimentary tracts of some animals is possible because of the presence of certain bacteria and/or protozoa which produce the enzyme cellulase that promotes the digestion of cellulose.

OTHER CELL WALL CONSTITUENTS

Several other substances, such as lignin, suberin, cutin, hemicellulose, callose, tannins, and minerals may become intermingled with cellulose and pectic compounds as the walls of certain cells increase in age.

Lignin.

Lignin is not a single compound but a mixture of chemically related substances (Figure 5 B). These amorphous substances, which are also produced by the living protoplasm of the cell, infiltrate the spaces between the cellulose micelles somewhat as soft plaster fills the spaces between laths. Also like plaster, the lignin hardens rapidly, lending strength and rigidity to the cell wall. It is the filling in and hardening of lignified cell wall layers which reduces their elasticity and increases resistance to bending, twisting, and other strains.

Lignin is especially characteristic of woody cells. It first appears in the middle lamella and primary wall and later in the secondary wall. Generally lignified cell walls are highly permeable to water and solutes. Although lignified plant tissues constitute the backbone of the lumber, furniture, and wood-construction industries, lignification increases the difficulty (and consequently the overhead cost) of obtaining cellulose from wood.

In many tissues, as soon as the walls of living cells become lignified, the protoplasm therein dies and the contents of the cell disappear. In this regard it is interesting to note that the trunk and older roots and branches of a tree are composed mainly of xylem cells and that most of these cells become lignified soon after they are formed. Therefore, the bulk of a tree is composed of dead cells of which only the lignified cell walls remain. However, the outer or younger layers of such cells (sap-wood) are still very important physiologically, since it is through them that the principal movement of water, minerals, and gases dissolved in the water occurs.

Suberin.

Suberin, a mixture of fat-like substances, forms a characteristic layer in the walls of cork cells and is also found in the walls of other types of cells (Figure 5 C). Suberin is formed from sugars as are fats and oils; however, the fatty acids in suberin differ from those in the common types of fats and oils. Suberin may become associated with cellulose in some cell walls which are said to be suberized. Suberin renders cell walls relatively impermeable to water and less vulnerable to invasion by fungi. The bark of older roots and stems in perennial plants is composed largely of suberized cork cells which greatly reduce the loss of moisture from the surfaces of these organs. Since very few organisms can digest it, suberin constitutes an important part of partially decomposed plant materials such as humus, muck, and peat. Derivatives of suberin are also important constituents of coal.

Cutin.

Cutin is similar in many respects to suberin. This complex of wax-like substances is found on the outer surface of epidermal cell walls of stems, leaves, flower parts, and fruits (Figure 5 D). There appears to be a relationship between the depositing of cutin and the atmosphere since cutin accumulates largely on the outer walls of epidermal cells exposed to the air. Different plants, as well as various organs of the same plant, differ in the amount of cutin produced and deposited in or on the walls of epidermal cells. The layer (or layers) of cutin is sometimes referred to as the cuticle, which greatly reduces the evaporation of water from such organs. Cutin and suberin differ in the kinds of fatty acids which constitute the two substances, and they occur in the cell walls of different plant tissues.

Hemicelluloses.

Hemicelluloses are found associated with cellulose in the cell walls of certain woody tissues and in the so-called storage cells of such seeds as onion, date, palm, coffee, and iris (Figure 5 E). Contrary to what the term implies, hemicelluloses are not "half-celluloses," but rather they are a complex of polysaccharides having very different chemical and physical properties from those of cellulose. In certain seeds hemicelluloses appear to serve as reserve food which may be digested and utilized by the embryo when active growth is resumed during germination. There is also evidence that the hemicelluloses which accumulate in the cell walls of certain tissues of young stems during the growing season may be digested and used as food when the stem resumes growth the following year.

Other Substances Found in Plant Cell Walls.

Many other substances may occur in the cell walls of certain tissues. Some of these are callose found in the sieve plates of the sieve tubes in phloem, resins and tannins found in woody tissues, mucilages found in some seed coats and the walls of several water plants, and inorganic materials such as silica, calcium, iron, and other minerals.

In concluding this discussion of plant cells, it should be emphasized that mature cell walls are dead; that the various substances which constitute plant cell walls are made primarily from foods by living protoplasm; and that the production of cell wall materials by the protoplasm is one phase of assimilation and differentiation which involves important physiological processes.

5.
WATER RELATIONS OF PLANTS

Diffusion, Imbibition, and Osmosis.

The principal process that determines the movement of water into, within, and out of plants is diffusion. Diffusion is dependent upon the movement of individual particles (ions, molecules, molecular aggregates) as a result of their own intrinsic kinetic energies. However, kinetic movement of particles alone is not diffusion. Diffusion occurs only when there are differences in areas of concentration of the particles of a particular substance, and it results in a net gain of the particles of that substance in the place of their lesser concentration and a net loss of the particles in the place of their higher concentration. In other words, diffusion is the net movement of the particles of a substance from a region of greater diffusion pressure of that substance to a region of lesser diffusion pressure of that same substance due exclusively to the intrinsic energy of the particles.

Diffusion pressure (occasionally indicated by the symbol DP) is the force or pressure developed by or resulting from the movement of the diffusible particles of a substance as they move from a place of their greater activity to an area of their lesser activity. The diffusing particles cause pressure which is proportional to the kinetic movement and number of such particles. The rate of diffusion is dependent upon factors which affect the diffusion pressure such as concentration of particles per unit volume and temperature (Chapter 3). Besides being the result of diffusion, diffusion pressure is also the cause of diffusion since there is a tendency for particles in an area of greater diffusion pressure to diffuse toward areas of their lesser diffusion pressure.

As explained in Chapter 3, when equal numbers of particles are diffusing in all directions simultaneously, a state of dynamic equilibrium is said to exist. For example, when equal numbers of water molecules are diffusing across a membrane in both directions per unit of time, the system is in dynamic equilibrium. Since under these conditions the activity of the molecules is equal on all sides (that is, there are no differences in areas of concentration nor diffusion pressure of the molecules), it is evident that at dynamic equilibrium there is no diffusion.

It should also be pointed out that when groups of particles are moved by extrinsic energy or forces originating outside of those particles (that is, by energy other than the intrinsic energy of the particles), the phenomenon is called mass movement, not diffusion. A log carried along by the flow of a river, a landslide, or the movement of bodies of air due to convection currents are examples of mass movement. Unless it affects temperature or pressure, mass movement will neither accelerate nor decrease the diffusion of the individual particles.

Imbibition.

A special kind of diffusion also involved in the movement of water molecules into plant cells is known as imbibition. In general, imbibition is the movement of water molecules into substances such as wood and gelatin, which swell or increase in volume as a result of this movement. In plants, imbibition is the diffusion of water into living and non-living parts of a cell or plant due to both a diffusion pressure gradient and adhesive attraction of the imbibant for water. The particular feature which distinguishes imbibition from simple diffusion is that for imbibition to occur, there must be adhesion between the imbibing substance and the diffusing molecules. For example, rubber will imbibe ether, but there is no adhesive attraction between rubber and water. Therefore, rubber in ether will swell, but rubber will not swell in water. Imbibition in plant cells is due primarily to diffusion of water molecules into colloidal substances. The water molecules are usually pictured as being adsorbed and tightly compressed in shells around the colloidal micelles. Such plant cell constituents as cellulose, starches, and proteins have the capacity of imbibing water molecules in increasing order. This explains in part why proteinaceous bean seeds swell to a greater extent than starchy corn grains. It also accounts for the fact that seeds frequently rupture their seed coats during germination since the seed coats are made up mostly of cellulose.

Seeds which are high in colloidal materials manifest considerable imbibition, the amount of water imbibed being directly related to the particular colloids involved. The resulting increase in volume of such seeds may be as much as 15 to 100 times the original size. This increase in volume, primarily due to imbibition of water, results in what is called imbibition pressure, which in many imbibing structures such as seeds, roots and wood, may assume tremendous proportions. It is said that the stone for the ancient Egyptian pyramids was quarried by drilling closely aligned holes in the rock face, driving tightly fitting wooden pegs into the holes, and then soaking the pegs with water. As the wood swelled, a force sufficient to break off a sizable slab of stone was created by imbibition. It should be kept in mind that the movement of water into substances by imbibition will occur only (1) when the diffusion pressure of the imbibed water molecules is less than the diffusion pressure of the water molecules of the water surrounding the imbibing substance, and (2) when there is an adhesive attraction between the imbibant and the water.

Osmosis.

Another kind of diffusion known as osmosis also plays a role in the movement of water into and within plants. As it applies to plants, the term osmosis is defined as the diffusion of water molecules through a differentially permeable membrane,—the membrane constituting the unique feature of this variation of the diffusion process. A differentially permeable membrane is a membrane through which the particles of certain substances, such as water molecules, may diffuse readily, but through which the diffusion of the particles of other substances is either retarded or prevented entirely. For example, the plasma, vacuolar, and nuclear membranes when alive function as differentially permeable membranes, but the cell wall seldom, if ever, does. In the mature plant cell with a central vacuole, the entire cytoplasm may function as a differentially permeable membrane. In order for movement of water molecules by osmosis to occur, there must be a difference in the diffusion pressure of the water molecules on opposite sides of the membrane. Where such a difference exists, diffusion will occur across the membrane from the area of high to the area of low diffusion pressure of the water molecules until a state of dynamic equilibrium is established.

When the net diffusion of water is into a living cell, a pressure is developed within the cell. This pressure, which is exerted against the cytoplasm and thence the cell wall, is called turgor pressure (TP). Turgor pressure is the actual pressure developed in a cell as a result of osmosis. A cell distended by turgor pressure is said to be turgid; a cell not so distended is said to be flaccid. Plasmolysis is the term used to denote the separation of the protoplasm from the cell wall due to excess outward diffusion of water from the vacuole over inward diffusion. The immediate effect of plasmolysis is the retardation of metabolic activities in cells. Continued water deficits will lead to permanent wilting of tissues and eventually to death by desiccation. Because of the wilting and browning of plasmolyzed plants, their manner of death is frequently termed "burning" by farmers and gardeners. Burning of plants may be caused by residues of insecticidal and fungicidal sprays and by the application of excessive amounts of fertilizers. The effect of plasmolysis in some instances is called physiological drought. On the contrary, the phenomenon of plasmolysis is employed in a number of practical ways such as the addition of quantities of salt to meat and fish and sugar to jams and jellies so as to plasmolyze bacteria and mold spores which could cause decay and spoilage; the salting of troublesome weeds and other obnoxious plants which are otherwise difficult to destroy; and the spreading of salt on clay tennis courts or in the cracks of brick walks to plasmolyze and thus kill grasses and other undesirable plants.

A Comparison of Turgor Pressure, Osmotic Pressure, and Diffusion Pressure Deficit.

The term osmotic pressure (OP) is frequently used in discussions of water relations in plants. In attempting to understand what is meant by osmotic pressure, we must first keep clearly in mind that the actual pressure developed in a living cell as a result of osmosis is turgor pressure, not osmotic pressure. What, then, is osmotic pressure? A hypothetical illustration may help to clarify the term. If pure water is placed in a membrane (bag) permeable only to water molecules, a maximum number of water molecules will be striking the inner walls of the bag at any given time if the temperature and pressure within the bag remain constant. Now, if a solute, such as sugar, is dissolved in the water in the bag, the sugar molecules will become dispersed among the water molecules and thus dilute the water molecules per unit volume. Hence under these conditions, fewer water molecules will be striking the walls of the bag per unit time (Figure 6). Therefore, the diffusion pressure of the water in the bag will be reduced in proportion to the amount of solute molecules introduced. The reduction in the diffusion pressure of the water caused by the interspersed sugar (solute) molecules causes a diffusion pressure deficit (DPD) of the water molecules in the bag.

If the bag containing the sugar solution is immersed in pure water,

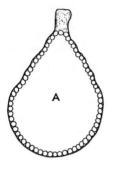 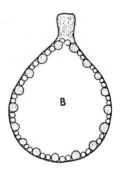

O = Water molecules

⊙ = Sugar molecules

Figure 6 Diagrammatic comparison of two differentially permeable membranes, A containing in the beginning 100 cc. of pure water, and B containing 100 cc. of a 20 per cent sugar solution. Both are immersed in distilled water. There is no change in A (a state of dynamic equilibrium prevailing from the start), but B will become distended due to the diffusion pressure deficit of water molecules within this membrane which results in an increase of turgor pressure.

the net movement of the water molecules will be into the bag, that is, from the pure water (place of greater diffusion pressure of the water molecules) into the solution in the bag (place of lesser diffusion pressure of the water molecules). In order to determine the osmotic pressure of the solution in the bag, it would be necessary to exert sufficient internal pressure on the solution to increase the diffusion pressure of the water in the solution enough to equal the diffusion pressure of the pure water in which the bag was immersed. In other words sufficient pressure must be exerted on the solution in the bag so that for every water molecule entering the bag from the surrounding pure water, a molecule of water will be leaving the bag from the solution within the bag. Stated another way, enough pressure must be exerted on the solution to prevent an increase in the volume of the solution in the bag due to the entrance of water. The amount of pressure thus required is called the osmotic pressure of the solution, and it is quantitatively equal to the imposed pressure. If the pressure required as explained above is 10 atmospheres, then the osmotic pressure of the solution is 10 atmospheres. Therefore, osmotic pressure may be defined as the maximum pressure which can be developed in a solution when the solution is separated from pure water by a membrane permeable only to water. That is, the amount (usually expressed in atmospheres) to which the diffusion pressure of the water molecules in a solution is less than the diffusion pressure of pure water is known as the osmotic pressure of the solution.

A living plant cell may be compared with the bag just described. The cytoplasm within the cell constitutes the differentially permeable membrane (bag) and the cell sap in the vacuole is an aqueous solution containing sugars and other dissolved substances. (Under usual circumstances, the cell wall may be ignored since it is permeable to both solute and solvent molecules). Since there are solute molecules dissolved in the water of the vacuole, the diffusion pressure of the water molecules in the vacuole solution is less than the diffusion pressure of pure water, that is, the solution in the vacuole has a definite osmotic pressure value. The reduction in the diffusion pressure of the water in the vacuole brought about by the interspersed solute molecules causes a diffusion pressure deficit of the water molecules in the vacuole. Now, if a pressure, such as turgor pressure resulting from osmosis, is exerted upon the water molecules in the vacuolar solution, the diffusion pressure of the water molecules in the solution will be increased accordingly. Thus if sufficient pressure is exerted upon the water molecules in the vacuolar solution, the diffusion pressure of the water molecules in the solution will be increased until it is equal to the diffusion pressure of the water surrounding the cell, and a state of dynamic equilibrium will be established.

In nature the osmotic pressure of the soil solution is usually less (approximately 1 atmos.) than the osmotic pressure in the epidermal cells or root hairs of the roots in which the vacuolar solution may have an osmotic pressure of from 3 to 5 atmos. Stated differently, the diffusion pressure deficit of the water molecules in the cell vacuoles is usually greater than the diffusion pressure deficit of the water molecules in the soil solution. Under these conditions, the net movement of the water molecules will be from the soil solution (place of lesser diffusion pressure deficit of the water) into the vacuoles of the epidermal cells and root hairs (place of greater diffusion pressure deficit of the water). It should be noted that the movement of the water molecules is from a place of lesser DPD to a place of greater DPD, and not from a place of greater osmotic pressure to a place of lesser osmotic pressure. The pressure resulting from the net movement of the water molecules from the soil solution into the vacuoles of the epidermal cells will cause the diffusion pressure of the water molecules in the vacuoles to be increased above that of the cells next toward the interior of the root. Thus a series of diffusion pressure gradients may be set up across the cortical cells of the root and on into the xylem conduits. Hence, in this process which is known as active absorption, water may reach the xylem.

In the plant cell, the increase in volume as a result of turgor pressure is counterbalanced by the resistance of the cell wall. The counteracting or back pressure exerted by the cell wall against and equal to the turgor pressure is designated as wall pressure (WP).

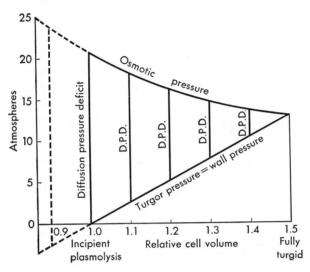

Figure 7 Interrelationships of osmotic pressure, turgor pressure, wall pressure, and diffusion-pressure deficit in an osmotic system representative of a plant cell. (*From* Plant Physiology, *Meyer, B.S. and D.B. Anderson. Copyright (1939), D. Van Nostrand Company, Inc., Princeton, New Jersey.*)

The interrelationships of the forces in an osmotic system representative of a plant cell are brought out in Figure 7. These interrelations may also be expressed by symbols in the following simple equations:

$$DPD = OP - WP$$
$$WP = TP$$

If these symbols are translated into values, it is evident that should the osmotic pressure in a cell be 10 atmos. and a turgor pressure of 6 atmos. is developed in that cell, the resulting diffusion pressure deficit of the cell will be 4 atmos., that is, the original OP of the cell will be reduced in proportion to the TP imposed.

It should now be clear that it is the diffusion pressure deficit that determines whether water molecules diffuse into or out of a plant cell.

Diffusion of water will occur only from areas of lesser to areas of greater diffusion pressure deficits. Our understanding of the osmotic mechanism may also be broadened by an illustration in which specific values are assigned to the osmotic pressures, turgor pressures, and diffusion pressure deficits of two adjoining cells. Figure 8 illustrates how DPD determines the direction of diffusion of water molecules between two adjacent plant cells. Water will diffuse from cell A to cell B because cell B has the greater DPD, and not from the cell with the higher OP to the cell with the lower OP.

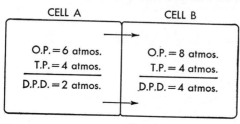

Figure 8   Diagram of two adjacent cells to show the direction of diffusion of water molecules.

A root hair surrounded by a soil solution provides another example as illustrated in Figure 9. The water will diffuse into the root hair since the solution in the root hair has a DPD of 4 atmos. as compared to a DPD of only 1 atmos. in the soil solution.

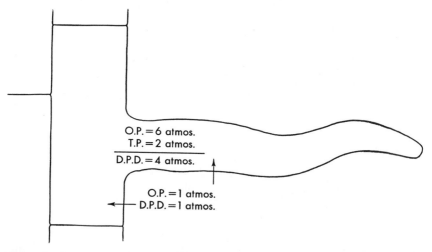

Figure 9   Diagram showing the diffusion of water from the soil solution into a root hair.

Diffusion pressure deficits are increased in plant cells either by an increase in the solute concentration (which increases the osmotic pressure), or by a decrease in turgor pressure. Solutions not in plant cells, such as the soil solution surrounding root systems, are not subject to turgor pressures. Consequently, the osmotic pressure of such a solution is equivalent to its diffusion pressure deficit.

Active Absorption.

Water movement into plant roots occurs in certain definite areas as shown in Figure 10. Diffusion of water into so-called "absorbing areas"

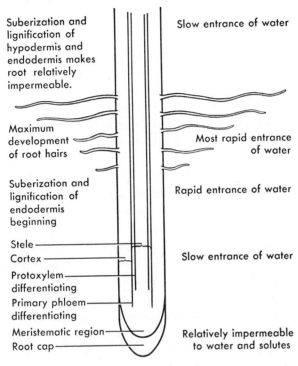

Figure 10 Water movement into plant roots occurs in definite areas. (*Modified from* Plant and Soil Water Relationships, *by P.J. Kramer. McGraw-Hill Book Company Inc., 1949.*)

of roots is possible only because the diffusion pressure deficits of the roots are greater than the diffusion pressure deficit of the soil water. However, the diffusion pressure deficit of the soil water system increases as the water is removed. Therefore, if water is to move continuously from the soil into the roots, either 1. diffusion pressure deficits must increase in the root absorbing cells to counterbalance the increasing soil water diffusion pressure deficits as the soil water declines, or 2. the water supply in the soil must be increased by rainfall or irrigation so as to lower the diffusion pressure deficit of the soil solution. Increases in diffusion pressure deficits in the roots as a result of forces which originate within the root cells, such as osmosis, are usually not in excess of 3 atmospheres. Thus water will diffuse across the cortical cells of the root, into the xylem vessels, and thence upward into the shoot only so long as the DPD of the root cells is greater than the DPD of the soil solution. This is known as active absorption, and it may cause exudations either from stumps that are left when the shoots are removed, or from specialized groups of cells called hydathodes which are found in the leaves of certain species. The pressure developed by the movement of the water into the roots is called root pressure, and the exuding of droplets of liquid water as a result of this pressure is known as guttation. Root pressure and guttation develop only under certain conditions and, as will be shown later, do not result in the movement of large quantities of water into plants. Guttation and root pressure occur most prominently when the atmosphere surrounding the shoot is high in water vapor (high relative humidity), the available soil water is abundant, and the soil temperature is above 25°C. Thus root pressure and guttation resulting from active absorption occur when transpiration is at a minimum, or when water is being absorbed by the roots in greater quantities than it is being lost by the tops (shoot).

The cause for active water absorption is often considered to be a purely physical phenomenon resulting from osmotic movements of water. However, within the past decade, physiologists have accumulated evidence which shows that active absorption is also a physiological mechanism. The results from stem exudation experiments have shown that the rate of exudation (guttation) can be affected by auxins, respiratory inhibitors, oxygen availability, and temperature. The temperature coefficient of active absorption has been shown to be 2 to 3, whereas for a strictly physical reaction the Q_{10} would be 1.2 to 1.3. Another feature of exudation as a result of active absorption is a curious rhythmic cycle in which exudation is high for a period of time, followed by a period of low exudation. It seems, then, that active absorption resulting in positive pressures in the xylem vessels is a result of both osmotic and physiological mechanisms. It is well to emphasize that active absorption plays only a minor role in water absorption of most plants, and it is of most importance in the early spring when the plants have only a few leaves and transpiration is not yet great. Although it is under these conditions that one can observe the result of active absorption, many plant physiologists are of the opinion that active absorption is the principle mechanism for restoration of turgidity in leaves at night following a day of high transpiration (see Figure 16 and the later discussion on absorption versus transpiration).

Passive Absorption and Transpiration.

Diffusion pressure deficits of more than 2 to 3 atmospheres in the root absorbing cells may be caused by tensions which develop in the conducting vessels as a result of forces which originate in the shoots, not in the root cells. In this case the root cells merely play a passive role in water movement. However, this is not to say that the living root absorption cells do not affect the rate of inward water movement under tension. In fact, a more rapid movement occurs through unsuberized dead absorption cells. Tensions developed in the xylem cells by forces which originate in the shoot result primarily from the evaporation of water from the mesophyll cells of the leaves (Figure 11), from the

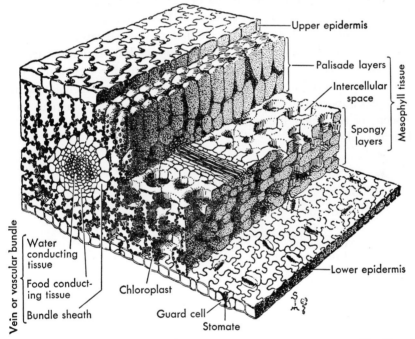

Figure 11 Model of a small portion of a leaf from the common periwinkle *(Vinca)*, showing cells and tissues. *(From Transeau, E.N. General Botany, World Book Company, 1924.)*

utilization of water in growth, or from both. The rate of water movement out of the xylem vessels of the shoots at times exceeds the rate of entrance of water into the xylem vessels of the roots; hence tensions are developed in the vessels. The tensions increase the DPD of the vessel sap which, in turn, induces water movements from the parenchyma cells of the roots into the xylem vessels, and thence to the stem and leaves. The DPD of a cell in a state of tension may be expressed by symbols in the following simple equation:

$$DPD = OP - (-TP)$$

It should be emphasized that this equation can be used only when plant cells are in a state of tension and is not to be thought of as a kind of osmosis. The only known mechanism that causes water to be in a state of tension in plant cells is transpiration pull.

Passive absorption is generally the cause of the absorption of the greatest amount of water by the rooted-green plant, and it is mainly associated with evaporation of water vapor from the leaves. The loss of water in the form of vapor from plants is called transpiration. Transpiration probably accounts for 95 per cent of all the water absorbed by plants. The remaining 5 per cent of the water is used for growth, cell hydration, and photosynthesis. Yet before water necessary for growth and other essential processes in plants is supplied, transpiration demands must be met. Hence, an adequate supply of water for agricultural crops becomes an exceedingly important phase of crop management, assuming equal importance with mineral nutrition or fertilizer practices. Some concept of the water transpired by single plants may be had from the data in Table 3.

Table 3   Water loss by transpiration per single plant for five kinds of plants during the growing season.

KIND OF PLANT	TRANSPIRATION DURING GROWING SEASON (GALLONS)
Cowpea	13
Irish potato	25
Winter wheat	25
Tomato	34
Corn	54

Perhaps an even more impressive way to illustrate the large amounts of water which are lost by transpiration is in inches of water required by an acre of a crop such as corn during a growing season. Data from Iowa show that for a yield of 70 bushels of corn per acre, 16 inches of rainfall are required, which, of course, must be well distributed throughout the growing season.

Transpiration demands must be met daily by at least sufficient absorption of water from the soil to balance water use in and loss from the tops. Without this water balance, water deficits are setup in the plant cells which result in cell plasmolysis. As previously pointed out, the immediate effects of plasmolysis are cessation of growth and decreased photosynthesis. However, the rate of photosynthesis is decreased less than the growth of young leaves, stems, and reproductive structures. The available photosynthate, under these conditions, is translocated to the growing regions of the root and root growth is accelerated. This is particularly true during the day when transpiration exceeds absorption. In some species of plants this available photosynthate may accumulate in leaves, stems, and other organs. A continued water deficit will lead to permanent wilting and eventually to death by desiccation.

Its importance having now been established, let us examine more closely the nature of transpiration and how it causes water movement from the soil into the roots. Perhaps the nature of the process can best be described by picturing the pathway of water movement into the plant as is shown in Figure 12. The substomatal cavities of leaves open

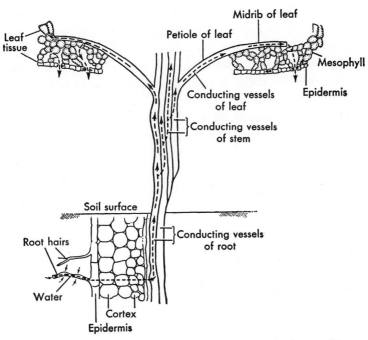

Figure 12 The pathway of water from the soil to the leaves. (*From College Botany, Revised Edition, by Harry J. Fuller and Oswald Tippo. By permission of Henry Holt and Company, Inc. Copyright 1949, 1954.*)

out to the atmosphere through the stomates, which lie between the guard cells. As a result of a generally higher vapor pressure of water molecules in the substomatal cavities than the vapor pressure of the water molecules of the atmosphere, diffusion of water molecules (vapor) occurs outward, that is, from the substomatal cavities into the atmosphere. The difference between the vapor pressure within the substomatal cavities and the vapor pressure of the atmosphere is called the vapor pressure gradient (VPG), and it regulates to a great degree the rate of outward diffusion of water vapor, or transpiration.

The outward diffusion of water molecules into the atmosphere causes other water molecules to diffuse from the walls of the mesophyll cells into the substomatal cavities. This then causes movement of water from the protoplasm of the mesophyll cells into the cell walls, and it results in an increase of the DPD in the vacuoles of the mesophyll cells. These increased DPD's in the mesophyll cells, in turn, cause diffusion of water into the mesophyll cells from the xylem vessels of the veins. Diffusion of water molecules from vein vessels to mesophyll cells, then to substomatal cavities, and thence out into the atmosphere occurs so rapidly that the water in the vascular conducting vessels is thrown into a tension. Under tension, the water in the vascular conducting vessels has the properties of a solid with the water columns hanging together tenaciously due to the tremendous cohesive forces among the water molecules. These water columns under tension extend into the roots and result in DPD's in the absorbing cells of the roots which cause an inward diffusion of water from the soil. This continues as long as the DPD's resulting from transpiration exceed the counter tensions exerted on the soil moisture by the forces of the soil particles. Thus the major movement of water into plants results from forces originating in the stems and leaves, and not in the roots. Therefore, the role of roots in water absorption is generally passive, and hence the name passive absorption which is given to this phenomenon.

Other evidence has shown that living roots actually offer resistance to water movement through the absorbing cells. Killed roots permit a much more rapid water absorption than living roots. The reason why living root cells offer resistance to water movement is thought to be due to lower permeability of living cells. Permeability to water in root cells is also decreased as carbon dioxide increases. Thus poor aeration in soils may decrease water movement into roots.

There is considerable experimental evidence to prove that passive absorption brought about by leaf and stem transpiration is the main cause of water absorption and movement in rooted-green plants. One of the most convincing types of observations is the comparison of the amounts of water lost through the influence of transpiration with those lost (exuded) as the result of active forces such as osmosis in the root. Data from such an experiment are shown in Table 4.

Table 4   A comparison of the amounts of water of transpiration and exudation from five species. (*From Kramer, P. J. Amer. Jour. Bot. 26: 784–791. 1939.*)

	TRANSPIRATION PER PLANT 1ST. HR.: 2ND. HR. *ml./hr.* *ml./hr.*		EXUDATION PER PLANT 1ST. HR.: 2ND. HR. *ml./hr.* *ml./hr.*		EXUDATION AS PER CENT OF TRANSPIRATION *per cent*
Coleus	8.6	8.7	0.30	0.28	3.2
Hibiscus	5.8	6.7	−0.01	0.05	0.7
Impatiens	2.1	1.9	−0.22	−0.06	
Helianthus	4.3	5.0	0.02	0.02	0.4
Tomato	10.0	11.0	−0.62	0.07	0.6

Other evidence in support of the transpirational theory of water movement is that DPD's in leaves are sufficient to cause tensions or DPD's in roots of 15 to 20 atmospheres as contrasted with maximum DPD's of only 3 atmospheres caused by active absorption or root pressure. The higher DPD's created by passive absorption thus cause a utilization of, or movement into the roots of, all the available water in soils (to the point of permanent wilting). Other support for the transpirational theory lies in the fact that the cohesive forces between water molecules is sufficient (more than 100 atmospheres) to cause the water columns to hang under tension in the xylem vessels. The high cohesiveness of the water molecules plus the high DPD's created by transpiration are sufficiently great, even considering friction in the vessels, to cause water movement to the tops of the tallest trees. This force is often called transpiration pull.

Factors Affecting Transpiration.

The rate of transpiration is affected by factors of the environment and by leaf characteristics. The major external factors which influence the rate of transpiration are total solar radiation (energy of sunlight) as it affects the internal temperature of leaves in relation to external temperature, and as it affects the opening and closing of the stomates, the atmospheric temperature, the vapor pressure of the atmosphere (that is, the concentration of water vapor in the atmosphere), the movement of air (wind velocity), available soil moisture, and soil temperature.

The principal leaf characters and/or internal factors which may affect the rate of transpiration are the opening and closing of the stomates, the number and spacing of the stomates, the length of time per day the stomates are open, the position of the stomates (whether they are located at the surface or are sunken), the internal vapor pressure (that is, the concentration of water vapor in the internal air spaces of the leaf in comparison with the concentration of water vapor, or vapor pressure, of the atmosphere), the temperature of the leaf, the ratio of internal to external leaf surface exposed to the air, the quantity of colloidal gels with high water-retaining capacity within the mesophyll cells, and the degree of cutinization of the outer walls of the epidermal cells.

Transpiration appears to be influenced principally by a combination of leaf characteristics and radiation which determines leaf temperature. Leaf temperature, in turn, affects the vapor pressure in the substomatal cavities. The higher the leaf temperature, the higher the vapor pressure. It is not unusual for leaf temperatures to be 10 degrees above air temperatures. It will be recalled that the difference between the vapor pressure of the air and the vapor pressure of the leaf is called the vapor pressure gradient, and that the greater the VPG, the greater the rate of transpiration. High transpirational rates generally occur during atmospheric conditions of moderate temperatures and high radiation which combine in establishing high VPG's.

The effect of air movement or wind velocity on transpiration is shown in Figure 13. These data show that transpiration is accelerated

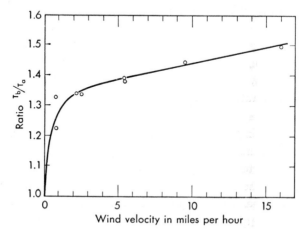

Figure 13 The effect of wind velocity on transpiration. *Data of Martin and Clements, 1935. (From* Plant Physiology, *Meyer, B.S. and D.B. Anderson. Copyright (1952), D. Van Nostrand Company, Inc., Princeton, New Jersey.)*

rapidly with increase in wind velocity up to 5 miles per hour, and then more gradually up to 15 miles per hour. Wind velocities of more than 15 miles per hour usually decrease transpiration by lowering temperatures and causing the closure of the stomates.

The effects of decreasing soil moisture are illustrated by the data in Figure 14. These data show that decreasing soil moisture results in decreased rates of transpiration.

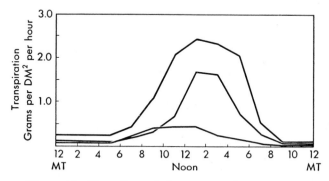

Figure 14 The effect of decreasing soil moisture on transpiration of bean *(Phaseolus vulgaris)* for three successive days. *Data of Chung. 1935. (From* Plant Physiology, *Meyer, B.S. and D.B. Anderson. Copyright (1952), D. Van Nostrand Company, Inc., Princeton, New Jersey.)*

Transpiration through the stomates (stomatal transpiration) is responsible for 85 to 95 per cent of the water vapor that diffuses from plants into the air. Vaporization through the cuticle (cuticular transpiration) may account for 5 to 15 per cent of the transpirational loss depending primarily upon the thickness of the cutin. However, transpiration can occur from flowers, fruits, tubers, roots, or any plant part exposed to air if the vapor pressure within the plant part is greater than the vapor pressure of the atmosphere. Even the bark of trees does not entirely prevent transpiration.

Practical recognition of the effects of transpiration is made by providing supplemental supplies of water through irrigation, by frequent watering of plants in homes and greenhouses, by the removal of weeds to conserve soil moisture, by the growing of tree wind-breaks bordering orchards and cultivated lands to reduce the desiccating effects of hot, dry air currents, by the placing of glass jars or cellophane caps over newly transplanted seedlings, by the packing for shipment of nursery stock in moist peat moss, by the periodic sprinkling of floors and crates in the storage of apples, by the florist when he wraps cut flowers in wax paper, and by the grocer who keeps a fine spray of water playing over his fresh, leafy vegetables. These and many other practices are employed to reduce transpiration and counteract the harmful effects of excessive water loss from plants or plant parts.

The Stomatal Apparatus.

In some species the stomates occur only in the lower epidermis, in other plants the stomates occur only in the upper epidermis, while in still others the stomates may occur on both surfaces. In the last type the number of stomates is usually greater in the lower epidermis than in the upper epidermis. Table 5 shows the number of stomates in the upper and lower surfaces of a few common leaves.

Table 5   Average number of stomates per square centimeter of leaf surface.

SPECIES	UPPER EPIDERMIS	LOWER EPIDERMIS
Corn	5,200	6,800
Wheat	3,300	1,400
Oat	2,500	2,300
Bean	4,000	28,100
Potato	5,100	16,100
Tomato	1,200	13,000
Cabbage	14,100	22,600
Apple	0	29,400
Peach	0	22,500
Cherry	0	24,900
Black Walnut	0	46,100
Willow Oak	0	72,300
Coleus	0	14,100
Geranium	1,900	5,900

The opening of the stomates is effected primarily by turgor pressure resulting from osmosis. Observation will reveal that the walls of the guard cells are thicker on the sides next to the stomatal opening (Figure 15).

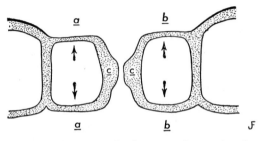

Figure 15   Longitudinal view of a pair of guard cells with the stomatal aperture slightly open.

When turgor pressure increases, the walls of the guard cells exert a counter pressure and give way first where they are thinnest and weakest (a a and b b). This changes slightly the shape of the cells, but sufficiently to separate c from c and thus enlarge the stomatal aperture. With a loss in turgor pressure, the guard cell walls tend to restore the original configuration of the cells and in this way the size of the stomatal aperture is reduced as c and c once more come closer to each other. As the guard cells lose turgidity, the surrounding epidermal cells exert a pressure against them which may also be instrumental in the closure of the stomates. It is doubtful that the stomates are ever completely closed.

One explanation of the opening and closing of a stomate may be briefly outlined as follows (5). From late afternoon and on into the night the acidity of the guard cells increases and the sugar in these cells is converted to starch. Starch is insoluble in water. Therefore, the water in the guard cells during the period of darkness is almost pure, that is, it contains very little, if any, solutes. This establishes a condition in which the concentration of water molecules per unit volume in the guard cells is greater (hence their diffusion pressure is greater) than it is in the surrounding epidermal cells which vary only slightly in this regard. Under such circumstances the net movement of water is out of the guard cells into the epidermal cells, which results in the guard cells shrinking and at least partially closing the stomates. Upon the advent of illumination (sunrise), the acidity of the guard cells decreases, apparently due to a photochemical reaction induced by the light. The change of the guard cells toward neutrality appears to favor the hydrolytic (starch to sugar) action of the complex of enzymes (amylase) which are present in the guard cells. As a result the starch which accumulated in the guard cells during the night is changed back to sugar. Sugar is soluble in water, and the sugar molecules become evenly dispersed among (and consequently dilute) the water molecules in the guard cells. In time a stage is reached in which the concentration of the water molecules per unit volume is greater in the surrounding epidermal cells, and consequently the net movement of water is into the guard cells,—the reverse of that which occurred during the night. The net inward movement of water into the guard cells increases the turgor pressure of these cells. Thus the guard cells are put under pressure and the stomatal aperture is widened.

In some species factors other than those described apparently influence the opening and closing of the stomates such as an excess accumulation of carbon dioxide in the guard cells. Regardless of what may be involved, it appears evident that when the guard cells are turgid, the stomates will be open. Conversely when the guard cells are flaccid, the stomates will be closed or nearly so. At present our knowledge does not enable us to postulate mechanisms which will explain the opening and closing of the stomates of all species under varying conditions.

The degree of opening of the stomates and the length of time that the stomates are open per day affect the rate of transpiration. The number and spacing of the stomates, however, is not usually considered to be a limiting factor in the transpiration of any particular species; although number and spacing of stomates may be major factors in causing the transpirational rates of different species to vary under conditions that are otherwise similar. Experimental evidence has shown that the rate of evaporation through a perforated membrane is often 50 times the rate of evaporation from an equivalent free water surface. The epidermis with its many open stomates constitutes such a perforated membrane. This coupled with the large amount of wet mesophyll cell surface exposed to the intercellular atmosphere (which may be 8 to 15 times more than the total external leaf surface) results in loss of water far in excess of that of free water surfaces of equal area exposed to the same evaporational stress. In other words, the leaf is a highly efficient evaporation mechanism when the stomates are open.

Sunken stomates impose longer distances through which water molecules must pass in diffusing from the substomatal cavities of the leaf into the atmosphere, and thus may decrease transpiration to some extent. Cuticular transpiration or transpiration directly through the epidermal cells is comparatively small, ranging from practically nothing in some species to as much as 15 per cent of stomatal transpiration in other species. During droughts, however, cuticular transpiration may assume considerable importance in certain species. Cuticular transpiration is generally of negligible importance in leaves with heavily cutinized epidermal cells.

Transpiration usually does not continue at high rates in the afternoon despite high VPG's because of a lag between absorption and the loss of water by transpiration as is shown in Figure 16. At night the rate of absorption exceeds that of transpirational loss. Thus loss of turgidity in plants during the day may be reversed during the night. When this sequence of events fails to take place, however, permanent wilting will occur and the plant may be killed by desiccation.

Desiccation, resulting when absorption fails to balance transpirational losses, can be caused either by excessive water (water-logged or flooded soils) or by excessive salts in the soil solution. The exact reason why flooded soils cause a decrease of water absorption by rooted-green plants

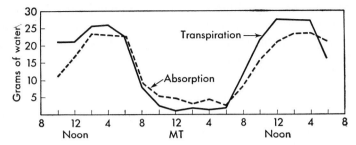

Figure 16 Comparison of transpiration and absorption in the loblolly pine *(Pinus taeda). Data of Kramer, 1937. (From* Plant Physiology, *Meyer, B.S. and D.B. Anderson. Copyright (1952), D. Van Nostrand Company, Inc., Princeton, New Jersey.)*

has never been fully explained. It appears that soil flooding is related to decrease in permeability of the root cells caused by increased carbon dioxide concentration together with reduced respiration in the cells of the submerged plant parts. The reason for high salt concentrations reducing water absorption is explainable on the basis of osmotic relationships. Increasing the salt concentration will bring about a rise in the osmotic pressure of the soil solution which, in turn, results in an increased diffusion pressure deficit of the soil solution. In time the DPD of the soil solution may become greater than the DPD of the cells of roots growing in the soil. Under such conditions, the net movement of water is from the roots into the soil even though there is an abundance of moisture in the soil. This phenomenon is frequently referred to as physiological drought. When the brine from an ice cream freezer is thrown upon grass, the grass usually dies, but not because the salt poisons the grass as is commonly believed. Rather the brine from the freezer causes the DPD of the soil solution to be so much greater than the DPD of the grass root cells that a net diffusion of water occurs from the grass roots into the soil and, as a consequence, the grass roots die of desiccation resulting from physiological drought. In crop management, particularly in sandy soils where high rates of fertilizer are applied, physiological drought is often a cause of damage or even death in crop plants during dry periods. These adverse effects have very often been erroneously attributed to toxicity of the fertilizer salts or to mineral deficiencies, when they were actually due to water deficiency.

Drought Resistance.
Certain species of plants are able to survive and grow in environments of low rainfall. Many of these plants are capable of survival in

these environments by virtue of special morphological features such as leafless stems, reduced numbers and sizes of leaves, and the occurrence in the cells of colloidal gels which have a high water-holding capacity including pectic compounds, mucilages and gums (the so-called water retention materials). As a rule such plants grow very slowly because reduction of leaf area also results in reduced photosynthesis. Therefore, restriction of leaf area is not a desirable characteristic to breed into crop plants, although it might help with the moisture problem in areas subject to droughts.

A method of measuring the problem has been to base drought resistance on water usage. This is called the water requirements of plants, and it is the amount of water lost per gram of dry matter. Research has shown that the ratio figure obtained by this method is a function of environment rather than a species characteristic. Hence, this method does not constitute a dependable basis for determining the drought resistance of individual species.

Increasing the survival chances of agricultural crops during droughts can be accomplished by growing crops insofar as possible with extensive and deeply penetrating root systems, such as alfalfa and sericean lespedeza. Plants having deep rooting systems, an abundance of water storage tissue, reduced leaf area, and similar features are now referred to as drought-enduring plants, rather than drought-resistant plants. The reason for this is that the protoplasm of such plants is no more resistant to high temperatures and loss of water than is the protoplasm of plant species without drought-enduring characteristics. True drought resistance, then, is a protoplasmic condition (toughness) that enables some plants to survive under high temperatures and limited drying out of their cells. This type of drought resistance is associated with the same physiological conditions that occur in plant tissues which can withstand temperatures below freezing, or which manifest cold resistance. Such protoplasmic endurance of high and low temperatures has now been shown to be an inheritable characteristic. The physiology of protoplasmic heat and cold tolerance has never been fully explained, but appears to be related to physical rather than chemical changes in the protoplasm.

Effects of Water Deficits on Plant Processes.

Under conditions of internal water deficits in plants (in which transpiration exceeds absorption), most of the processes in plants are affected. Growth, a very sensitive indicator of water deficits, decreases in proportion to the deficit. One of the best ways to illustrate this relationship is to plot growth against decreasing supplies of soil moisture. Such data are plotted in Figure 17. As these data show, growth declines in proportion to the decrease in available soil moisture which, in turn, causes an internal water deficit in the plant.

A lack of water balance in leaves causes a reduction in the rate of photosynthesis. The rate of photosynthesis is said to be a very good indicator of the degree of turgidity of leaf cells. However, the reduced rate of photosynthesis is probably not due entirely to a shortage of water for the process, but it is attributed chiefly to an upset of the balance of proper conditions in the protoplasm, probably in a large measure of an enzymatic nature.

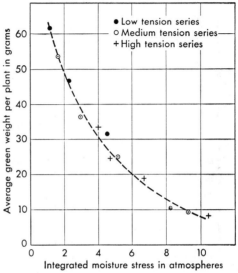

Figure 17 Growth declines in proportion to decreasing available soil moisture. (*From Wadleigh, C.H. and A.D. Ayers.* Plant Physiology *20:106–132, 1945.*)

It is interesting to note, moreover, that whereas declining water supplies cause reduced rates of photosynthesis, other processes of a hydrolytic nature are accelerated in leaves by limited water deficits; for example, during periods of low water availability, starch is converted to sugar and proteins are hydrolyzed to amino acids. Thus in leaves, sugars and amino acids tend to accumulate during droughts; or, as has been shown in cotton, sugars and amino acids are translocated to and accumulate in the stems. It is also interesting that respiration in leaves is increased during water deficits,—just the reverse of that which occurs in seeds as the available water declines. While loss of moisture results in increased respiration and hydrolysis of organic substrates in leaves, the same conditions induce condensation in curing seeds.

Another important effect which frequently accompanies reduced growth is the utilization of hydrolyzed organic substrates in the process of assimilation which results in an accumulation of assimilation products. Assimilation products, such as latex (natural rubber), are valuable plant products utilized by man. Since assimilation products are increased by periodic water deficits, it is, of course, desirable that plants grown for such assimilation products undergo occasional water deficit conditions. Another effect of internal water shortages which may also be desirable in plant shoots is the tendency of water deficits to cause more sugar translocation to the roots. Consequently, root growth is accelerated while shoot growth is being checked, an effect which may subsequently result in a restoration of water balance in the shoot. Extensive top growth not accompanied by periods of water deficits results in plants with large leaf areas (which contribute to loss of water by transpiration), but with inadequate root development. Such plants have a poor chance for survival during droughts.

Controlled partial drying of plants is also desirable for hardening plants against injury due to freezing. Thus under conditions where it can be done, it may be advisable to lower gradually the water available to plants in the soil prior to periods of freezing weather.

Several of the important facts concerning water relations of plants may be summarized as follows:

1. Movement of water into, within, and out of plants is due mainly to particular kinds of diffusion such as imbibition, osmosis, and transpiration.
2. Diffusion is the net movement of the particles of a substance from a region of greater diffusion pressure of that substance to a region of lesser diffusion pressure of that same substance due exclusively to the intrinsic energy of the particles.
3. Imbibition is the diffusion of water molecules into colloidal substances, such as gelatin, wood, and plant cells, which causes the colloidal substances to swell. Imbibition will occur only when there is adhesive attraction between the colloid (imbibant) and the water molecules.
4. Osmosis is the diffusion of water through a differentially permeable membrane.
5. The actual pressure of the water molecules developed within a membrane as a result of osmosis is called the turgor pressure.
6. The maximum possible pressure which can develop in an ideal osmotic system is referred to as the osmotic pressure. Osmotic pressure is a physical index of the solute concentration of a solution.
7. The actual diffusion pressure of the water molecules in an osmotic system at any particular time is calculated in terms of the diffusion pressure deficit of the water molecules.
8. In a plant cell, the pressure opposite to and exerted against the turgor pressure by the cell wall is called the wall pressure.
9. Since diffusion pressure deficit indicates the actual diffusion pressure of the water molecules in a plant cell, water movement in plants is determined by diffusion pressure deficit gradients, and it occurs from cells of low DPD's to cells of high DPD's:

$$DPD = OP - WP$$
$$WP = TP$$

10. Under atmospheric conditions which cause low transpiration and with soil moisture near field capacity, active water movement occurs into plant roots and upward into the shoots due to osmosis and other physiological phenomena originating in the root absorbing cells. Active water absorption results in root pressure and guttation, but it cannot account for the large amounts of water absorption by plants.

11. Diffusion pressure deficits in shoot cells, usually in the leaves as a result of transpiration, exert a tension on the water conducting system which, in turn, causes movement of water from the soil, through roots, and upward in continuous, unbroken water columns. Transpiration and the resulting transpiration pull which causes water movement into plants are responsible for passive absorption, because the root cells play no active part in the inward movement of water under these conditions. This relationship in terms of the individual plant cell is expressed as follows:

$$DPD = OP - (-TP)$$

Passive absorption is responsible for the large amounts of water which move into, within, and out of plants, and is determined primarily by the rate of transpiration.

12. The transpiration rate in leaves is a function of both leaf characteristics and environmental factors. Important leaf characteristics affecting transpiration are stomatal opening, sunken stomates, amount of exposed internal cell surfaces, and cutinization of epidermal cells. Environmental factors affecting transpiration are solar radiation, air temperature, air vapor pressure, wind velocity, and soil moisture.

13. Water balance in plants occurs when absorption and transpiration are equal, whereas unbalance results when transpiration exceeds absorption. Water absorption is reduced by decreasing soil moisture, flooded soil, and increased solute concentration in the soil solution (physiological drought).

14. Lack of water balance in plants results in declining growth of shoots, decreased photosynthesis, acceleration of hydrolytic bioreactions, and increased root growth. Continued lack of water balance, however, will result in death by desiccation.

15. True drought resistance in plants is characterized by "tough" protoplasm which survives at low hydration and high temperature. Drought resistance is basically an inherited attribute.

6.

MINERAL NUTRITION

Relation of Water Absorption to Mineral
Absorption and Translocation.

In Chapter 5, it was pointed out that water movement into rooted-green plants was caused by the mechanisms of active and passive absorption. The various minerals which are present in soils are thought by most plant physiologists to move into roots as individual anions $(-)$ or cations $(+)$. Recent research with radioactive P^{32} showed that P^{32} ions were absorbed mainly by the root hairs and cells in the region of cell elongation, while only small amounts of P^{32} ions were absorbed by the meristematic cells. However, the greatest accumulation of P^{32} ions was in the meristem. This research, along with other radioactive isotopic tracer studies which dealt with the entire plant, have caused many workers to re-examine the relationship between mineral (or ionic) absorption and water absorption.

Prior to 1950, a majority of plant physiologists believed that the experimental evidence was sufficiently conclusive to state that the amount of minerals absorbed is not proportional to the amount of water absorbed. The reason for such a conclusion is illustrated by the data which compare the absorption rates of Br^- ions and water in barley plants (data based on 168 20-day-old barley plants) during a 10½-hour period (Figure 18). These data clearly showed that as many milliequivalents of Br^- ions were absorbed during the low transpiration period as were absorbed during the high transpiration period. The data also showed that Br^- ion absorption was not affected by light and dark. Other experiments have demonstrated that detached roots will absorb as high concentrations of minerals as will the same size root system attached to a rapidly transpiring shoot. Although this is true in laboratory experiments, data from such studies do not constitute sufficient proof that water absorption and mineral absorption are unrelated. Living root cells accumulate

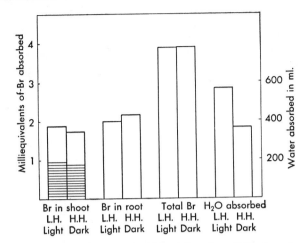

Figure 18 Absorption and translocation of Br ions in young barley plants under conditions of high and low transpiration. *(From Hoagland, D.R.* Inorganic Plant Nutrition. Chronica Botanica Co., 1948.)*

large concentrations of mineral ions in their vacuoles independently of transpiration pull, but as will be shown later, the ions in the vacuoles are probably unavailable for translocation via the xylem to the shoot.

The older concept postulated that ions accumulated in the vacuoles of the root absorption cells due to a process called active absorption. The accumulated ions were then thought to be released into the xylem by some unexplained mechanism. In the xylem, the rate of upward translocation of the ions was considered to be related to transpiration. Accumulation of ions, however, was not always highest in the more rapidly transpiring leaves, rather the greater concentrations of ions were found to be in rapidly growing tissues such as buds, fruits, and seeds.

In contrast to the above classical concept of ionic movement into and within intact rooted-green plants, numerous recent isotopic tracer studies have led to the following concept. The transpiring plant, by means of the transpiration pull-passive absorption mechanism, causes water movement in the root absorption cells to occur mainly through the cell walls, thus bypassing the living protoplasm. According to this explanation, water and ions move together in a mass flow through the root cell walls into the xylem and thence upward. This concept offers the most acceptable explanation at present, and it is consistent with numerous radioactive tracer studies which show a rapid upward movement of ions within plants. This rapid upward movement is not tenable with the old theory of accumulation and then release of ions through a cytoplasmic system into the xylem.

Mechanisms of Mineral Absorption.

Entry of minerals into plant roots was for many years viewed as a process of diffusion. The mineral ions were thought to combine within organic molecules and with each other in root tissues, thus causing a gradient for diffusion. Undoubtedly such combination occurs in the root cells to some degree, but many of the ions remain in the uncombined state in cell vacuoles. Furthermore, many of these ions, particularly cations such as K^+, Na^+, and Ca^{++}, accumulate in vacuoles in concentrations many hundreds of times those in the external solution. From such experimental evidence, the only plausible inference to be drawn is that many ions move into root cells against a gradient, and diffusion alone is thus an untenable and inadequate explanation.

Accumulations of ions in the vacuoles of cells is clearly demonstrated in algal cells, and data on this phenomenon are presented in Figure 19. Similar data, obtained from experiments with roots of higher plants, have given rise to the belief that accumulation of ions in cells can be attributed to the energy of metabolism being used to hold the ions against a gradient. This has been proved in a large number of experiments using both chemical analysis and radioactive tracer techniques.

That metabolic activity controls the amount of ionic accumulation in vacuoles can be demonstrated experimentally by showing the effects

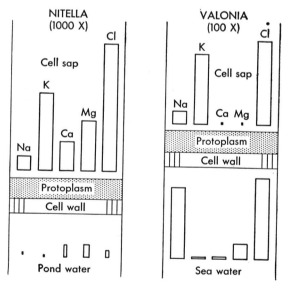

Figure 19 Relative concentrations of several ions in the cultural medium and in the vacuolar sap of algal cells. (*From Hoagland, D.R. Inorganic Plant Nutrition. Chronica Botanica Co., 1948.*)

of temperature, oxygen, sugar concentration in cells, and respiratory inhibitors upon such accumulation. These effects all suggest that ionic accumulation is in some manner related to the respiratory process. Although several elaborate theories (9) have been advanced to explain the role of respiration in ionic accumulation or movement against gradients, the exact nature of this interrelationship is at present unexplainable. The very striking effect of temperature and oxygen supply on the rate of inward movement of radioactive K^+ into barley roots is shown in Figure 20.

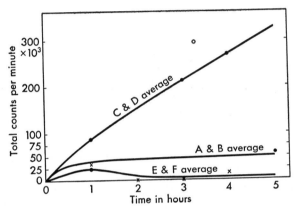

Figure 20 Effects of temperature and oxygen on absorption of radioactive potassium. A & B = 0.5°C & oxygen, C & D = 20°C & oxygen, and E & F = 20°C & no oxygen. (*From* Mineral Nutrition of Plants. *Emil Truog. The University of Wisconsin Press, 1951.*)

The accumulation of large concentrations of ions in root cells occurs chiefly in the meristematic region of the root tip, and this is called primary absorption. However, primary or active absorption, as it is sometimes named, is not limited entirely to meristematic cells, but it is also characteristic of elongating cells and root hairs as well as some kinds of storage cells.

Moreover, inward movement of ions is not confined to primary absorption. Ionic movement in cells also results from a process called ionic exchange which is often referred to as secondary absorption. Some workers believe that secondary absorption is a necessary step preceding primary absorption of ions. Secondary absorption, or ionic exchange, results from H^+ ions in the cells being exchanged for cations, such as K^+, Ca^{++}, Mg^{++}, etc., in the external solution; while OH^- and/or HCO_3^- anions in the cells are exchanged for anions, such as SO_4^{--}, Cl^-, NO_3^-, etc., in the external solution. Exchangeable ions are easily displaced from the root cells by other ions of like charge. For example, when excised barley roots were placed in a salt solution of radioactive potassium sulfate ($K_2S^*O_4$) for 90 minutes, the radioactive sulfate ion ($S^*O_4^{--}$) underwent maximum absorption in 30 minutes. When these same roots were transferred to a salt solution of calcium sulfate ($CaSO_4$), there was an exchange of the radioactive sulfate ions ($S^*O_4^{--}$) for the nonradioactive SO_4^{--} ions of the external solution in a period of 60 minutes.

At present some plant physiologists visualize ionic absorption as a combination of diffusion, ionic exchange, and active absorption. Portions of living plant cells have certain areas (sometimes called outer space) into which simple diffusion of ions occur from the external solution and vice versa. Ions in the outer space are either exchanged for ions in the cells, or such ions combine with carriers. Ions in combination with carriers are then released into the cell vacuoles. The ions within the vacuoles cannot be exchanged or move to other cells, and these ions may remain in the vacuoles until the death of the cells. This theory postulates that the vacuolar membrane is impermeable to free ions, but freely permeable to the carrier-ion complex. As mentioned previously, the accumulated ions in the vacuoles are not the ions which are translocated upward in the transpiration stream.

Factors Affecting Mineral Absorption.

The rate of entry of the ionic minerals into roots, as already stated, is affected by internal cellular metabolic activity. However, any particular ion is affected by other factors which complicate even further our understanding of mineral absorption. The most obvious of these other factors is the external concentration. It is a long established fact that the rate of accumulation of an ion in root cells is proportional to the external concentration of that ion. Monovalent ions accumulate more rapidly than do divalent ions. The rate of absorption of a particular ion is markedly influenced by the nature of the accompanying ion of opposite charge.

Extensive research has demonstrated the effects between various ions on their rates of absorption. The earlier studies usually were associated with increasing the absorption of ions by counteracting the effect of a single ion present in high concentration in the external solution. This phenomenon, called antagonism, is thought to be related to permeability. A classical example is the counteracting effect of Ca^{++} on Na^+. In contrast to counteracting the effect of one ion at high concentration with the addition of another, it was soon learned that interionic effects existed between ions at low concentrations. This interionic effect has been well investigated between such ions as: Ca^{++} and K^+, Ca^{++} and Mg^{++}, K^+ and Mg^{++}, Ca^{++} and BO_3^{---}, Fe^{+++} and Mn^{++}, NO_3^- and PO_4^{---}, and Fe^{+++} and PO_4^{---}. These experiments have led to attempts to show the best ratios, for example Ca/K, that would cause the maximum growth of a particular species of plant. Wide ratios have been shown not only to depress growth, but also to cause mineral deficiency symptoms. For example, a high proportion of iron to manganese causes manganese deficiency symptoms.

Concentrations of minerals in plants are not only controlled by internal and external conditions, but are also a function of the hereditary potentialities of plants. That such differences exist can be shown by growing various species of plants in the same mineral nutritional solutions. The results of such an experiment are shown in Figure 21. Differences have been long observed by practical agriculturists. For example, legumi-

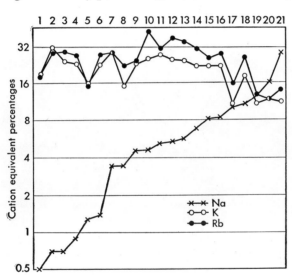

Figure 21   Differential accumulation of cations by various species of plants. Numbers at top indicate species.

1. *Fagopyrum* (Buckwheat).
2. *Zea* (Indian corn).
3. *Helianthus* (Sunflower).
4. *Chenopodium* (Goosefoot).
5. *Salsola* (Saltwort).
6. *Pisum* (Pea).
7. *Nicotiana* (Tobacco).
8. *Solanum* (Nightshade).
9. *Spinacia* (Spinach).
10. *Avena* (Oat).
11. *Aster* (Aster).
12. *Papaver* (Poppy).
13. *Lactuca* (Lettuce).
14. *Plantago* (Plantain).
15. *Melilotus* (Sweetclover).
16. *Vicia* (Vetch).
17. *Atriplex* (Saltbush).
18. *Sinapis* (Mustard).
19. *Salicornia* (Glasswort).
20. *Plantago* (Plantain).
21. *Atriplex* (Saltbush).

(From Collander, R. Plant Physiol. 16:691–720, 1941.)

nous plants will absorb large amounts of calcium while non-leguminous plants growing in the same soil will absorb smaller amounts of calcium.

From the preceding discussion it should now be clear that movement of minerals into plant roots is mainly affected by metabolic activity, interionic effects, and hereditary potentialities. There is one other external factor which has been assigned a role far more important than careful experimental evidence would justify. This factor is pH (degree of acidity or alkalinity). The degree of hydrogen-ion concentration has been shown to have little effect on plant growth within a relatively wide range of hydrogen-ion concentrations. An example of one of the numerous plants used to demonstrate that pH has no direct injurious effects is shown in Figure 22. For all species of plants investigated, Arnon and his co-

Figure 22   Effect of external pH on the growth of lettuce. From left to right: pH3, 4, 5, 6, 7, 8, and 9. *(From Arnon, Daniel I. and C.M. Johnson, Plant Physiol. 17:525–540, 1942.)*

workers were able to show that a pH of 3.0 was markedly injurious. For other pH's, if the mineral salts remained in solution, neither mineral absorption nor plant growth was depressed.

Translocation of Mineral Ions in the Intact Plant.

As already discussed, ionic absorption into roots occurs mainly in the region of cell elongation and in the root hairs. Some ions either accumulate in the vacuoles of cells or become chemically combined into organic molecules as the result of numerous cellular metabolic processes, while other ions remain free in the outer space of the cells from whence they can move via the transpirational stream across the cortex into the xylem. Research shows that uncombined ions in the vacuolar sap cannot diffuse back out. Therefore, ions can be translocated upward into the shoot only by the passive mass flow process. However, there is too much experimental data to enable the acceptance of mass flow as the only process involved. As has already been shown (Figure 18), ions are translocated upward during the dark period as well as during the light period. Furthermore, the bleeding sap from a stump contains a rather high concentration of ions. Other ions may move downward and accumulate in the root apical meristem. At present a process which explains all the known facts has not been forthcoming. Present opinion, however, strongly favors diffusion as being the principal cause. The ions move in the outer free space of the cell cytoplasm and also from cell to cell by means of the plasmodesms. Thus, it is seen that ions can diffuse across the cortex and into the xylem without ever entering the vacuoles of the cortical cells.

Upward movement of minerals occurs almost entirely in the xylem. The fact that minerals move upward in the xylem was established in 1939 by Hoagland by separating the phloem from the xylem and using radioactive tracers. As the minerals are swept upward in the xylem vessels of the shoot, they may be distributed as follows: a portion will diffuse laterally into the cambium and phloem; a portion will move laterally via rays into actively metabolizing cells; a portion will be moved into the leaves via the transpiration stream; and a portion will move into the actively metabolizing meristems. The highest concentrations invariably occur in the region of highest growth rate.

Some of the ions that have been translocated from the roots via the xylem tissue into leaves, and into such growing areas as bud meristems, fruit, and seeds, may not remain in these cells. Probably only a small proportion of the ions is translocated out of growing cells of leaves, buds, etc. However, radioactive tracer studies have shown that ions can be translocated out of any of these organs. These studies have established that such ionic movement is by way of the phloem tissue. Probably the largest amount of total ionic movement is from mature leaves. Whatever the origin of an ion in the phloem tissue, the ion will move rapidly in the phloem (Table 5-A). Once in the phloem, ions either are translocated upward to growing leaves and buds or downward to the root cells in the regions of cell division and cell elongation. In these cells, ions either move into the xylem again or outward into the external medium. Thus, ions can circulate in the rooted-green plant.

Table 5-A The rates of translocation of several ionic species in the phloem tissue of several kinds of plants as determined by radioactive isotopic tracer studies (*From various sources in the literature*).

KIND OF ION	KIND OF PLANT	TRANSLOCATION RATE
		cm/hr
Iron	Bean	43
Phosphate	Bean	60
Phosphate	Cotton	21
Sulfate	Bean	41

Many studies have shown that not all ions are freely mobile for phloem translocation. The highly mobile ions are NO_3^-, SO_4^{--}, PO_4^{---}, K^+, Na^+, Mg^{++}, Mn^{++}, and BO_3^{---}. Ions that are less mobile are Fe^{+++}, Cu^{++}, and Zn^{++}. Calcium is thought to be entirely non-mobile. The above pattern of ionic mobility is useful in explaining why the older leaves show mineral deficiency symptoms earlier than do younger leaves. This is true only for the mobile essential-mineral ions.

The mobile ions translocated out of leaves via the phloem are the kinds of essential-mineral ions which may be used in foliar application of fertilizers. Within the last decade, a great deal of research has been done on the foliar application of fertilizers. In general these studies have shown that expanding leaves with little cutinization absorb most readily water soluble mineral salts. However, only the mobile ions are translocated via the phloem from the leaves in sufficient quantities to maintain growth in meristematic areas. Many problems yet remain to be solved in foliar application of fertilizers. For example, one of these problems concerns essential minerals being applied as foliar sprays in organic forms (chelates and urea-nitrogen). Injury has often resulted from the application of these organic forms of fertilizers. Foliar sprays of essential-mineral ions in agriculture were first successfully used with the essential microminerals such as Zn^{++}, Cu^{++}, BO_3^{---}, and Mo^{--}.

Another interesting fact about ion mobility is its application to the growth cycle in the rooted-green plant. As vegetative growth proceeds in such annual plants as corn, cotton, etc., the lower mature leaves have as much as 40 to 90 per cent loss of the more mobile ions to the upper growing leaves and meristematic areas. The greatest loss occurs from leaves to growing fruit and seeds.

The Essential Elements.

Rooted-green plants, when growing in soils, absorb all mineral elements which are present in an available form. A majority of the 92 elements have been found in plant tissue. However, it was not until the middle of the last century that plant physiologists began to formulate and understand the essential element concept. During this period, basic concepts were established which indicated that plant dry matter was made up mainly of carbon, oxygen, and hydrogen (Figure 23). The carbon and oxygen were shown to come from the air in the form of carbon dioxide, and the hydrogen from water. The remaining dry matter, constituting about 10 per cent (or 2 per cent of the fresh weight), was composed of minerals absorbed from the soil. Prior to 1870, carbon dioxide was thought to be absorbed by the roots from soil humus. Growing of plants in aqueous mineral solutions devoid of humus and of other organic materials by Knop and Sachs was the experimental basis for clarifying the origin of the essential elements.

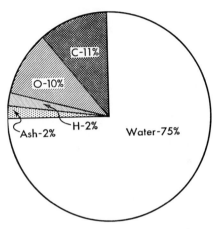

Figure 23 Percentage distribution (on a fresh weight basis) of the main constituents of green plant tissue. (*From Lyon, T.L. and H.O. Buckman.* The Nature and Properties of Soils. *The Macmillan Company, 1943.*)

In 1920, as a result of mineral nutritional solution studies, it was believed that 10 chemical elements were essential for normal plant growth. These were carbon, hydrogen, oxygen, nitrogen, phosphorus, sulfur, calcium, potassium, magnesium, and iron. These are designated as the macronutrients. However, plant physiologists continued their search for other possibly essential mineral elements. By careful purification of the salts used in mineral nutritional solutions, by using insoluble glass containers, and by removal of contaminating minerals from distilled water, various investigators have now added boron, zinc, copper, manganese, molybdenum, and chlorine to the essential element list. As shown in Table 6, the essential role of the last six elements was demonstrated rather recently. These investigations revealed that the six elements were needed in the nutrient solutions only in very low concentrations (0.5 to 0.01 parts per million). For this reason, the last six essential elements have been designated as minor or trace elements, or micronutrients. At present plant physiologists are of the opinion, after very careful nutrient solution research, that probably 15 or 16 chemical elements are essential for plant growth.

Table 6   Discovery of the essentiality of the micronutrients in plant nutrition.

MICRONUTRIENT	YEAR DISCOVERED	DEMONSTRATED BY
Manganese	1922	McHargue
Boron	1923	Warington
Zinc	1926	Sommer and Lipman
Copper	1931	Lipman and MacKinney
Molybdenum	1939	Arnon and Stout
Chlorine	1954	Broyer, Carlton, Johnson, and Stout

Table 7   The approximate non-toxic amounts in whole plant and the roles of essential elements in rooted-green plants.

ESSENTIAL ELEMENT	APPROXIMATE AMOUNT IN WHOLE PLANT	PRINCIPAL FUNCTION
1. Carbon	45%	All cellular constituents.
2. Oxygen	43%	All cellular constituents.
3. Hydrogen	6%	All cellular constituents.
4. Nitrogen	1–3%	All living matter, amino acids, proteins.
5. Potassium	0.3–6.0%	Enzyme system in the change of sugar to starch, citric acid synthesis, in the change of amino acids to proteins, respiration, interaction with iron enzymes, photosynthesis, buffer.
6. Calcium	0.1–3.5%	Cell wall, cell permeability, buffer.
7. Sulfur	0.05–1.5%	All living matter, proteins, allyl oils of mustards, chlorophyll synthesis, nodulation in legumes.
8. Phosphorus	0.05–1.0%	All living matter, nucleoproteins, lipoids, phosphorylation enzymes.
9. Magnesium	0.05–0.7%	A part of the tetrapyrrolic chlorophyll molecule, enzyme activator of hexokinase, phosphorylase, carboxylase, dehydrogenase, peptidase, photosynthesis, buffer.
10. Chlorine	100–300 p.p.m.	Unknown.
11. Iron	10–1500 p.p.m.	A part of the porphyrin compounds, cytochrome enzyme system, chlorophyll synthesis.
12. Manganese	5–1500 p.p.m.	Chlorophyll synthesis, stabilization of H-atoms split from H-OH by hydrogenation in photosynthesis, reduction of nitrates to nitrites, activator of arginase, carboxylases, and dehydrogenases.
13. Zinc	3–150 p.p.m.	Tryptophane synthesis (precursor for auxin), phosphorylation enzymes, enzymes in chloroplasts.
14. Copper	2–75 p.p.m.	Enzyme in synthesis of ascorbic acid, activator of polyphenoloxidase, laccase, and oxidase.
15. Boron	2–75 p.p.m.	Phosphorylation enzymes, glutamine synthesis, nodulation in legumes.
16. Molybdenum	Very minute	Nodulation in legumes, tannin synthesis, reduction of nitrates to nitrites.

With a knowledge of the essential elements necessary for higher plants, plant physiologists have exerted considerable effort toward an understanding of how each of the elements functions in plant metabolism. A summary of the known functions of essential elements is given in Table 7. The establishment of the essentiality of an element is determined by whether: 1. withholding of the element affects normal growth; 2. withholding of the element causes a deficiency disease; 3. the element is a part of organic molecules; and 4. the element participates in a bio-chemical reaction.

Nutrient Solutions.

The growing of plants in nutrient solutions containing mineral salts dissolved in water has enabled plant physiologists to establish which elements are essential for plant metabolism and to study the effect of the absence of each of the 12 mineral elements on deficiency symptoms and growth. Many combinations of salts have been used in nutrient solutions. Formulae of four of the more common nutrient solutions are given in Table 8. One of the earliest solutions was that prepared by Knop which he used for plant growth studies in 1865. However, he did not supply his nutrient solutions with minor elements because their essentiality was not established; nevertheless, the minor elements were probably present as contaminants in his salts. This lack of knowledge of minor elements still prevailed through the 1920's, which accounts for the fact that the widely used solution of the American plant physiologist, Shive, did not contain minor elements. In the early 1930's, minor elements were found to be essential and, since that time, have been added to nutrient solutions. At present, solutions composed of salts which furnish 12 elements are extensively used. Hoagland's solutions are used by many investigators of plant nutrition at present.

Examination of the four solutions reveals that considerable variation exists in the concentrations of their macronutrients. Each of these solutions has been acclaimed as being suitable for growing a large number of different species of plants. However, an examination of other nutrient solutions used by many different investigators for a wide variety of crops reveals considerable variation among the various solutions in their effects upon plant growth. One such investigation (10) showed that various species of plants grew much better in one solution than in the other solutions. It would seem that a single nutrient solution acceptable for the growth of all plant species is not available, although modification of a basic solution, such as Hoagland's will cause it to be a suitable nutrient solution for a particular plant.

Table 8   A comparison of the composition of four nutrient solutions.

SALT	KNOP'S SOLUTION	SHIVE'S SOLUTION	HOAGLAND'S SOLUTION (1)	HOAGLAND'S SOLUTION (2)
	gm/liter	gm/liter	gm/liter	gm/liter
$Ca(NO_3)_2 \cdot 4H_2O$	0.8	1.23	1.18	0.95
KNO_3	0.2	. . .	0.51	0.61
KH_2PO_4	0.2	2.45	0.14	. . .
$MgSO_4 \cdot 7H_2O$	0.2	3.70	0.49	0.49
$FePO_4$	trace	0.005	. . .	. . .
$FeC_4H_2O_6$	. . .	. . .	0.005	0.005
$NH_4H_2PO_4$	. . .	. . .	. . .	0.12
H_3BO_3	. . .	. . .	0.0029	0.0029
$MnCl_2 \cdot 4H_2O$	. . .	. . .	0.0018	0.0018
$ZnSO_4 \cdot 7H_2O$	. . .	. . .	0.00022	0.00022
$CuSO_4 \cdot 5H_2O$	. . .	. . .	0.00008	0.00008
$H_2MoO_4 \cdot H_2O$	. . .	. . .	0.00002	0.00002

Nutrient solutions have proved to be a valuable tool in determining the mineral nutritional requirements for the maximum growth of crop plants. Such basic information as to how variations in concentrations and variations in ionic ratios affect crop growth is studied by means of nutrient solution techniques. This type of basic research has been carried out only on a few crop plants, but applied plant scientists are now making greater use of the nutrient solution method. Use of nutrient solutions is not limited to a water medium, and it has been widely adapted to other media such as sand and gravel (11). For the sand and gravel media, the solutions are pumped upward through the media and then allowed to drain downward. At suitable intervals, the solutions are pumped upward in order to keep the water and nutrient at an optimum to prevent drying of roots and to insure continued supplies of water and nutrients to the roots.

Nutrient solutions, as a scientific tool in mineral nutritional research, are not devoid of problems. Maintenance of ions in an available form has proved troublesome. Keeping ions in an available form is mainly dependent on preventing the nutrient solution from shifting from an optimum pH of about 6.0 as the plant absorbs certain ions such as No_3^- more rapidly than others. A pH of near 6.0 is maintained in some nutrient solutions by adding a buffer such as $NH_4H_2PO_4$ (Hoagland's Solution (2), Table 8). Adjustment of pH, however, did not overcome the troublesome problem of maintenance of iron in an available form. Iron is easily tied up with the phosphate ion and precipitated out. Recently this problem has been successfully solved by using a complex organic form of iron in compounds such as chelates. Chelated iron was at first thought to be a reservoir of iron that slowly released the Fe^{+++} ion which could then be absorbed by the root. However, radioactive tracer studies later showed that the entire chelated molecule was absorbed from which iron was released in the plant cell for use in certain metabolic processes. The chemists call the chelated compound either potassium or sodium ethylene-diamine tetraacetate.

Limitation of oxygen supply in nutrient solutions restricts both root growth and mineral absorption. This has been overcome by means of continuous aeration, which is now a standard practice. In a water medium, air under pressure is bubbled from various aerators such as porous stones and fritted glass discs.

On a commercial scale, the growing of plants in nutrient solutions is known as hydroponics. Hydroponic culture of plants is accomplished in large, shallow tanks constructed of concrete, sheet metal, or wood, in which the chemical solutions, with or without sand or gravel, are placed. Use of sand or gravel has many advantages over a water medium. For example, these media serve as anchors for the plant roots as well as overcoming some of the difficulties of supporting the shoot. However, use of impure sources of sand or gravel or improper purification of these materials may cause mineral nutritional disturbances in some plant species. The culture tanks are usually equipped with pumping devices and empty auxiliary tanks so that the solutions may be pumped out of the growth tanks and circulated at suitable intervals to insure adequate aeration of the nutrient solutions.

Mineral Deficiency Symptoms.

The absence or deficiency of any of the essential minerals in the soil or in a nutrient solution will cause decreased growth and/or deficiency symptoms in shoots and roots. By use of certain nutrient solutions, these effects are reproducible in plant species and an exact knowledge is obtained as to which mineral deficiency causes a particular symptom. Under natural conditions, however, because of a similarity of symptoms for more than one mineral and differences due to plant species, it is often difficult to diagnose exactly which mineral is deficient. Nevertheless, in a general way, the symptoms of a given mineral deficiency are similar in all species of plants. A key to mineral deficiency symptoms is presented in Table 9.

It is now generally accepted that deficiency of minerals can cause definite abnormal appearances in plants (Figure 24). For many years some of the mineral deficiency symptoms were confused with effects due to pathological causes such as fungi, bacteria, and viruses. Mineral deficiencies from nitrogen, phosphorus, and potassium often cause a

Table 9 A key to mineral deficiency symptoms. *(From McMurtrey. Diagnostic Techniques for Soils and Crops. American Potash Inst., 1950.)*

SYMPTOMS	ELEMENT DEFICIENT
A. Older or lower leaves of plant mostly affected; effects localized or generalized.	
B. Effects mostly generalized over whole plant; more or less drying or firing of lower leaves; plant light or dark green.	
C. Plant light green; lower leaves yellow, drying to light-brown color; stalks short and slender if element is deficient in later stages of growth	Nitrogen
CC. Plant dark green, often developing red and purple colors; lower leaves sometimes yellow, drying to greenish brown or black color; stalks short and slender if element is deficient in later stages of growth	Phosphorus
BB. Effects mostly localized; mottling or chlorosis with or without spots of dead tissue on lower leaves; little or no drying up of lower leaves.	
C. Mottled or chlorotic leaves, typically may redden, as with cotton; sometimes with dead spots; tips and margins turned or cupped upward; stalks slender	Magnesium
CC. Mottled or chlorotic leaves with large or small spots of dead tissue.	
D. Spots of dead tissue small, usually at tips and between veins, more marked at margins of leaves; stalks slender	Potassium
DD. Spots generalized, rapidly enlarging, generally involving areas between veins and eventually involving secondary and even primary veins; leaves thick; stalks with shortened internodes	Zinc
AA. Newer or bud leaves affected; symptoms localized.	
B. Terminal bud dies, following appearance of distortions at tips or bases of young leaves.	
C. Young leaves of terminal bud at first typically hooked, finally dying back at tips and margins, so that later growth is characterized by a cut-out appearance at these points; stalk finally dies at terminal bud	Calcium
CC. Young leaves of terminal bud becoming light green at bases, with final breakdown here; in later growth, leaves become twisted; stalk finally dies back at terminal bud .	Boron
BB. Terminal bud commonly remains alive; wilting or chlorosis of younger or bud leaves with or without spots of dead tissue; veins light or dark green.	
C. Young leaves permanently wilted (wither-tip effect) without spotting or marked chlorosis; twig or stalk just below tip and seedhead often unable to stand erect in later stages when shortage is acute	Copper
CC. Young leaves not wilted; chlorosis present with or without spots of dead tissue scattered over the leaf.	
D. Spots of dead tissue scattered over the leaf; smallest veins tend to remain green, producing a checkered or reticulating effect	Manganese
DD. Dead spots not commonly present; chlorosis may or may not involve veins, making them light or dark green in color.	
E. Young leaves with veins and tissue between veins light green in color	Sulfur
EE. Young leaves chlorotic, principal veins typically green; stalks short and slender	Iron

Figure 24 Tobacco plants showing various mineral deficiencies. Letters indicate: B—nitrogen, C—phosphorus, D—potassium, E—boron, F—calcium, G—magnesium, and A—all essential nutrients. *(From Hunger Signs in Crops. 1941. Courtesy of the National Plant Food Institute.)*

striking reduction in growth or dwarfing of plants. Other minerals cause a yellowing in various patterns in leaves which is called chlorosis. Deficiencies of several of the trace minerals and of calcium cause a disturbance in meristematic regions which results in distorted and twisted growth of young leaves and stem. Diseases caused by deficiencies of trace minerals are summarized in Table 10.

Table 10 A summary of diseases in various plants caused by trace mineral deficiencies.

| PLANT SPECIES | DISEASE CAUSED BY A DEFICIENCY OF | | | |
	MANGANESE	ZINC	BORON	COPPER
Oats	Grey speck			Yellow tip
Sugar cane	Pahala blight			
Sugar beet	Speckled yellows		Heart rot	
Peas	Marsh spot			
Tung oil	Frenching	Bronzing		
Pecan		Rosette		
Fruit trees		Little leaf	Internal cork	Die-back
Citrus		Little leaf		
Corn		White tip		
Cauliflower			Browning	
Celery			Cracked stem	
Alfalfa			Yellow top	
Tobacco			Top sickness	

Sources of Essential Minerals

As has already been pointed out (Table 7), 12 of the essential minerals are absorbed by plant roots from the soil environment. Of these 12 minerals, by strict definition only 11 are minerals or have their origin from the weathering of parent material rocks. The twelfth mineral, the nitrogen in the soil utilized by plants, does not originate from weathering of parent material rocks, but instead comes ultimately from the atmosphere.

Atmospheric nitrogen, before becoming available for higher plants, must be fixed or combined with other elements. This combination or fixation is accomplished by symbiotic and free-living microorganisms in soils and by lightning discharges in the atmosphere. The symbiotic bacteria *(Rhizobium)* which cause nodulation of leguminous plant species utilize free nitrogen gas from the air, and in their metabolism fix nitrogen into a combined form. The combined nitrogenous compound, probably amino nitrogen, is absorbed by the legume host and utilized in protein synthesis. It should be emphasized that the legume plant does not fix atmospheric nitrogen itself, but obtains it from its nitrogen fixing bacteria. In the soil other bacteria *(Azotobacter* and *Clostridium)*, which live entirely as saprophytes, are capable of nitrogen fixation. The symbiotic and saprophytic bacteria are the main sources of combined nitrogen in the soil. Combined organic nitrogen in dead legume and bacteria tissues is broken down by various microorganisms to the nitrate-nitrogen form. Nitrates are then utilizable by non-leguminous plants. Animals obtain their food either from plants or other animals, and utilize some of the nitrogenous foods in the synthesis of their proteins, while some nitrogen is excreted as urea. The protein in animal tissues, upon death, is returned to the soil as is the urea, and both groups of compounds are broken down by microorganisms to nitrates. The nitrogenous compounds in dead plant and animal tissues (and their wastes) are decomposed in several stages by various soil microorganisms, thus:

$$\text{Organic residues} \xrightarrow{\text{Ammonification}} NH_3 \xrightarrow{\text{Nitrification}} NO_2 \longrightarrow NO_3$$

The above discussion has shown that atmospheric nitrogen passes through a series of stages into living organisms and back again into the soil as combined nitrate. This series of steps, called collectively the nitrogen cycle, is diagrammatically summarized in Figure 25. Included in the nitrogen cycle, along with the nitrogen pathway from air to living organisms to soil, is also illustrated the manner in which nitrogen is lost from the soil. Nitrogen is lost from the soil as nitrates by the move-

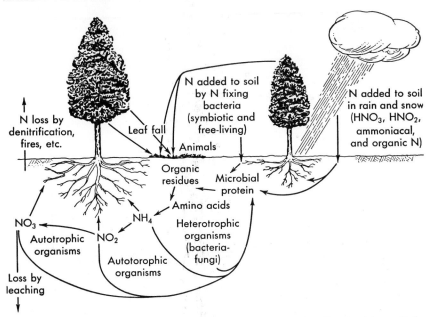

Figure 25 The nitrogen cycle. (*From Lutz, H.J. and R.F. Chandler, Jr.,* Forest Soils. *John Wiley and Sons, Inc., 1946.*)

ment of soil water into the ground water (leaching) and by soil erosion. Nitrogen is returned to the air as free nitrogen gas by denitrifying bacteria and by burning either plant or animal residues.

Effects of Mineral Supply on Plant Growth.

Provided all other essential minerals are not limiting and in proper ratios, recognition of the effect of the amount or concentration of any particular mineral in an available form on plant growth and yield has been an established principle in crop management for many years. This principle was founded mainly on fertilizer investigations. However, more exacting research with nutrient solutions has substantiated this concept. Increases in concentration of a mineral may cause corresponding increases in plant growth or yield. If concentrations are increased beyond a certain critical level, however, further growth or increase in yield does not occur, although the concentration of the mineral may continue to increase in the plant parts. This excess in mineral is called luxury consumption since it does not contribute to further yield. By plotting either external concentration of a nutrient or tissue concentration against growth, a curve of the type shown in Figure 26 is obtained. Tissue concentration is probably a better indicator of the critical level required

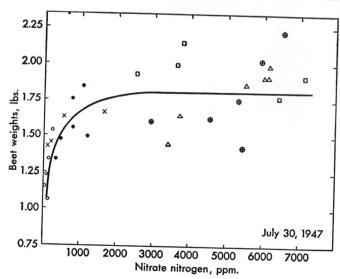

Figure 26 Relationships of beet root weights (green) and nitrate-nitrogen concentration (dry weight) of recently matured sugar beet leaves. (*From Ulrich, Albert.* Annual Review of Plant Physiology. 1952.)

for a particular mineral than is soil analysis, because tissue measurement shows the actual absorption by the plant. It should be emphasized, however, that the critical level associated with maximum yield must be worked out for each species of plant. Furthermore, the concentration required for maximum growth varies with each season, so that under field conditions the required concentration of any particular mineral must be tested over several growing periods. Although tissue analysis is believed to be an excellent guide for determining mineral requirements, consideration must also be given to each field condition in order to set up fertilizer practices for maximum yields. This entire problem is far from being adequately solved by plant scientists. Far too much emphasis has been placed on field fertilizer trials as a solution to mineral nutritional problems, and too little emphasis has been given to controlled experiments with nutrient solutions, combined with above-ground environmental factors such as temperature and light.

Several of the important facts concerning mineral nutrition of plants may be summarized as follows:

1. Absorption of mineral ions by the individual living plant cell is due to diffusion, ionic exchange, and active or metabolic absorption. Accumulation of such ions as the K^+ ion in the cell vacuole against a diffusion gradient is a result of converting metabolic or respiratory energy into osmotic energy.

One plausible theory is that active absorption is by means of a carrier (an unknown organic constituent) which diffuses with its ions into the vacuole and there releases them. The vacuolar membrane is permeable to the carrier but not to ions separately. Thus the vacuolar sap ions are irreversibly absorbed.

2. Ions that are translocated upward into the shoot from the root absorption cells either move across the cortex into the xylem by the transpirational-pull mass-flow mechanism via the cell walls, or they diffuse through the outer free space in the cytoplasm by means of the plasmodesms. It is thought that ions accumulated in the vacuoles are not available for translocation.

3. Mineral absorption is affected by: (a) metabolic activity of the absorption cells, (b) the concentration of the ions in the external solution, (c) cell permeability, (d) kind and nature of the ions, (e) interionic effects of one ion on another ion, and (f) the hereditary potential of the species.

4. Upward translocation of minerals from the roots occurs in xylem. Movement of minerals from leaves to meristematic regions in the shoot and downward to the root occurs in phloem. Minerals accumulate in greatest concentrations in those parts of shoots which are actively growing, or the meristematic regions.

5. There are 15 or 16 elements now known to be essential for normal plant growth. These are carbon, hydrogen, oxygen, nitrogen, phosphorus, potassium, sulfur, magnesium, calcium, iron, boron, manganese, zinc, copper, molybdenum, and chlorine. All these essential elements except carbon and oxygen are absorbed from the soil by plant roots.

6. The essential elements function in plant metabolism as constituents of cell components, as buffering agents in the vacuolar sap, and as participants in essential enzyme systems in biochemical reactions.

7. Nutrient solutions are valuable scientific tools in mineral nutritional research; plants may be grown in these solutions alone or in these solutions in sand or gravel media.

8. Deficiency of an essential mineral will cause retardation in plant growth and/or the development of definite mineral deficiency symptoms in plants, some of which closely resemble symptoms due to pathogens.

9. Growth and yield of plants are directly proportional to external mineral supply. Maximum yield is associated with a definite optimum concentration of any particular mineral. Absorption of a mineral above the optimum concentration required for maximum growth is called luxury consumption.

7.
PHYSIOLOGICAL SIGNIFICANCE
OF SOILS AND SOIL MOISTURE

The Origin of Soils and Some General Concepts.
Most higher green plants have their root systems in that portion of the earth's surface called the soil. Since it is in the soil environment that roots grow, it is necessary to have an understanding of soils in studying water and mineral relationships of rooted-green plants. The water and minerals which are essential for both top and root growth move into plants through roots. The water and minerals which move into the roots are a part of the soil complex, which we shall now examine.

Soil may be defined as the outermost portion of the earth's surface which is usually a mixture of mineral and organic materials. Soils can be better understood if we know their origin and the processes involved in their formation. Soils are derived from parent materials, which are formed as a result of rock weathering. Soils, then, result from the interaction of parent materials, climate, organisms, and topography over varying periods of time (17).

Table 11 Classification of parent material according to geological origin. *(From Thompson, Louis M. Soils and Soil Fertility. McGraw-Hill Book Company, Inc. 1952.)*

	TRANSPORTING AGENCY	ORIGIN	CLASSIFICATION
I. Sedentary	Weathered in place	Residual	Residual
II. Transported	Water	Marine	Marine
		Lacustrine	Lacustrine
			Alluvial fan
		Alluvial	Delta
			Flood plain
			Terrace
	Ice	Glacial	Ground moraine
			Terminal moraine
			Outwash plain
			Loess
	Wind	Aeolian	Volcanic ash
			Adobe
			Dune sand
	Gravity	Colluvial	Colluvial

The soil body therefore results primarily from the action of climate and living organisms on the parent material. Parent materials, however, are not necessarily derived from weathered rocks in place, but may be of various other origins as shown in Table 11.

As a result of soil formation factors, a soil has certain definite structural and positional characteristics which form what is known as a soil profile. Three distinct horizons or levels are distinguishable in a well-developed soil. These horizons, usually designated from the surface downward as A, B, and C, vary tremendously in different soils. The degree of horizon development depends primarily on the age of the soil. A hypothetical soil profile is shown in Figure 27. A further simplification is illustrated in Figure 28. Plant roots generally are confined to the A and B horizons. The A horizon in a well developed soil is usually somewhat

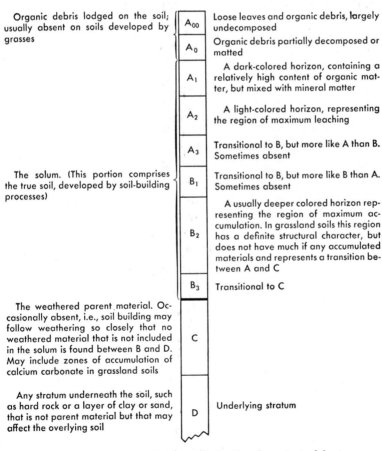

Figure 27 A hypothetical soil profile having the principal horizons (*From Soils and Men.* Yearbook of Agriculture. *U.S.D.A. 1938.*)

sandy, whereas the B horizon is often high in clay content. The B horizon, as a result of the downward movement of the finer clay particles, frequently becomes almost impermeable to water movement and is often poorly aerated, resulting in an environment unfavorable to root development. This type of accumulation of clay in the B horizon often results in what is commonly called a "hard-pan."

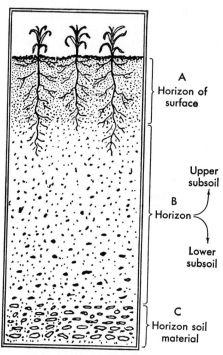

Figure 28 A simplification of a soil profile showing the three main horizons. (*From Lyon, T.L. and H.O. Buckman. The Nature and Properties of Soils. The Macmillan Company, 1943.*)

Some Soil Properties.

The soil horizons are made up of materials in three different states,—solid, liquid, and gaseous. The distribution of the three phases in soils for several soil types from various parts of the United States is shown in Figure 29. The solid portion is composed of organic and inorganic matter. Air and water occupy the pore spaces within the solid framework of the soil and also spaces within some of the soil particles. The solid phases are the source of minerals in the soil solution. Organic matter is an excellent storehouse for nitrogen, phosphorus, and sulfur.

The mineral particles of the soil are classified in descending order of size into three principal groups called sand, silt, and clay. Varying proportions of these particles of different sizes determine the soil texture classes. Several of these textural classes are illustrated in Figure 30.

Soil texture, while descriptive of the distribution of the soil separates, does not describe their arrangement. The arrangement of soil particles is known as soil structure. A sandy soil has a single grain type of structure which is well drained and aerated, but with little water holding capacity. The heavier clay soils have their structure arranged into either a tight, non-crumb structure which is poorly aerated and slowly permeable to water, or into the crumb type of structure which is well aerated, permeable, and with a high water holding capacity.

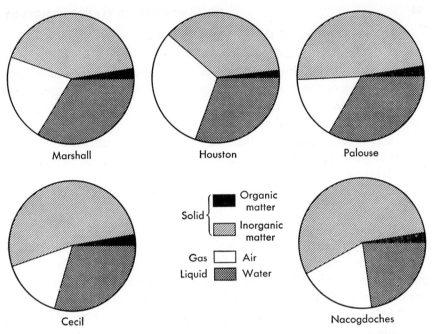

Figure 29 Proportions of various constituents of soils by volume at comparable moisture contents. (*From Soils and Men.* Yearbook of Agriculture. *U.S.D.A., 1938.*)

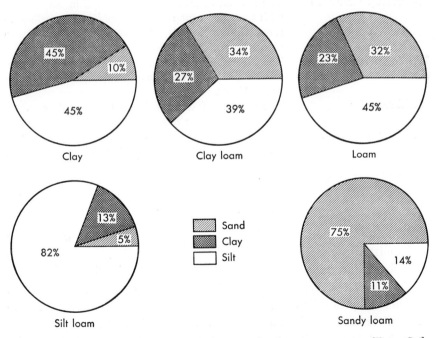

Figure 30 Per cent of sand, silt, and clay in soils of various textures. (*From Soils and Men.* Yearbook of Agriculture. *U.S.D.A. 1938.*)

The maintenance of the heavier soil types in a crumb structure is one of the most important problems in soil management for the growth of agricultural crops. Such soils are very productive since they have high mineral contents. Crumb structure is a result of formation of aggregates of the soil particles. Aggregates are made up of the silt, clay, and organic fractions of the soil held together by electrostatic bonds between the clay and organic fractions. Some of the binding is attributed also to sticky organic cementing substances secreted by soil microorganisms. This type of aggregation is only temporary, however, and must be periodically renewed by additions of organic matter. Organic matter functions not only as a source of minerals for plants, but it is equally important in causing soil aggregation.

Directly related to and controlled by texture and structure is soil moisture. Soil moisture is held in the soil by certain soil forces and is moved into the plant by forces which originate within the plant, as described earlier. Soil moisture variations may be grouped into soil moisture equilibrium points which are extensively used in describing plant-soil moisture relationships. These may be summarized as follows:

Equilibrium point	Description of value
Hygroscopic moisture	The amount of water held by the soil in equilibrium with 98.2 per cent relative humidity (according to some workers). This moisture is not available to plants because it is held by soil forces.
Wilting percentage	The soil moisture content at which the soil moisture is not sufficiently available to prevent permanent wilting of plants.
Field capacity	The amount of water held in the soil after excess gravitational water has drained off.
Moisture equivalent	This moisture content is approximately equivalent to field capacity and is the amount of water removed from soil by a force 1000 times gravity.
Available moisture	The soil moisture obtained by taking the differences between field capacity and wilting percentage. This is the water that is available for movement into plants.

Moisture in soils is in a highly dynamic condition and the above static soil moisture points are useful only in understanding the relationships of soil moisture to plants and in the classification of soil moisture categories. A better picture can be given through a graphic presentation developed by Edlefsen and Anderson as shown in Figure 31. An examination of this illustration reveals that if wet by rainfall or irrigation, soils do not retain water indefinitely since the soil moisture is acted upon by

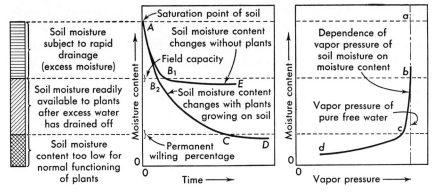

Figure 31 Relation among permanent wilting percentage, field capacity, range of readily available moisture, drainage, vapor pressure, and moisture content. (*From Baver, L.D., Soil Physics, John Wiley and Sons, Inc., 1948.*)

certain forces. The force of gravity will drain most of the water from the non-capillary or macropore spaces to the point B_1. If plants are not growing in the soil, the moisture remaining in the capillary or micropore spaces will be at equilibrium with the capillary-holding forces of the soil particles. This is indicated by the line B_1E. Movement of moisture within the capillary range is extremely slow and assumes importance only when the rooted-green plant is introduced into a soil.

When a plant grows in soil, water moves into the roots mainly by forces originating from transpiration of the plant. This will reduce the moisture content of the soil to the point of permanent wilting C unless the absorbed water is replaced. This reduction occurs only in a narrow zone around the absorbing zone of the roots. As previously mentioned, movement of moisture in the capillary zone is too sluggish to replace sufficiently the water absorbed by the plant. The soil moisture in regions around the roots then becomes constant as shown by the portion of the curve CD in Figure 31. Although within this entire range the vapor pressure is the same as that of free water, the water vapor is not absorbed by plants. Even below the permanent wilting point, the soil air is essentially saturated. Therefore, despite the presence of water at permanent wilting, movement of soil moisture by forces arising within the plant cannot cause a sufficient amount of water movement into the plant to prevent death by desiccation. It should now be clear that soil moisture is held within the soil by definite forces. Soil physics has developed means of expressing these forces.

All present knowledge of soil moisture is based on concepts which visualize the water in the soil as being held by attractive forces of the soil particles. One of the most common units of measurement of such attraction is based on the tension exerted on the soil water by the soil particles, expressed as the pressure (of a water column of a given number of centimeters in height) which must be applied to remove the soil water at various soil-moisture contents. As is shown in Table 12, this necessitates the use of rather large and cumbersome figures. As a substitute, these figures are converted to logarithmic values and the term pF is applied to such values. Another unit of measurement applied to moisture tensions is stated in terms of atmospheres of pressure required to remove water from the soil at a given soil-moisture content. A summary of these units at various soil moisture constants is given in Table 12.

Table 12   Soil moisture retention points and tension equivalents.

SOIL MOISTURE RETENTION POINTS	TENSION EQUIVALENT TO		
	CM. OF WATER	PF	ATMOSPHERES
Saturated	1.0	0.0	0.001
Field Capacity	344.0	2.5	0.333
Wilting Point	15,000.0	4.2	15.000
Hygroscopic	31,623.0	4.5	30.600
Oven dry	10,000,000.0	7.0	10,000.000

These figures illustrate the magnitude with which the attractive (soil) forces exerted on soil moisture are increased as water is moved out of the soil by plants. Other terms have been used to express these forces, namely, capillary potential, free energy, moisture stress, and diffusion pressure deficit.

Data are presented in Figure 32 which illustrate the relationship between the various classifications of soil moisture and tension forces as expressed in pF units, and the primary soil property which determines the amount of soil moisture held at these various tensions. These data show that the amount of soil moisture is a function of soil texture at any given soil tension. For example, at pF 2.7 the sandy loam has 20 per cent moisture, whereas at the same pF the clay loam has 40 per cent moisture. The moisture available to plants is almost three times as great in the clay loam as in the sandy loam. If maintained in good crumb structure which establishes aeration conditions conducive to root growth, a clay loam soil has obvious advantages over a sandy loam soil for crop survival during droughts. The influence of soil texture on available soil moisture for a wide range of soil types in the southeastern United States is clearly brought out in Figure 33.

It is now generally accepted that soil texture is the major soil characteristic which controls the amount of moisture in soils. A question which often arises is this: does not organic matter also affect the amount of soil

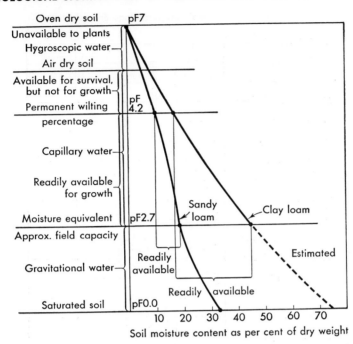

Figure 32 Classification of soil moisture in relation to pF for a sandy loam and clay loam soil. (*By permission from* Plant and Soil Water Relations, *by P.J. Kramer. Copyright 1949. McGraw-Hill Book Company, Inc.*)

moisture? In the field, experiments have conclusively shown that organic matter does not appreciably increase the available soil moisture in the capillary or micropore spaces because under natural conditions the organic content of soils is usually so low that it is not significant. The main effect of organic matter in field soils is to improve soil structure. This prevents the formation of an impermeable surface layer and reduces the run-off of rainfall. Furthermore, the improved soil structure permits water to move downward via the macropore spaces, thus increasing what is called the infiltration rate. Organic matter therefore functions mainly in facilitating the movement of rainfall into the soil, but it does not materially increase the water content of agricultural soils in the range available for plants. In greenhouses and pots where large amounts of organic matter are added to soils, moisture-holding capacity is definitely increased by organic matter, but the wilting point is also raised, which largely counteracts the higher moisture-holding capacity. Therefore, available soil water for plants is not increased appreciably by addition of organic matter to soils.

The effect of the water table on soil moisture relationships has a

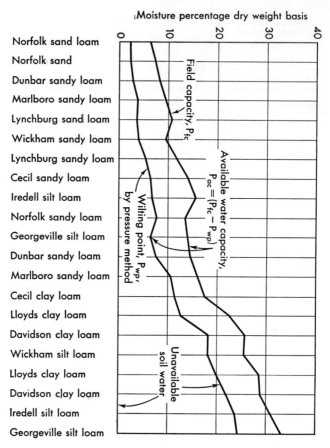

Figure 33 Field-moisture capacity, wilting point, and available water capacity for various soil types of the southeastern United States. *(From Israelsen, O.W.,* Irrigation Principles and Practices, *John Wiley and Sons, Inc., 1950.)*

definite bearing on plant growth. The water table may be defined as the upper limit of the part of the soil or underlying material wholly saturated with water. A water table near the soil surface causes the soil to have poor aeration and results in poor root growth. Usually such soils are occupied only by plants which have root systems tolerant of low oxygen environments. Therefore, these soils need to be drained before being utilized for the growth of most agricultural crops.

A common opinion held by many is that moisture can move upward from water tables by capillarity and provide adequate moisture for plants. If this were true, loss of crops during droughts would not occur. Experimental facts now show that upward movement of moisture by the forces of capillarity does occur, but that sufficient amounts of moisture to supply plants occur only within the soil region 18 inches above the water table. Consequently, water tables, which are usually 6 feet or more below the soil surface of most upland soils, do not furnish water for plants.

In the last several paragraphs attention has been given to physical properties and moisture relations of soils. The chemical nature of soils is equally important in influencing soil constituents related to plant growth. Collectively the soils of the world probably contain all the known chemical elements, but there is a great deal of variation in the numbers of elements in any particular soil type.

The chemical elements in soils are present in the solid phase and, with the exception of nitrogen, are a part of the inorganic mineral constituents. These mineral constituents are derived by weathering from rocks. The classes of soil minerals are silicates, phosphates, oxides, carbonates, sulphates, and sulphides. The chemical composition of the earth's crust and of the A and B soil horizons are given in Figure 34. These soil data are mean values of 18 soil types, and the constituents are expressed as oxides for comparative purposes and not necessarily as the forms in which the constituents exist in soils.

Weathering of parent material causes soils to contain fewer bases, such as calcium, magnesium, and potassium, and more silica and aluminum than the parent material. The loss of basic materials through soil formation processes is much greater in humid than in arid soils. There may also be less accumulation of organic matter in humid soils due to more continuous decomposition by microorganisms. These facts are illustrated in Figure 35. These data present pertinent evidence to show that the soils of the southeastern United States, for example, were deficient in essential minerals even before they were utilized for agriculture by the white man.

The alumina-silicate minerals constitute the bulk of the soil mineral structure. The essential elements comprise only a small part with potassium being the most abundant (approximately 2.0 per cent). Calcium, phosphorus, magnesium, and sulfur are found in quantities of less than 1 per cent. The other minerals essential for plant growth are found only in traces.

The essential minerals for plant growth occur in soils in aqueous solution, adsorbed on organic and inorganic colloids, as insoluble inorganic compounds, and as constituents of organic compounds. When in the available form, the essential minerals are either cations (Ca^{++}, Mg^{++},

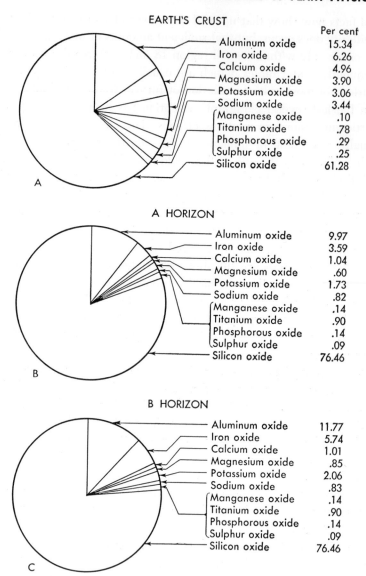

EARTH'S CRUST

	Per cent
Aluminum oxide	15.34
Iron oxide	6.26
Calcium oxide	4.96
Magnesium oxide	3.90
Potassium oxide	3.06
Sodium oxide	3.44
Manganese oxide	.10
Titanium oxide	.78
Phosphorous oxide	.29
Sulphur oxide	.25
Silicon oxide	61.28

A

A HORIZON

Aluminum oxide	9.97
Iron oxide	3.59
Calcium oxide	1.04
Magnesium oxide	.60
Potassium oxide	1.73
Sodium oxide	.82
Manganese oxide	.14
Titanium oxide	.90
Phosphorous oxide	.14
Sulphur oxide	.09
Silicon oxide	76.46

B

B HORIZON

Aluminum oxide	11.77
Iron oxide	5.74
Calcium oxide	1.01
Magnesium oxide	.85
Potassium oxide	2.06
Sodium oxide	.83
Manganese oxide	.14
Titanium oxide	.90
Phosphorous oxide	.14
Sulphur oxide	.09
Silicon oxide	76.46

C

Figure 34 The approximate composition of the earth's crust and mean composition of the A and B horizons of 18 representative soils. (*From Soils and Men.* Yearbook of Agriculture. *U.S.D.A. 1938.*)

K^+, Fe^{+++}, Mn^{++}, Zn^{++}, and Cu^{++}) or anions (sulfates, phosphates, borate, and molybdate). Nitrogen occurs either in the ammonium (cation) or nitrate (anion) form. Many of the cations and anions combine in the soil solution forming salts which have varying degrees of solubility as shown in Table 13.

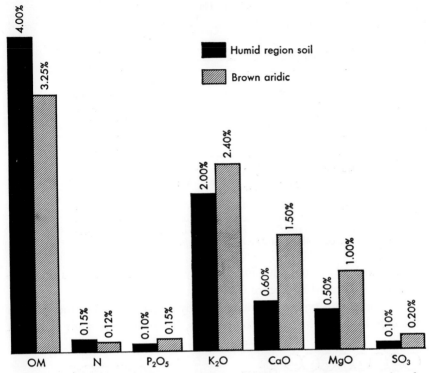

Figure 35   Chemical analysis of a representative humid region surface soil and a brown aridic surface soil. (*From Lyon, T.L. and H.O. Buckman.* The Nature and Properties of Soils. *The Macmillan Company, 1943.*)

Table 13   Solubility of mineral salts.

SOLUBILITY	SALTS
Completely soluble	Nitrates, chlorides
Less soluble	$Ca(H_2PO_4)_2$, $CaHPO_4$, $CaSO_4$, $CaCO_3$, $MgCO_3$, $FePO_4$, $AlPO_4$
Insoluble	$Ca_3(PO_4)_2$, $CaSO_4$, Colloidal salts

Minerals are absorbed by plants principally from the soil solution and from the colloidal clays. The colloidal clays play a very prominent role and much attention has been directed to them. The colloidal clay particles are negatively charged and have positively charged cations adsorbed in the electrostatic field around them. This arrangement is shown in Figure 36.

The crystal clay particles are now known to have a definite structure. This structure is known as a crystal lattice, two groups of which occur in soils. These are the kaolin group or the 1:1 type of crystal lattice, and the montmorillonite group or the 2:1 type of lattice. The 1:1 type means one silica sheet to one alumina, whereas the 2:1 type is composed

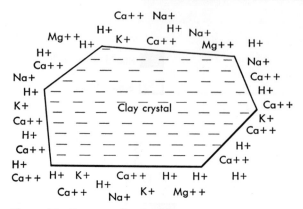

Figure 36 Diagram of a clay crystal showing the various cations that usually occupy the exchange complex. *(From Lyon, T.L. and H.O. Buckman. The Nature and Properties of Soils. The Macmillan Company, 1943.)*

of 2 silica sheets to one alumina. The crystal-lattice makeup is diagrammatically illustrated in Figure 37.

The kaolinite type is characterized by slight hydration and low ion exchange capacity. Montmorillonite clays, however, have high hydration

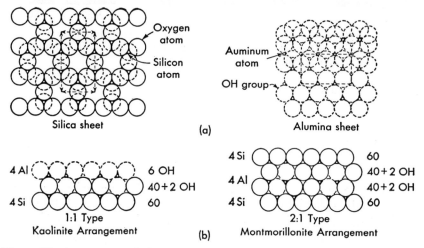

Figure 37 Arrangement of the atoms in the kaolinite and montmorillonite crystal lattice colloidal clays. *(From Baver, L.D., Soil Physics, John Wiley and Sons, Inc., 1948.)*

and high ion exchange capacity. The most important property from the plant nutritional viewpoint is the exchange capacity and the nature of the predominant adsorbed ions.

The exchange capacity is the relative cation adsorptive power of a clay. This is expressed as milliequivalents per 100 grams of dry soil. The exchange capacity of a soil is broken down into two components. The first portion is the exchangeable bases (not including hydrogen) and is expressed as percentage base saturation. A soil with a high percentage base saturation is one which has its clay colloidal complex saturated with cations such as calcium and sodium. On the other hand, a soil which is low in percentage base saturation has its colloidal clay saturated with hydrogen ions. A soil high in exchangeable hydrogen is an acid soil with a low pH. Conversely a soil with a high percentage base saturation is a neutral to alkaline soil with a high pH. The cations held by the clays are exchangeable, that is, hydrogen may displace sodium or calcium may displace hydrogen. The cations can be arranged in series as to their rate of release or ease of displacing other cations. The usual rate by which cations can be released is in the order of $Ca>Mg>Na>K$. The usual rate at which the cations may displace each other on the soil colloids is in the order of $H>Ca>Mg>K>Na$.

Table 14 Relation of pH values to acid and base normality and moles per liter of H^+ and OH^- ions. A simplification of the pH scale is shown below the table.

		MOLES PER LITER	
NORMALITY	*pH*	H^+	OH^-
1.0	0.0	1	10^{-14}
0.1	1.0	10^{-1}	10^{-13}
0.01	2.0	10^{-2}	10^{-12}
0.001	3.0	10^{-3}	10^{-11}
0.0001	4.0	10^{-4}	10^{-10}
0.00001	5.0	10^{-5}	10^{-9}
0.000001	6.0	10^{-6}	10^{-8}
Neutral	7.0	10^{-7}	10^{-7}
0.000001	8.0	10^{-8}	10^{-6}
0.00001	9.0	10^{-9}	10^{-5}
0.0001	10.0	10^{-10}	10^{-4}
0.001	11.0	10^{-11}	10^{-3}
0.01	12.0	10^{-12}	10^{-2}
0.1	13.0	10^{-13}	10^{-1}
1.0	14.0	10^{-14}	1

5.5	6.0	6.5	7.0	7.5	8.0	8.5
pH						pH
Strongly Acid	Medium Acid	Slightly Acid	Very Slightly Acid	Very Slightly Alkaline	Slightly Alkaline	Medium Alkaline	Strongly Alkaline

Soil solutions may be either acid or alkaline in reaction. In measuring the degree of acidity or alkalinity of a soil, a method is used which indicates the proportion of H^+ to OH^- ions. The proportion of H^+ to OH^- ions is expressed as the logarithm of the reciprocal of the hydrogen ion concentration (Table 14). If one understands that a change of pH is a logarithmic change, then the true meaning of the pH scale as an indicator of acidity or alkilinity becomes clear. A more accurate measurement of soil reaction, both in terms of the inorganic nutrients present and of lime requirement, is the millequivalents of hydrogen per 100 grams of dry soil.

Soils which have a low pH are sometimes deficient in the essential minerals for plant growth. This is particularly true of sandy soils. However, in heavier soils, such as silt and clay loams, pH readings on the acid side may not mean soils of low fertility. With the heavier textured soils it is necessary also to know the kind of clay mineral and the amount of organic colloid as well as available phosphorus. Thus, use of pH measurements of a soil to indicate its inorganic nutrient capacity is often misleading and erroneous. As was explained previously, soil solutions which have a low pH are not toxic to plants because of their high concentration of H^+ ions, but they may interfere with mineral absorption.

In a discussion of soils, a review of the organic fraction or soil organic matter is important. The organic fraction of soils is a stable complex of the more resistant constituents of plant and microbial residues. The original plant residues are not soil organic matter, but are rather a source of energy for the soil microbial population, and as such, are either resynthesized into the bodies of the microorganisms or released by their respiratory activity as CO_2 and H_2O. The exact chemical nature of the more resistant portion of the soil organic matter is not fully understood, but it is postulated to be a ligno-protein complex combined with the clay colloidal fraction.

When plant residues are added to a soil, the rate at which they decompose is dependent upon the ratio of carbon to nitrogen within the residues, provided soil moisture, aeration, temperature, and minerals are not limiting. Plant residues of wide C/N (high carbon—low nitrogen) ratios, such as oat straw, decompose slowly, whereas a plant residue of a leguminous origin with a narrow C/N (less carbon—more nitrogen) ratio decomposes rapidly. The wider C/N ratio in plant materials usually causes the available nitrogen in the soils to be lowered due to microbial activity which results in rapid utilization of the available nitrogen. This is known as immobilization which, unless corrected by application of nitrogen fertilizers, will cause a nitrogen deficiency in plants growing in such soils. During the decomposition process, minerals in the organic molecules of the plant and microbial residues are returned to the soil solution where they can be reutilized by growing plants. This process is known as mineralization.

The soil organic matter is an important part of soils because of its role in plant growth. First, as an organic colloid, it functions like clay crystals as an adsorbent of cations. As a result, organic matter has exchange capacity. In fact, organic colloids have much higher exchange capacities than do clay crystals. Second, organic matter is an important storehouse for some essential inorganic nutrients, namely, nitrogen, phosphorus, and sulfur. Finally, organic matter is probably the key to crumb structure or aggregate formation in heavier soils and thus indirectly affects aeration and water relations of soils.

8.
SOIL-ROOT RELATIONS

Generally the root system is that part of the plant in immediate contact with the soil or other substrate. In many species the root system constitutes the bulk of the plant body. Dittmer (18) found that the roots of a four months old winter rye plant had a combined length of 387 miles and a surface of 6,875 square feet, and the plant bore a total of approximately 14 billion root hairs. Although the greater portion of the root systems of many trees may be found in the top 4 or 5 feet of the earth's crust, the lateral spread of the roots may extend through the soil considerably beyond the tips of the longest branches of the crown (Figure 38). Thousands of plants including fungi, algae, liverworts and

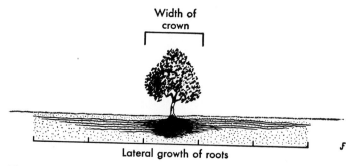

Figure 38 The lateral spread of the root system of a tree growing in an open field and not in competition with the root systems of other trees for available soil water may be considerably more than the diameter of the crown of the tree.

mosses, do not have true roots, although root-like structures may be found in many of these species. True roots are likewise absent from some higher seed plants such as spanish moss, mistletoe, dodder, and some orchids.

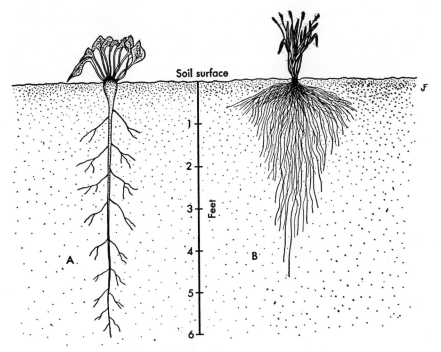

Figure 39 The tap roots (A) of species such as sugar beet, carrot and parsnip, and the fibrous root systems (B) of corn, wheat, and other grasses may penetrate the soil much below the depth broken by the plow.

Contrary to popular belief the roots of most crop plants penetrate the soil to depths much below that turned by the plow. This is especially true if the subsoil is loose and if neither an impenetrable "hard-pan" nor the water table is close to the surface (Figure 39). In many species, particularly in the monocots, the primary root stops growing and may even die while the plant is comparatively young. In these plants adventitious roots develop from the lower nodes of the stem and form a fibrous root system which takes over the functions of absorption and anchorage previously performed in part by the tap root and its affiliated secondary or lateral roots.

It seems appropriate at this point to dispel a prevalent and persistent fallacy which emanates from a misunderstanding of soil-root relationships. One frequently hears, even in professional circles, that "plants send their roots deeper into the soil in search of moisture." Such a statement implies that the plant has foresight, that it is capable of knowing there is available water at greater depths, and consequently that it directs the roots to go deeper to obtain moisture. No one has ever demonstrated the presence of such mental processes in plants. It has been conclusively shown, however, that when the water content of a root per unit volume is greater than that of the soil, water will move from the root into the soil, resulting in the cessation of growth of the root, since an abundance of water in that organ is necessary for continued development. Therefore, roots will not grow through "dry" soils, that is, soils in which the concentration of available water per unit volume is less than that in the roots (Figure 40).

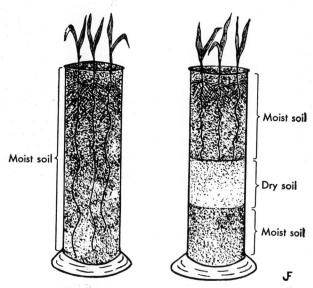

Moist soil

Moist soil

Dry soil

Moist soil

Figure 40   Effects of dry soil on the growth of roots.

That green plants obtain food from the soil is another erroneous concept. Suffice it to state that minerals (including fertilizers), water, and gases are not foods; rather they are raw materials which are utilized by green plants in making their own foods. A food is an organic compound which furnishes energy and/or builds protoplasm.

A root system may serve plants in five major capacities: as the principal structure through which water, and mineral salts and gases dissolved in water, pass into the plant; as the channels through which these raw materials move on into the stem; as a depository in which water and foods accumulate; as the holdfast which anchors the plant and gives support to the shoot; and as a means of asexual or vegetative reproduction.

Fuller and Tippo (19) point out that roots are economically important in many ways. The growth of higher plants upon which man depends for food, clothing, shelter, and other necessities would be impossible without roots. Numerous roots are valuable for pharmaceutical and medicinal products including goldenseal, aconite, asafetida, gentian, licorice, rhubarb, valerian, marshmallow, and ginseng, the alleged values of the last named apparently arising from Chinese superstition. The principal root crops used as food by man are sweet potatoes, yams, carrots, turnips, rutabagas, beets, salsify, parsnips, radishes, and cassava (tapioca). Spices and other aromatic substances are obtained from the roots of such plants as sassafras, horseradish, sarsaparilla, angelica, and turmeric. The roots of alkana and madder furnish important dyes, the latter being the source of the widely used "turkey red." In addition to these uses, the importance of roots as soil-binders and preventers of erosion should be emphasized.

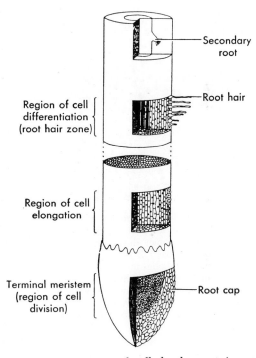

Region of cell differentiation (root hair zone)

Region of cell elongation

Terminal meristem (region of cell division)

Secondary root

Root hair

Root cap

Regions of the Root Tip.

Examination of a longitudinal section of a root tip under a microscope will reveal that it is composed of regions which gradually merge into each other (Figure 41). It will be observed that the apex is enclosed in a cone of parenchymatous cells much as a thimble

Figure 41   Regions of cell development in a root tip showing terminal meristem. (*From Sampson, H.C., Work Book in General Botany. Harper & Brothers.*)

covers the end of a finger. These cells form the root cap. They are larger and more loosely arranged at the periphery, becoming smaller and more compact in the vicinity of the adjacent terminal meristem from which they were originally derived. As the root tip extends through the soil, its root cap protects the enclosed cells of the terminal meristem from mechanical injury. The abrasive action of hard soil particles causes the rupture and death of the outer cells of the root cap. The remnants of these cells are being constantly sloughed off and just as constantly replaced by other cells at the inner surface of the cap. When the surface cells of the root cap are torn by the soil particles, the liquids within them pass into the soil. Thus a comparatively dry soil adjacent to the root cap might be somewhat moistened and softened, a condition which some workers think facilitates the elongation of the root tip through the soil. Even when formed in moist air, that is, when not subjected to soil pressure, the root

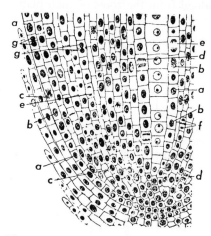

cap has only limited development, probably because limited food supplies reach these cells.

The terminal meristem, often referred to as the region of cell division, occurs immediately posterior to (above) the root cap. Although its extent varies according to the species, the region of cell division is often less than a millimeter in depth (Figure 42). Nevertheless, the cells in this region are capable of rapid division, and it is here that the cells of both the root cap and the other primary tissues of the young root are formed. When a terminal meristem mother cell divides, it forms two daughter cells of about equal size, each of which contains approximately one-half of the cytoplasm of the mother cell. Before undergoing division

Figure 42 Meristematic region of a root tip of onion. A series of stages in the behavior of chromosomes during vegetative cell division (mitosis) is represented and labeled: a. metabolic nucleus; b. prophase; c. metaphase; d. anaphase; e. telophase; f. cell plate formation; g. two new daughter cells. (*From Transeau, E.N., General Botany. World Book Company, 1924.*)

or otherwise becoming modified, each daughter cell enlarges to about the size of the mother cell. This growth involves among other things the production of more cytoplasm and cell wall materials. The potentialities for differentiating into the several kinds of cells in the root tip reside in the protoplasm of the meristematic cells, and the manifestation of these potentialities usually follows a definite pattern.

Just back of (above) the terminal meristem is a region commonly referred to as the region of cell elongation. As the name implies, it is here that the young cells undergo maximum growth, especially in length; therefore, it is here that the major increase in length of the root occurs. It will be observed that the cells in this region are more transparent than those of the terminal meristem. This is due to the fact that the inward movement of water causes many of the small vacuoles to enlarge and coalesce, forming in each cell one or a few large vacuoles through which light passes readily. The pressure created by the molecular energy of the water molecules which diffuse into the vacuoles forces the cytoplasm and its contents against the inner faces of the cell walls.

Illustrations of root tips frequently lead to the fallacious notion that the cells produced in the terminal meristem move back into the region of cell elongation where they enlarge. That this is a misconception becomes apparent when it is recalled that a cell enlarges and matures in the same spot where it was formed. The region of cell elongation today was occupied by the terminal meristem yesterday. By the constant addition of new cells, the terminal meristem has moved forward much as a garden wall increases in height by the addition of new layers of bricks or stone to the top. In attempting to clarify this phenomenon, it has been found helpful to explain it in terms of a familiar unit of measure such as the inch. Let us assume that yesterday the region of cell division of a root tip was 6 inches below the surface of the ground. Today the same region, due to the piling up of new cells during the interim, is 7 inches below the ground surface. The cells which were formed yesterday by the meristem at the 6 inch level are today undergoing enlargement. Those formed today at the 7 inch depth will be enlarging tomorrow and the meristem will have moved ahead in the meantime.

If we continue our observations of the young root tip in a direction proximal to (above) the apex, our eyes move from the region in which the cells are undergoing elongation into the region of cell differentiation. Here the cells become conspicuously modified through processes of maturing. In the center will be seen rows of comparatively long, broad cells. Bordering these are rows of long, narrow cells. The centrally located cells are often called the provascular strands because some of these cells mature into vascular tissue (primary xylem and phloem). Pith cells are generally absent except in certain monocots and some herbaceous dicots (Figure 43). External to the provascular cells are several rows of cubical or rectangular cells which form the cortex. The surface is made up of a single layer of elongated cells called the epidermis. It will be observed that many of the surface cells have developed lateral protuberances which we recognize to be root hairs. This accounts for the fact that this region is sometimes referred to as the root hair zone. Although occasionally seen in the older part of the region of cell elongation, root hairs are produced most abundantly by the epidermal cells in the region of cell differentiation.

The region of cell differentiation in a root, then, is distinguished by two characteristics: the development of distinct cell or tissue types, and the production of root hairs. Since in many species the major absorption of water occurs through the root hairs, this function might also be considered a prominent feature of this region.

Every plant, in fact every living organism whether plant or animal, in its adult form is the result of these three basic and essential biologic processes, namely, cell division, cell enlargement, and cell differentiation.

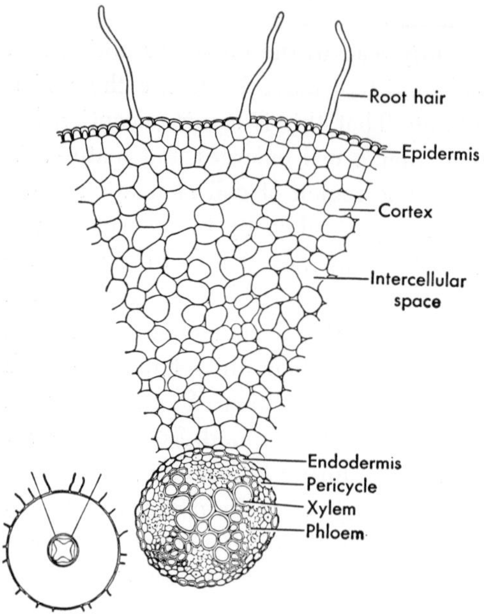

Anatomy of a Young Dicot Root.

A brief general description of a plant organ is rendered difficult by the numerous variations which occur in the organs of different species. There is no such thing as a typical root, stem, or leaf. Regardless of this fact, a cross section of a young root will usually reveal three well-defined regions: a central stele, enclosed by a relatively broad cortex, which is covered by an epidermis such as that previously described (Figure 43).

Figure 43   Cross section of a young dicot root, *Ranunculus. (From Dietz, S.M.,* Laboratory and Field Problems in Botany. *Wm. C. Brown Co., 1940.)*

The cortex is composed of several layers of loosely-arranged, living parenchymatous cells among which are many conspicuous intercellular spaces. Staining discloses that these cells in many species contain numerous starch grains. The innermost layer of the cortex is generally called the endodermis, which in roots is usually more prominent than its counterpart in the stem. In some plants, such as *Ranunculus,* it frequently forms a conspicuous ring or chain of alternating groups of thick- and thin-walled cells surrounding the stele (Figures 43 and 44).

Except in certain monocots and some herbaceous dicots, the center of the young root is occupied by primary xylem, that is, xylem which has been formed by differentiation of cells originally produced by the terminal meristem. The larger elements (cells) which compose the core of the stele are xylem vessels. Radiating from this central group of vessels are two or more projecting ridges or strands of tracheids. Lying between or alternating with the xylem ridges are groups of primary phloem tissue. The remainder of the stele is made up chiefly of parenchymatous cells (Figure 44).

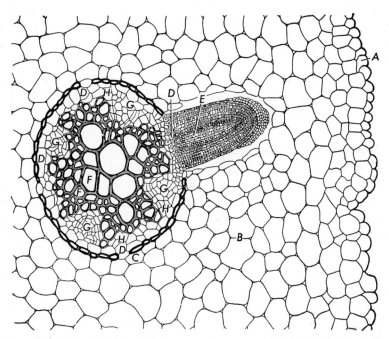

Figure 44 Cross section of a young dicot root, *Ranunculus*, showing the origin of a secondary root from the pericycle. A, epidermis. B, cortex. C, endodermis. D, pericycle. E, branch root originating from pericycle. F, xylem. G, phloem. H, parenchyma of stele. *(From College Botany, Revised Edition, by Harry J. Fuller and Oswald Tippo. By permission of Henry Holt and Company, Inc. Copyright 1949, 1954.)*

As a dicot root matures, the parenchymatous cells abutting the primary xylem differentiate into vascular cambium, forming a border completely surrounding the xylem and separating it from the primary phloem. When it becomes functional, the cambium produces secondary xylem to the inside and secondary phloem on the outside. At first the cambium is more active at the base of the trough internal to the phloem. As a result of this difference in the rate of cell production, the xylem soon becomes a circular core with the cambium developing the form of a ring or cylinder around it. The phloem likewise develops into a cylinder enclosing the vascular cambium.

Lateral or secondary roots originate in the layer of parenchymatous cells called the pericycle, usually just above the root hair zone (Figures 41 and 44). These branch roots generally develop at the extremities of the primary xylem ridges. Pericycle cells at these points just inside the endodermis become meristematic. By repeated divisions these cells form a young lateral root with a root cap and other regions identical with those of the primary root. Mainly due to the pressure resulting from growth and perhaps partly by digestion of the tissues through which it grows, the lateral root penetrates through the tissues external to it and emerges into the soil where it continues to develop and becomes an integral part of the root system. The xylem, phloem, and other tissues of the lateral root are connected with those of the primary root.

Anatomy of an Older Dicot Root.

If a cross section of a dicot root is made at a point just before it merges into the stem, it will be observed to consist of a central core of primary and secondary xylem completely encircled by a single layer of vascular cambial cells. The latter, in turn, will be enclosed by secondary phloem. In the roots of perennial plants at this stage the development of cork cambium and the subsequent formation of cork cells usually results in the death and sloughing off of the epidermis, cortex and primary phloem. Thus the periphery of an older perennial root is made up chiefly of cork cells which constitute an almost impervious outer bark somewhat comparable with that of stems (Figure 45).

Since water and minerals move upward to other parts of the plant primarily through the xylem, it is apparent that these raw materials must first pass through a number of living cells between their entrance into the root hairs or epidermal cells of the young root and their arrival at the xylem (Figure 43). It is obvious also that, since an older root is covered with a highly water repellent bark, the major absorption occurs in young root portions prior to the formation of cork cells (Figure 45).

Characteristics of Root Systems.

The term "root system" is applied to the entire mass of roots of a single plant. In general, root systems may be classified as tap, semi-fibrous, and fibrous root systems.

The tap root type is illustrated by the alfalfa root shown in Figure 46. This kind of root system has a prominent primary root from which smaller lateral or secondary roots branch. In a perennial dicot plant, the main tap root usually develops annual rings of xylem and lives as long

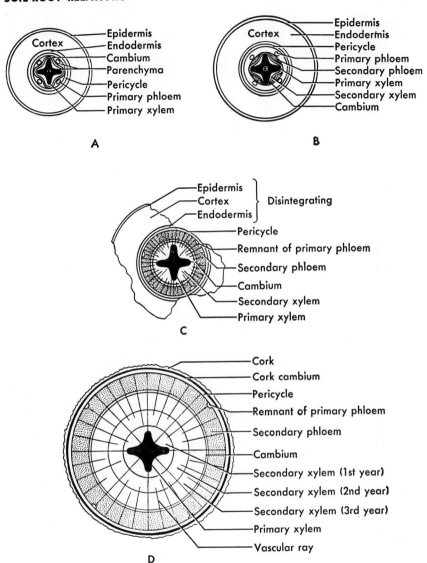

Figure 45 Diagrammatic representation of secondary growth in a dicotyledonous root. A, primary tissues only. B, beginning of secondary growth. C, secondary growth continuing with outer tissues sloughing off. D, three-year-old root, with three secondary xylem rings. (*From* College Botany, *Revised Edition, by Harry J. Fuller and Oswald Tippo. By permission of Henry Holt and Company, Inc. Copyright 1949, 1954.*)

as the plant. A tap root is developed by many trees. Carrot and dandelion are herbaceous plants with tap root systems (Figure 47).

Semi-fibrous root systems are characteristic of many species. The

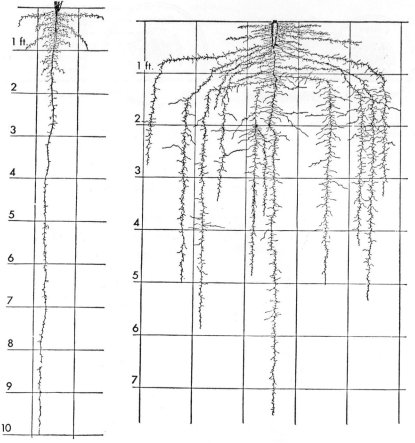

Figure 46 Two-year-old alfalfa root. (*By permission from* Root Development of Field Crops, *by John E. Weaver. Copyright 1926. McGraw-Hill Book Company, Inc.)*

Figure 47 Root system of a mature carrot plant. (*By permission from* Root Development of Vegetable Crops, *by John E. Weaver and William E. Bruner. Copyright, 1927. McGraw-Hill Book Company, Inc.)*

semi-fibrous root system does not display as much branching as fibrous root systems, but it has more extensive branching than tap root systems. The semi-fibrous root systems of corn and lettuce are shown in Figures 48 and 49.

The fibrous root system is characteristic of most members of the grass family, at least in the later stages of development. Fibrous root systems of grasses have an amazing number of roots with extensive branching, as the already cited work of Dittmer indicates.

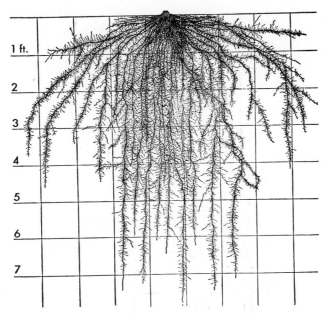

1 ft.

2

3

4

5

6

7

Figure 48 The mature root system of corn. *(By permission from* Root Development of Field Crops, *by John E. Weaver. Copyright, 1926. McGraw-Hill Book Company, Inc.)*

In Figures 50 and 51 the effect of the soil environment on root development is strikingly demonstrated. Where the soil is well aerated in the A, B, and C horizons, the western wheat grass root system is well developed in all horizons. On the other hand, when the B horizon is poorly aerated (Figure 50) but the A and C horizons have sufficient oxygen, the western wheat grass has extensively branching roots only in the A and C horizons. The purple three-awn grass has its root development restricted primarily to the A horizon since the B and C horizons of soils in which this species flourishes are usually tight and restrictive to root development.

The above illustrations further demonstrate that root systems often penetrate the soil to considerable depths and spread laterally many feet from the mother plant. Trees probably have the greatest lateral root development, their lateral roots often extending as far as 15 to 50 feet or more from the parent plant. Quantitative data of the total length of roots per individual plant clearly show that roots ramify soils (see Table 15) exposing large surface areas which facilitate the absorption of water and minerals.

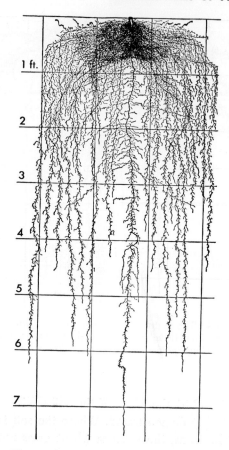

Figure 49 Mature root system of lettuce. (*By permission from* Root Development of Vegetable Crops, *by John E. Weaver and William E. Bruner. Copyright, 1927. McGraw-Hill Book Company, Inc.*)

Table 15 Total length of roots per individual plant for a few species of plants.

SPECIES OF PLANT	TOTAL LENGTH OF ROOT SYSTEM
	miles
Squash	15.9
Wheat	44.0
Wild oats	54.0
Crested wheat grass	315.0

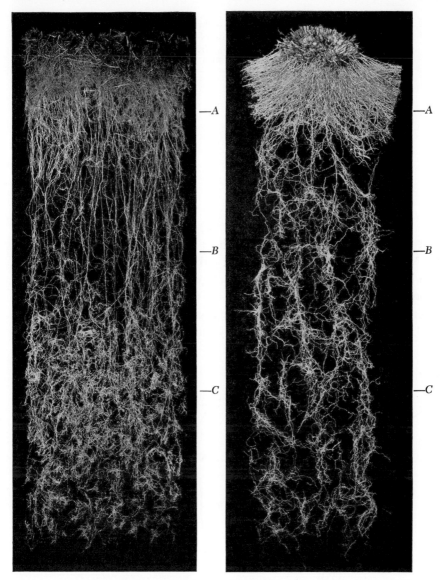

Figure 50   Root system of western wheat grass. Note restricted root development in the B soil horizon. *(From Weaver, J.E. and R.W. Darland,* Ecol. Monographs *19:303–338, 1949.)*

Figure 51   Root system of purple three-awn grass. Note restricted root development in all but the surface layer of soil. *(From Weaver, J.E. and R.W. Darland,* Ecol. Monographs *19:303–338, 1949.)*

The quantity of dry matter of the roots of various kinds of plant covers is shown in Table 16.

Table 16 The dry weight yield of roots of various kinds of plant cover *(From Ward, H.S., Jr. Ecol. Mono. 19: 145–171, 1949).*

KIND OF PLANT COVER	YIELD OF DRY MATTER
	lbs. per acre
Bird-foot trefoil	3,073.0
Sericea lespedeza	2,927.0
Big bluestem	13,344.0
Switch grass	9,319.0
Indian grass	10,522.0
Kentucky bluegrass	7,213.0
Oak-Hickory	15,172.0

Factors Affecting Root Growth.

The rate of root growth of most crop plants is from ½ to 2½ inches in length per day. For maximum root growth, the soil environment must have certain optimum factors, one of the most important of which is aeration. The effect of soil aeration has already been shown in Figures 50 and 51. In Figure 52 the root systems of corn, blue lupine, tomato,

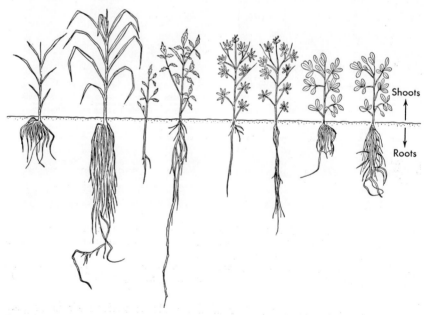

Figure 52 The effects of aeration on corn, tomato, blue lupine, and peanut when grown in nutrient solutions. The plant specimen to the left for each kind of plant is the non-aerated treatment.

and peanuts are shown from aerated and non–aerated solution cultures. In all instances, and particularly in corn, a far more extensive root development occurred in the aerated cultures.

The effect of poor aeration as a limiting factor on root growth has been the subject of considerable research. Results of these investigations show that restriction of root growth is not due to high CO_2 concentration in the soil. Root growth was not restricted by CO_2 concentration as high as 25 per cent so long as the oxygen concentration remained above 5 per cent. Thus it is evident that oxygen, not CO_2, is the limiting factor. However, roots of some plant species such as rice grow very well in anaerobic environments.

As has been pointed out, the region of growth in length of roots is restricted to a narrow band of tissue just back of the root apex. For these areas of the root to carry on growth, moisture must move into the cells from the soil. If these root tips come into contract with soil moisture which is held below the permanent wilting point, root growth will not occur. On the other hand when root tips contact soil in the available moisture range, root growth will occur. Hence the soil moisture conducive to root development is the available moisture. Soils with their pore spaces saturated with water are poorly aerated and although moisture is available, oxygen is restrictive. Some investigators have shown that root growth is most rapid when there is approximately 50 per cent available moisture in the soil, or when soil moisture is in the lower capillary range.

The texture and structure of soils are often mentioned as factors affecting root growth. These two soil properties indirectly influence root growth in that soil moisture and aeration are controlled by texture and structure. The relationships involved have already been explained.

The cells of roots, like the cells of stems and leaves, require essential minerals for their metabolic activities. Therefore, root growth can be inhibited by absence or inadequate supply of any of the essential minerals in the soil. It is not only necessary that the essential minerals be available in the soil, but each mineral must occur at a proper concentration. Certain minerals in high concentrations, such as boron, aluminum, and sodium, are toxic to root cells.

There is considerable erroneous thinking about the effect of particular minerals on root growth. Statements such as that nitrogen restricts root growth and phosphorus and potassium stimulate root growth are misleading. Actually nitrogen, phosphorus, and potassium are all essential for root growth as are the other essential minerals.

Soil acidity or alkalinity is often mentioned as affecting root growth. Unless the pH is so high or so low that essential minerals become unavailable or toxic to the roots, root development is usually not restricted; in the pH range from 4 to 9, root growth of most species is ordinarily not inhibited.

A factor in the soil often overlooked as affecting root growth is temperature. Roots appear to make little growth below 10°C. Optimum root growth for many plants is from 25°–30°C. At soil temperatures of 35°C. to 40°C., root growth is either slow or ceases altogether. The effect of temperature on root growth of loblolly pine is shown in Figure 53. Be-

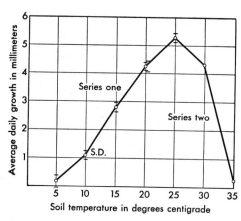

Figure 53 The effect of temperature on the rate of growth of loblolly pine roots. (*From Kramer, P.J.* Plant and Soil Water Relationships. *McGraw-Hill Book Company, Inc., 1949.*)

fore the plant has developed sufficient leaf area to shade the soil surface, it is very probable that the young seedling has its roots restricted in growth by high soil temperatures. High soil temperatures may inhibit root growth of young seedlings of woody plants so as to cause insufficient root surface for water and mineral absorption and so result in the development of both drought and mineral deficiency symptoms in the tops. Soil temperature also has an indirect effect on root growth and may even contribute to the death of roots when soils become flooded with water. Flooded soils at high temperatures have low oxygen contents; whereas at lower temperatures, the oxygen content of such soils is somewhat higher. As a result, roots survive longer when the temperature of flooded soils is low. Whether this interrelationship between oxygen and temperature in saturated soils is the primary cause of death of plants in flooded soils still remains a debatable question.

Favorable soil conditions alone will not suffice for root growth. Other essential factors must come from the plant shoot. The basic food (sugar) for root nourishment is translocated into roots from leaves, since photosynthesis does not occur in non-green root cells. Likewise, root growth will not occur unless minute quantities of vitamins are translocated to the roots from the shoot. For the roots of many species, thiamine is essential; whereas for other species, pyridoxine and nicotinic acid are essential. The plant growth hormone, indoleacetic acid, is also required for root growth and is translocated into the roots from apical buds and young leaves. The dependence of roots on shoots for these substances serves to illustrate that higher green plants are made up of interrelated parts, that each plant part is dependent on the other parts, and that their processes are inter-related. Roots, while obtaining food and growth substances from shoots, furnish water and minerals to the shoots, which shoots require for the synthesis of foods, vitamins, and hormones.

Aeration, moisture, and essential minerals in proper balance are the soil factors which exert the most directly important effects on the physiology of root growth. However, other soil environmental factors also influence root growth. The presence of roots of other plants of the same or of different species may cause a decrease in root development. The reciprocal effect of the roots of the same species is attributed mainly to competition for water and minerals. On the other hand, depression of root growth of one species by the roots of a different plant species has been thought by some investigators to be due to secretion of toxic substances by these roots. Such toxic effects may result, however, from organic substances released into soils by decomposition of dead root tissue. In contrast, some kinds of plants contribute to increased root growth of other species. An example of the latter is the growth-stimulating effect of the release of nitrogenous compounds from the nodules of leguminous roots and the absorption and utilization of these nitrogenous substances by non-leguminous plants.

In addition, the soil environment contains organisms which may destroy living roots. Among these are several species of parasitic bacteria and soil fungi which cause root rots. The various species of nematodes (roundworms) may also be very destructive to root systems.

Growth of root hairs is influenced by the same factors which affect root growth. It should be remembered that root hairs are not present on roots of all species of plants. For example, root hairs are absent from the roots of many species of conifers, peanut plants, and others. Root hairs are most abundant on the roots of certain species of the grass family. The number of root hairs on the roots of three kinds of plants is shown in Table 17.

Table 17   Number of root hairs per square centimeter
of root surface of three species of plants.

SPECIES OF PLANT	NO. OF ROOT HAIRS/SQ. CM. OF ROOT SURFACE
Loblolly pine	217.0
Black locust	520.0
Winter rye	2,500.0

Several important facts concerning soils and soil-root relationships may be summarized as follows:

1. Soils are derived from parent materials as a result of the action of climate, organisms, and topography over varying periods of time.
2. Soil building processes frequently result in the formation of a soil profile made up of horizons designated in descending order by the letters A, B, and C.
3. Soils consist of solids, liquids, and gases in varying proportions.
4. The distribution of sand, silt, and clay in soils determines the soil property called texture.
5. The arrangement of the sand, silt, and clay particles into aggregates is referred to as soil structure.
6. Moisture in soils is held by the attractive forces of the solid particles; these forces increase as soils pass from the wet to the dry state.
7. Moisture in soils is classified into gravitational, capillary, and hygroscopic moisture. The available moisture for plants is chiefly the capillary moisture held in soils, which ranges from field capacity to the permanent wilting point.
8. The amount of moisture held in soils is a function of texture, whereas the rate of movement of moisture into and within the soil is a function of soil structure.
9. Minerals essential for plant growth are found in the soil solution, adsorbed on the clay particles, and as a part of the organic matter.
10. The amount of minerals adsorbed on the clay crystals of soils is called the exchange capacity.
11. Soil acidity and alkalinity are expressed by the symbol pH which represents the logarithm of the reciprocal of the hydrogen ion concentration.
12. Organic matter of soils consists of residues of plant and animal bodies and their waste products, and of microorganisms.
13. In soils conducive to optimum root growth, the root systems of many kinds of plants develop extensively, penetrating to depths of 6 feet or more and growing laterally as much as 30 to 50 feet.
14. Root growth is primarily affected by aeration, available moisture, and available minerals in the soil; secondarily, root growth is influenced by parasitic bacteria and fungi (root rots), nematodes, and competition with other roots. Root growth is likewise affected by shoot development. Restriction of shoot growth results in a limited supply of sugar and growth substances which must be translocated from the shoots to the roots if good root growth is to occur.

9.
RADIANT ENERGY AND THE CHLOROPLAST PIGMENTS

We shall now study the ways in which raw materials entering plants from the soil and the atmosphere are synthesized into foods in higher green plants. For simplicity a food may be defined as an organic substance which upon oxidation in living cells yields energy, or which may be converted into the protoplasm and walls of which cells are composed. Foods are broadly classified as carbohydrates (sugars and starches), fats and oils, proteins, and intermediate products of these three major categories. It is now generally accepted that sugar in some form is the first stable food made by green plants, and that all other kinds of foods are produced by chemical alterations of this sugar, or of intermediate products of photosynthesis which develop just prior to the formation of sugar.

Although scientists regard the foods of green plants to be similar to those of animals, the processes by which green plants produce foods are unique. Contrary to popular belief, green plants do not secure food from the soil, air, or water. Rather, food is synthesized within green plants from inorganic substances obtained from the soil, air, and water. In contrast, all animals and non-green plants (except a few simple forms) cannot synthesize food from these inorganic substances, and are therefore directly or indirectly dependent upon green plants for their sustenance.

Mineral salts, water, and gases (also fertilizers and other so-called "plant foods") are raw materials. They are not included in the category of foods since higher plants cannot obtain energy directly from them, nor can these raw materials, if uncombined, be used in the production of more cell wall materials, protoplasm, enzymes, hormones, and other essential organic constituents of living cells.

Before considering how carbon dioxide and water are utilized within

117

the chloroplasts of plants in the synthesis of carbohydrates, we shall first investigate the factors or conditions essential for the production of sugar.

Radiant Energy.

Light is a form of radiant energy. The sun is the original source of all radiant energy on the earth. How is this radiant energy propagated across approximately 93 million miles of space which separates the earth from the sun?

Many years ago it was learned that if the "white light" of the sun is passed through a prism, it is separated into the color bands of which the sun's light is composed. As in a rainbow, the color bands range from violet through blue, blue-green, green, yellow, orange and red. This is called the visible spectrum because it can be seen with the human eye. Later, it was theorized that light (radiant energy) is transmitted across space as undulatory waves. It was reckoned that violet light is composed of the shortest waves—the wave lengths of such light ranging from 390 mμ (millimicron = one-millionth of a millimeter) to 430 mμ from the crest of one wave to the crest of the next wave—and that red light has the longest wave lengths, ranging from 650 mμ to 760 mμ from wave crest to crest. The wave lengths of the other color bands were thought to lie between these extremes as shown in Figure 54.

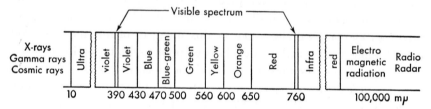

Figure 54   Total and visible spectrums of radiant energy.

However, when a scientific effort was made to explain the effect of light on photographic paper, it was found that the movement of light through space could not be explained on the basis of waves alone. This and other observations led to the theory that light is transmitted across space in tiny bundles (particles) of energy called photons. When these photons impinge against a suitable substance, they may impart their energy to the electrons of that substance and cause a photochemical reaction.

Although the latter theory requires that light moves by the medium of photons, the older wave length idea is still useful to designate or delimit the energy values of different kinds of colored light. For example, violet light, which was considered to have a wave length of 390 mμ to 430 mμ, is now known to be composed of photons having the greatest energy value, and hence a greater amount of radiant energy than any other light. On the other hand, red light, supposedly ranging from 650 mμ to 760 mμ, is considered to have photons of lesser energy value and thus to have the least radiant energy of any part of the visible spectrum. The energy value of any given color of light is calculated in terms of quantums of radiant energy. A photon has one quantum of energy; however, the energy value of quantums decreases from violet to red light. Roughly, a quantum of ultraviolet radiation has four times the energy value of a quantum of violet light and approximately eight times that of red light. Thus, the quantums of radiant energy in the various color bands of light in the visible spectrum range from violet with the most to red with the least.

The light which we see (visible spectrum) makes up only a small part of the total spectrum (Figure 54). Beyond the violet are the invisible bands of radiant energy known as ultraviolet, X-rays, gamma rays, and cosmic rays. Extending beyond the red are the invisible bands of infrared and electromagnetic radiation (radio, radar). Interestingly, however, it is the light which we are able to see that is also the light which green plants use in food synthesis.

When considering radiant energy in relation to plants, we must take into account three aspects of light, namely, intensity, quality, and duration. Intensity of light is dependent upon the number of quantums impinging upon a given area of surface per second regardless of the energy value of the quantums. In light of low intensity several plants have been observed to grow vegetatively for many years without bearing flowers and fruits. It is not known definitely whether the failure of flower formation under low light intensities is due to decreased photosynthesis, retarded hormone effects, or some other factor or combination of conditions. Quality refers to the color bands which make up any given kind of light. The light from a tungsten bulb is relatively rich in red and poor in blue light, whereas the quality of the light from a fluorescent tube is richer in blue than it is in red light. In the initiation of flower primordia, red light is apparently more effective than blue, and green light is least effective of all. Duration is the term used to designate the number of hours of illumination per day to which a plant is exposed and is frequently called the photoperiod. Certain so-called long-day plants, such as corn, produce flowers only when exposed to about 12½ hours of light per day; others, called short-day plants, such as tobacco, bloom only when exposed to fewer than 12½ hours of light daily; whereas in a third group of plants, such as tomatoes, the initiation of flowers occurs during either long or short photoperiods. Species of this last group are often referred to as indeterminate or day-neutral plants.

The Chlorophylls and Carotenoids.

It is generally accepted that photosynthesis occurs only in the chloroplasts of higher plants, since the chloroplasts are the only cell structures which contain the chlorophyll pigments necessary for photosynthesis. However, it has been shown that chloroplasts isolated from living cells can carry on photosynthesis. Consequently, the living cell is not absolutely necessary in the photosynthetic process, although in nature photosynthesis occurs only in living cells. Because of their primary importance in photosynthesis, chloroplasts must be considered from the standpoint of their nature and behavior. In general the metabolic functions associated with the chloroplasts are photolysis of water, photosynthetic phosphorylation, fixation of carbon dioxide, and the synthesis of carbohydrates. Each of these will be discussed under photosynthesis, Chapter 10.

Chloroplasts in higher plants are usually disc-shaped protoplasmic bodies with diameters frequently ranging from 4 to 6 μ. Structurally chloroplasts consist of units called grana which are dispersed in a protein ground substance (matrix). A single granum contains several million chlorophyll molecules. It is probable that these grana are composed of molecular units of protein, chlorophyll, and fatty materials.

The photosynthetic process is generally associated with the green pigments, the chlorophylls; however, other pigments are also present in the chloroplasts. If green leaves are warmed in ethyl alcohol, methanol, ether, acetone, or chloroform, a green extract of chlorophyll is obtained. If the chlorophyll is extracted in alcohol then shaken with petroleum ether and allowed to stand for a few minutes, this extract will separate into two portions,—one layer containing chlorophyll *a* and carotene, and the other layer containing chlorophyll *b* and xanthophyll. Further separation by chemical means will disclose that the chloroplast pigments are composed of four major pigment complexes known as chlorophyll *a*, chlorophyll *b*, carotene (or carotin), and xanthophyll. Chlorophyll *a* and chlorophyll *b* are spoken of together as the chlorophylls, whereas carotene and the xanthophylls are known collectively as the carotenoids or carotenols.

The chlorophylls are not water soluble, but, as explained, separation of the *a* and *b* components is possible by organic solvents. A more recent method of separation is to pour the leaf pigments (extracted in acetone) and dissolved in petroleum ether into a tube containing an adsorbent such as magnesium oxide. Creation of a slight vacuum in the tube facilitates the movement of the pigments through the column. A beautiful and distinct separation of the four chloroplast pigments into horizontal bands is made in this manner.

Some ten different chlorophylls are known, but in higher plants only chlorophyll a and chlorophyll b are present. Although the chlorophylls alone absorb sufficient radiant energy for photosynthesis, it has been shown that the yellow and red pigments (carotenoids) can absorb light which may be utilized in photosynthesis. Whereas the absorption of light by the carotenoids is not considered to be important in higher plants, it may assume considerable importance in certain algae and bacteria. It is not known whether the non-green pigments transfer radiant energy directly into carbon dioxide reduction, or whether the radiant energy is first transferred from the non-chlorophyllose to the chlorophyll pigments and is then used in the photosynthetic mechanism. It can be confidently asserted, however, that light absorption by pigments other than the chlorophylls is not required for the completion of the process of photosynthesis in higher plants.

On a fresh weight basis, the leaves of most plants contain only from 0.10 to 0.45 per cent of chlorophyll a plus chlorophyll b. However, the concentration of the chlorophylls in the chloroplasts is from 4 to 5 times that of the leaf as a whole. Mosses and algae, which grow in low-light-intensity environments, have higher chlorophyll contents, amounting to nearly 2.0 per cent of the fresh weight. Chlorophyll content is not considered to be a limiting factor in the photosynthetic rate of plants unless the amount of chlorophyll is greatly reduced through mineral deficiencies, injury, or in some other abnormal manner.

Table 18 presents a brief comparison of these four pigment groups.

Table 18   Comparison of the chloroplast pigments.

PIGMENT COMPLEX	CHEMICAL (MOLECULAR) FORMULA	CHARACTERISTIC COLOR IN SOLUTION	OCCURRENCE
Chlorophyll a	$C_{55}H_{72}O_5N_4Mg$	Blue-green	In all green plant tissues (chlorenchyma).
Chlorophyll b	$C_{55}H_{70}O_6N_4Mg$	Green or yellow-green	In all green plant tissues.
Carotene	$C_{40}H_{56}$	Orange-red	In all green tissues, in roots of carrots, and in many fruits, flowers, and seeds.
Xanthophylls	$C_{40}H_{56}O_2$	Light yellow	In many plant tissues both green and non-green.

The chlorophylls and carotenoids are products of the synthetic activities which occur in living cells of plants. From the above table it is apparent that carbon, hydrogen, oxygen, nitrogen, and magnesium are necessary for the synthesis of chlorophyll in plants, since they are constituents of the molecules of these pigments. In addition to these, several other conditions or factors are essential for the production of chlorophyll. The absence of any one of the factors will prevent chlorophyll synthesis and result in a condition technically called chlorosis or "yellowing" of plants. Plants grown in darkness fail to become green, a condition called etiolation. The major factors which influence chlorophyll synthesis are listed in the following outline:

Genetic Factors.	Unless it possesses the proper inheritance, a plant cannot synthesize chlorophyll even if all other conditions are favorable for its formation. Example: albino corn.
Light.	Light is necessary for the production of chlorophyll in most plants. Exceptions include certain algae, mosses, ferns, conifers, and a few angiosperms such as the seedlings of the water lotus and the cotyledons of citrus fruits.
Oxygen.	If oxygen is absent, seedlings will not develop chlorophyll even when illuminated under conditions favorable for chlorophyll formation. Evidently oxidation is essential for the chemical transformations involved in the formation of chlorophyll.
Carbohydrates.	The carbon, hydrogen, and oxygen atoms in the chlorophyll molecule are apparently derived from carbohydrates. Etiolated leaves which have been placed in darkness and depleted of carbohydrates, will rapidly develop chlorophyll if floated on a sugar solution exposed to light.
Nitrogen and Magnesium.	These elements, absorbed from the soil, are also parts of the chlorophyll molecule, and they are obtained from the environment. Symptoms of chlorosis are early evident in plants grown in soils deficient in nitrogen and/or magnesium.
Iron, Manganese, Copper, and Zinc.	Although not parts of the chlorophyll molecule, these elements are essential catalytic agents in the synthesis of chlorophyll. In the absence of manganese and iron in an available form, and copper and zinc in traces, plants are unable to produce chlorophyll.
Suitable Temperature.	Like most other physiological processes in plants, chlorophyll synthesis is limited by extremes of temperature. Below 38°F. or above 118°F. there is little or no chlorophyll production. In many plants the maximum rate of chlorophyll formation occurs between 78°F. and 86°F.
Water.	A highly aqueous medium is essential for the most efficient operation of practically all physiological processes in living cells. Desiccation of chlorenchyma not only prevents the

formation of chlorophyll, but lack of water appears to speed up the disintegration of any chlorophyll already present. Example: the browning of grass and other plants during droughts.

The Living Cell.   As yet no one has been able to synthesize chlorophyll artificially, that is, outside of living cells. Many other conditions in addition to those listed may cause partial or complete chlorosis of plants. Some of these factors are lack of essential minerals other than those already discussed, deficient aeration of the roots, attacks of insects, and bacterial, fungus or virus diseases.

Absorption of Light by Chlorophyll.

The absorption of radiant energy by the chloroplast pigments collectively and individually has been measured both under artificial and natural conditions. These experiments show that the absorption of light by the chloroplasts of living leaves differs somewhat from the absorption of light by various chlorophyll extracts (Figure 55). This is particularly

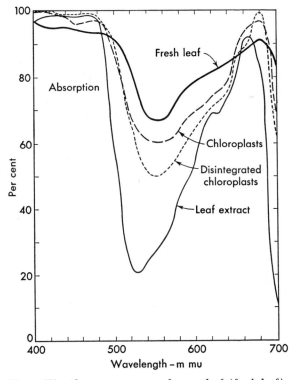

Figure 55   Absorption spectra of intact leaf (fresh leaf), leaf extract, and extracted chloroplasts of spinach. (*From Moss, R.A. and W.E. Loomis*, Plant Physiol. 27:370–391, 1952.)

true as regards the green region of the spectrum. Living leaves absorb large amounts of green light, whereas chlorophyll extracts display only minor absorption in this area. Nevertheless, it is evident that both chlorophyll *a* and chlorophyll *b* solutions show heavy absorption bands in the red and other bands in the blue and violet, but little absorption in the green. In contrast, the carotenoids absorb light only in the violet-blue region. Therefore, it is apparent that the maximum absorption of light by the collective chloroplast pigments occurs in the red and violet-blue regions of the visible spectrum. It will also be recalled that violet-blue light has greater energy value than any other kind of visible radiant energy.

10.
PHOTOSYNTHESIS

In the preceding chapters it was shown that several processes are involved in the movement of water, minerals, and gases into plant tissues. In some of these tissues, the living cells contain chloroplasts possessing a pigment system capable of absorbing light energy which is converted into chemical energy. Although chloroplast-containing cells are present in other tissues, we shall concentrate our attention upon the mesophyll of leaves. Mesophyll cells are supplied with minerals, water, and CO_2 which are the building blocks essential for the conversion of light energy into the chemical energy of organic molecules, especially carbohydrates. From these molecules, living cells can synthesize other foods, assimilate a whole host of organic cell constituents (other than foods), and release the energy needed for the many biosyntheses which occur in living tissues. The process in which light energy is converted into chemical energy in living plants is called photosynthesis.

It is generally accepted that photosynthesis is the most important physiological process in the world. The facts gathered to date indicate that the material make-up of all living organisms is dependent upon chemical derivatives of photosynthesis. It is also known that the potential energy in photosynthetic products is the primary source of the chemically-bound energy supply of all organisms. Most of the energy that man transforms by various means into heat, light, electricity and mechanical motion may be traced back through a series of processes to the potential energy bound during photosynthesis. In addition, photosynthesis is the principal process through which oxygen is returned to the earth's atmosphere and through which the oxygen content of the earth's atmosphere is kept approximately constant.

The Magnitude of Photosynthesis.

Some concept of the magnitude of the product made in photosynthesis may be had by examining a few figures. It is estimated that 15.5×10^{10} tons of carbon are fixed annually by the photosynthetic activity of the plants of all the world's oceans; whereas, in comparison, land plants fix only 1.9×10^{10} tons of carbon per year. In other words, marine plants are responsible for about eight times as much carbon fixation as all land plants. The total annual production of sugar of all plants amounts to approximately 300 billion tons, or 1,000 times the world's yearly production of steel.

The agriculturally and industrially important plant, corn, provides another striking illustration of the magnitude and importance of photosynthesis. An average corn plant produces five grams of sugar, about half a lump, in a 14-hour day. In 100 days, Iowa's 100 billion corn plants will produce 30 million tons of glucose, or 400 pounds for each man, woman, and child in the United States (26).

The amounts of glucose synthesized at maximum rates of photosynthesis by several plants are shown in Table 19.

Table 19   Amounts of glucose synthesized at maximum
rates of photosynthesis by several plants.

KIND OF PLANT	GRAMS OF GLUCOSE/SQ. M. LEAF/HOUR
Pumpkin	1.80
Corn	1.19
Cowpeas	0.85
Soybeans	0.80
Cotton	0.74
Apple	0.45
Red oak	0.45
White oak	0.38
Loblolly pine	0.25
Dogwood	0.19

It should be obvious to the agricultural student that photosynthesis is extremely important in the growth of plants since it accounts for 95 per cent or more of the dry weight of a crop, whereas only about 4 per cent of the dry weight results from materials obtained from the soil.

The Efficiency of Photosynthesis.

Management of cultivated land to produce greater yields of food and fiber for the constantly increasing human population has been directed primarily to the planting of the best crop varieties, to proper mineral fertilization, and, when possible, to irrigation. Thick spacing of crops has also become a popular management practice. All this has resulted in more leaf area per acre and consequently greater carbon fixation in foods through photosynthesis.

Of interest in this connection is the question of how efficient is the photosynthetic process? Of even greater interest are two other questions, namely, does the photosynthetic process vary greatly with individual species, and can the efficiency of the process be increased? Present evidence indicates that under optimum conditions, each species of plant, through the process of photosynthesis, can convert into chemical energy about 25 per cent of the absorbed light. Therefore, it seems unlikely that the efficiency of the photosynthetic process in separate species can be increased appreciably. Moreover, under average crop conditions, the efficiency of photosynthesis is probably somewhat less than the 25 per cent obtained under experimental conditions. Although 25 per cent of the absorbed light is converted into chemical energy by photosynthesis, only about one per cent of the total incident solar energy and about 2.5 per cent of absorbed visible radiation is utilized by field crops and forests during the summer growing season.

Another approach to a more efficient utilization of solar energy by plants might be through the growing of those plants which yield the maximum dry matter per acre. A comparison of a few plants as to yield per acre is given in Table 20.

Table 20 Utilization of sunlight by plants. (*From Daniels, F. Solar Energy. Sci. 109: 51–57, 1949.*)

CROP	CROP YIELD/ACRE/YEAR
	Tons
Corn (1946 average, U.S.)	0.9 (grain)
Wheat (1946 average, U.S.)	0.5 (grain)
Hay, tame (1946 average, U.S.)	1.5
Hay, wild (1946 average, U.S.)	0.9
Florida pine	3.0 (total wood)
Wisconsin aspen	2.0 (total wood)

These data show that Florida pine yields the maximum dry matter per acre from photosynthesis. By modern industrial chemical processes, a large part of this dry matter could be converted into animal and human food. It is very probable that pasture plants are the next best utilizers of solar energy. In the future man might make greater use of nature's photosynthetic process in green plants if he grew algae in large tanks supplied with optimum amounts of essential minerals and carbon dioxide. At any rate the process of photosynthesis is still the only means of permanently accumulating solar energy in plant organic matter for use as food and as a raw material in industry.

Factors Which May Influence the Rate of Photosynthesis.

The rate of photosynthesis is dependent primarily upon the interrelations of several environmental factors, various structural conditions of leaves, and the effectiveness of organic and inorganic substances, such as enzymes and minerals, which are essential for the process.

External factors such as the intensity, quality, and duration of light; the concentration of carbon dioxide in the environment; temperature; the amount of available moisture; atmospheric dust; insect attacks; disease; and indirectly aeration of the roots; may greatly influence photosynthesis.

Structural conditions which have an important role in photosynthesis are the number and distribution of stomates; the abundance of leaf intercellular spaces as related to the surface exposure of the chlorophyll-containing cells, particularly of the mesophyll of leaves; the number and distribution of veins; the total leaf surface exposed to the atmosphere; and to a lesser extent the thickness of the cuticle.

The chief organic and inorganic conditions involved, in addition to the supply of carbon dioxide and water, are the amounts and distribution of chlorophyll and enzymes, the acidity of the cells, and the abundance of those elements essential for chlorophyll synthesis. To this list might also be added a plentiful supply of foods, especially carbohydrates and proteins.

It is evident that one or a combination of these factors or conditions may retard or accelerate photosynthesis. The effect of any one factor is probably always influenced to some extent by the relative potency of the other factors involved. Likewise, the general physiological activity of a plant, as it is influenced by the numerous other processes necessary for life, may have a direct bearing upon the photosynthetic rate. The effect of the major external factors and internal conditions will be briefly discussed.

Light.

The energy source of photosynthesis is, of course, light. Except for a few bacteria, plants deprived of light will make no sugar even though other conditions are favorable for photosynthesis. Light is not only necessary for the formation of chlorophyll in most plants, but it is the source of the energy which becomes chemically bound in carbohydrate molecules. As previously explained, the chloroplast pigments absorb radiant energy, that is, the photons of light, upon striking the electrons of the chlorophyll atoms, impart energy to them. During the several intermediate chemical reactions which follow, this energy is transferred from one product to another apparently by enzymes, and finally becomes a part of the sugar molecules which are produced in the process of photosynthesis.

The daily light intensity in which a plant can survive on the sugar made is often referred to as the critical light intensity. The critical light intensity varies with different species and with alteration of external factors such as temperature, available moisture, and carbon dioxide concentration. Land plants which endure low light intensities are generally known as "shade plants," whereas those which require high light intensities are called "sun plants." The light intensity which results in the best yields of flowers, fruits, and vegetables is of deep concern to greenhouse operators and other practical plant growers. Many ways of supplementing natural light by artificial means have been studied in an effort to increase photosynthesis. It should be kept in mind, however, that increasing the length of exposure to light is quite different from increasing the intensity of light, since length of day (photoperiod) may greatly influence the vegetative and/or reproductive processes of a plant.

If the original light intensity is low and other factors remain constant, most plants will show an increase in the rate of photosynthesis as the intensity of light is increased up to that required for maximum sugar production. However, in many species maximum photosynthesis occurs at intensities considerably below that of full sunlight as shown in Table 21.

The data in Table 21 show that maximum carbon dioxide fixation (photosynthesis) occurs at light intensities varying from 200 to 10,000 foot candles. For example, 9,000 foot candles of light intensity will cause 3.5 milligrams of carbon dioxide fixation in loblolly pine while only 1,500 foot candles of light intensity will cause 6.0 milligrams of carbon dioxide fixation in red oak. Less carbon dioxide fixation (photosynthesis) occurs on a per plant basis than on a per leaf basis. This is probably attributed to only a portion of the leaves of an entire plant being exposed to full sunlight. It is of interest to note that cotton, a plant of sunny environment and maximum light saturation, at 3,500 foot candles has a carbon dioxide fixation of 18.0 milligrams while philodendron, a plant of shady environment and maximum light saturation, at 500 foot candles has a carbon dioxide fixation of 4.0 milligrams.

Table 21   The apparent maximum rates of photosynthesis, light saturation, and compensation point of various kinds of plants.

KIND OF PLANT	UNIT OF MEASUREMENT	LIGHT SATURATION	COMPEN- SATION POINT	CO_2 FIXATION AT LIGHT SATURATION
		ft-c	ft-c	mg/dm²/hr
Elodea	Plant	10,000	. . .	. . .
Loblolly pine	Plant	9,000	300	3.5
Scotch pine	Plant	6,400	. . .	3.0
Wheat	Plant	5,300	. . .	. . .
Alfalfa	Plant	4,700	. . .	. . .
Sugar beet	Plant	4,400	. . .	. . .
Apple	Plant	4,400	. . .	4.5
Cotton	Leaf	3,500	150	18.0
Dogwood	Plant	3,500	. . .	3.1
Potato	Leaf	3,000	. . .	14.0
Sunflower	Leaf	3,000	100	18.0
Tomato	Leaf	2,500	150	21.0
Tobacco	Leaf	2,500	200	15.0
Corn	Leaf	2,250	. . .	16.0
Soybean	Leaf	2,200	200	17.0
Bean	Leaf	2,200	100	20.0
Castor bean	Leaf	2,100	200	18.0
Coleus	Leaf	2,000	75	8.0
White oak	Plant	2,000	. . .	5.2
Red oak	Plant	1,500	300	6.0
Oxalis	Leaf	1,000	50	4.0
Saintpaulia	Leaf	1,000	50	5.0
Nephrolepis	Leaf	600	50	2.0
Philodendron	Leaf	500	25	4.0
Dryopteris	Leaf	200	25	3.0

Carbon Dioxide Concentration.

Although the percentage of carbon dioxide in the atmosphere is usually about 0.03 per cent (3 parts in 10,000 parts of air), it may vary greatly near the surface of the earth, especially if there is much decaying organic matter in the soil. Measurements have revealed that the concentration of CO_2 in the air of the first few inches above a rich soil may range from 0.06 to nearly 0.30 per cent. If other factors are favorable, this increased CO_2 concentration is sufficient to step up greatly the rate of photosynthesis in low-growing broad-leaved crops, especially if air movement is negligible. It has been shown also that the rate of photosynthesis at a given light intensity is directly correlated with the available carbon dioxide, and vice versa. With the temperature at 22°C. and the relative humidity at 70 per cent, the rate of photosynthesis did not increase in wheat seedlings at light intensities beyond 40 per cent when the available CO_2 was only 0.01 per cent. However, when the CO_2 concentration was increased to nearly 0.04 per cent, the rate of photosynthesis increased more or less directly with increase in light intensity up to 100 per cent of full sunlight (Figure 56). This experiment illustrates the interrelations between two different environmental factors and the rate of photosynthesis. As shown the rate of photosynthesis at a given light intensity depends upon the available CO_2, and vice versa.

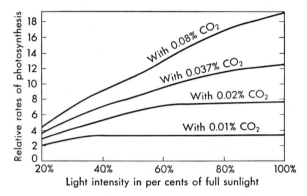

Figure 56 Rates of photosynthesis in relation to light intensity and the concentration of carbon dioxide. *Data from W.H. Hoover, E.S. Johnson and F.S. Brackett. (From Transeau, E.N., H.C. Sampson, and L.H. Tiffany. Textbook of Botany. Harper & Brothers, 1953.)*

Although increasing the carbon dioxide concentration surrounding the leaves of plants when other factors are favorable will accelerate the rate of photosynthesis, it is doubtful whether CO_2 is often a limiting factor for plants under field conditions. This fact is demonstrated by yield data of crops. Such data show that even though the plants are spaced much more closely than is the usual practice, the plants produced from 5 to 20 times the average yields when provided with an adequate supply of water and minerals.

Photosynthesis is a carbon dioxide utilizing process and, unless the CO_2 fixed into the dry matter of plants is returned to the atmosphere, the 0.03 per cent concentration (by volume) of CO_2 in the air would eventually be exhausted. It is of interest, therefore, to examine the cycle of carbon dioxide in our world. This can be shown by the paths of the carbon cycle as illustrated in Figure 57. As is indicated by the heavier black line, plant decay is the major process by which CO_2 is returned to the atmosphere. Other important processes through which CO_2 is released into the air are respiration in plants and animals which involves the oxidation of food, combustion which involves burning of dry matter such as wood, coal, and gas, and the release of CO_2 through various industrial processes.

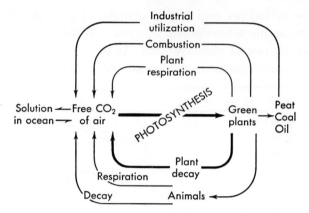

Figure 57 The carbon cycle. (*From Franck, James and W.E. Loomis.* Photosynthesis in Plants. *Iowa State College Press, 1949.*)

Temperature.

It has also been demonstrated that the rate of photosynthesis in potato leaves exposed for 10-minute periods to full sunlight varies with temperature and the concentration of carbon dioxide in the air. For example, with the CO_2 concentration at 0.03 per cent, the maximum rate of photosynthesis in the potato leaves was attained at a temperature of 20°C. However, when the CO_2 concentration was increased to 1.22 per cent, a much greater rate of photosynthesis was attained at 30°C. (Figure 58). Here again certain interrelations are evident between two different environmental factors and the rate of photosynthesis. It is

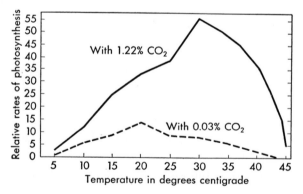

Figure 58 Rates of photosynthesis in potato leaves in relation to temperature and the concentration of carbon dioxide. *Calculated from data by H.G. Lundegardh. (From Transeau, E.N., H.C. Sampson, and L.H. Tiffany.* Textbook of Botany. *Harper & Brothers, 1953.*)

also known that, as in chlorophyll synthesis, extremes of temperature will greatly diminish, if not inhibit, photosynthesis.

Water.

Available moisture may influence the rate of photosynthesis in several ways. Water is one of the necessary raw materials in photosynthesis, and if the supply of water becomes greatly diminished, the rate of photosynthesis will be reduced accordingly. Moreover, a reduction in water supply will frequently cause closure of the stomates and thus limit the entrance of carbon dioxide into the leaves and young stems. When plants wilt, photosynthesis is sharply decreased, first because the water content of green leaf cells is lower, and second because the stomates become closed or nearly so. Furthermore, as previously pointed out, a highly aqueous medium is essential for the many interrelated chemical processes which occur in all living cells, including the chlorophyll-containing cells of the chlorenchyma.

Other Factors.

Although not as extensive as the other factors listed, dust in the atmosphere, especially in and around industrial centers, may clog the stomatal apertures sufficiently to interfere materially with the inward diffusion of CO_2 and consequently with photosynthesis. By reduction of total leaf surface and in other ways, grasshoppers, leaf hoppers, red spiders, aphids and other insects may lower photosynthesis. Leaf spot disease and other fungus, bacterial, and virus diseases may be so destructive as to wipe out entire fields of crops or horticultural plantings causing damage amounting to millions of dollars. Insufficient available oxygen to root systems may indirectly reduce photosynthesis since poor aeration of the roots may greatly interfere with the movement of water and essential minerals into the roots and thence to the leaves.

Structural Conditions.

The leaves of various species of plants differ as to the amount of cutin on the epidermis; the physiological behavior and numbers of stomates per square centimeter of leaf surface; the thickness of the leaf; the compactness of the chlorenchyma and the number of chloroplasts per cell in this tissue; and the size, number, and distribution of the intercellular spaces as these govern particularly the exposure of the mesophyll cells to the internal atmosphere of the leaf. All these structures may influence the entrance of carbon dioxide into the cells of the chlorenchyma and thus affect the rate of photosynthesis. Although some carbon dioxide may enter the leaf through the cells of the epidermis, many tests show that the major part of the CO_2 used in photosynthesis is that which diffuses into the mesophyll through the stomates. The physiological behavior of stomates has previously been discussed. However, as related to the rate of photosynthesis, the stomates of many plants during hot, dry weather may be open mainly at night and closed during the day. In other plants, the stomates may be open only for a few hours in the early morning. In certain cacti and other succulents, the stomates may remain open twenty-four hours each day. Three points should be mentioned here. First, it is doubtful whether stomates are ever completely closed. Second, stomates that appear closed may be open wide enough to permit sufficient inward movement of CO_2 molecules. (The shortest diameter of a fully opened stomate is several million times the diameter of a molecule of carbon dioxide.) Third, the rate at which CO_2 passes through a stomate is more directly proportional to the periphery of the stomate than to its total area. For this reason, the amount of CO_2 that diffuses through a stomate is several times greater than would be expected on the basis of its area. Furthermore, when the stomates are very closely spaced, less CO_2 passes through each one. These facts indicate that stomatal behavior may greatly influence the rate of photosynthesis through its effect on the passage of CO_2 into leaves.

The Chloroplasts.

In higher plants the chlorophyll pigments are found only in the colloidal matrix of specific protoplasmic bodies called chloroplasts. It is apparent, therefore, that photosynthesis occurs only in the chloroplasts of these plants. Beneath each square centimeter of leaf surface there may be millions of chloroplasts in the mesophyll cells. Consequently, the number and distribution of chloroplasts as well as the abundance of chlorophyll in them may influence the rate of photosynthesis in various plants.

Enzymes.

Enzymes are catalyzers which occur in all living cells. These usually complex substances may initiate, accelerate, or decrease chemical reactions without losing their identity or being destroyed by the reactions. It is highly probable that all physiological processes which occur in living protoplasm involve the activity of one or more groups of enzymes. Without enzymes the chemical changes in cells would probably be so slow that living organisms could not survive. The effectiveness of enzymes in controlling chemical changes evidently results from their ability to facilitate the transfer of energy and the formation of unstable intermediate compounds. When the chain of reactions is completed, the enzymes are liberated intact and are again functionally effective. The activity of enzymes in living cells is influenced by many factors such as temperature, available moisture, acidity, light (perhaps as it photochemically affects acidity), the substances acted upon, and the accumulation of end products. Therefore, it is apparent that in photosynthesis, as in many other physiological processes, enzymatic activity plays an important role.

The Mechanism of Photosynthesis.

Some of the outstanding plant physiologists and chemists of the past and present have devoted their scientific careers to an attempt to unravel the problem of how green plants entrap and convert solar energy into chemical energy; still, the mechanism of photosynthesis appears far from a complete explanation. During the twentieth century, however, some revealing research has given us a better understanding of the photosynthetic process.

The first notable contribution was made in 1905 by the English plant physiologist, Blackman. He demonstrated that photosynthesis is not a single photochemical reaction, but consists rather of two major reactions. The first of these is a rapid reaction and requires light energy for its acceleration. The second reaction does not use light energy and can go on equally well in either light or darkness. It appears highly probable that the light reaction produces unstable intermediate compounds which are converted by enzymes of the dark reaction into stable molecules. It is also very likely that the unstable molecules produced photochemically are formed much too rapidly for all of them to be converted into stable molecules by the slower dark reaction. Thus it appears that the dark reaction is the "bottleneck" in photosynthesis.

Although Blackman's contribution was made in 1905, it was not until 1937 that Hill showed the possible nature of the light reaction. He was able to demonstrate that if their enzyme systems were unimpaired, isolated chloroplasts could be resuspended in water, and in the presence of light and a suitable oxidizing agent (hydrogen acceptor), the chloroplasts could cause a photodecomposition of water as shown by the following equation.

$$4\,Fe^{+++} + 2H_2O + (\text{light, chloroplasts}) \longrightarrow 4\,Fe^{++} + 4H^+ + O_2$$

No carbohydrate can be produced by such a system, however.

Facts obtained from the Hill reaction appear to demonstrate that the light reaction of photosynthesis is a photodecomposition of water into H_2 and O_2. Other research with isotopic oxygen (O^{18}) has shown that the carbohydrate molecules formed by photosynthesis contained none of the O^{18}. This definitely demonstrates that the oxygen in the carbohydrate comes from CO_2 and not water, and that the oxygen from the water is released as free oxygen. These two facts together enable the mechanism of photosynthesis to be more clearly understood as a chemical reaction. Therefore, the elementary, over-all photosynthetic equation becomes:

$$6\ CO_2 + 12\ H_2O + Energy \longrightarrow C_6H_{12}O_6\ (simple\ sugar) + 6\ H_2O + 6\ O_2$$

Thus it is established that water is not combined with CO_2 to form a carbon hydrate. Rather the water is decomposed, and its hydrogen is used in the reduction of CO_2.

After photodecomposition of water, the hydrogen must be quickly accepted by what is called a hydrogen acceptor and transferred to the reluctant CO_2 molecule which is not readily reduced by hydrogen. Light-excited chlorophyll is thought to function as the hydrogen acceptor and it transfers this hydrogen to the CO_2. As a result, the CO_2 molecule is reduced. This can be shown as follows:

$$CO_2 + 4\ H \longrightarrow C(H_2O)_2$$

Thus 4 hydrogen atoms are required to reduce one molecule of CO_2, and this requires 112 kilocalories. One quantum is equal to 40 kilocalories, and a minimum of 4 quanta would be needed since there is some loss in the transfer of energy. This would give an efficiency of 70 per cent (112/160), which seems improbable. More likely, as experimentation has shown, 8 quanta are required which would give an efficiency of 35 per cent (112/320).

Attempts to arrive at a comparable basis of understanding of the dark reaction (or reduction of CO_2 by use of the radioactive tracer C^{14}) have been made since 1945. These studies indicate that carbon dioxide is reduced by the hydrogen derived from the photodecomposition of water, after which the reduced carbon is transformed independently of light into carbohydrate molecules. This has suggested to many that the dark reaction in photosynthesis may be the reverse of respiration, and that the enzymes involved, as well as the intermediate organic acids formed, are similar.

Recently it has been shown that the earliest product identified from

CO_2 tracer studies is phosphoglyceric acid ($C_3H_5O_3 \cdot H_2PO_4$) which is mid-way between CO_2 and sugar ($C_6H_{12}O_6$). This 3 carbon phosphoglyceric acid must be preceded by a 2 carbon compound, ribulose-1, 5-diphosphate. The 3 carbon phosphoglyceric acid is, in turn, reduced to fructose, 1, 6-diphosphate by several intermediate steps and the fructose, 1, 6-diphosphate is then converted into sugar. The intermediate compounds between phosphoglyceric acid and fructose, 1, 6-diphosphate have not been definitely identified. By omitting many of the individual steps involved, we may represent the light and dark reactions of photosynthesis diagrammatically as shown in Figure 59. For further details, the student is referred to *Photosynthesis In Plants* (27).

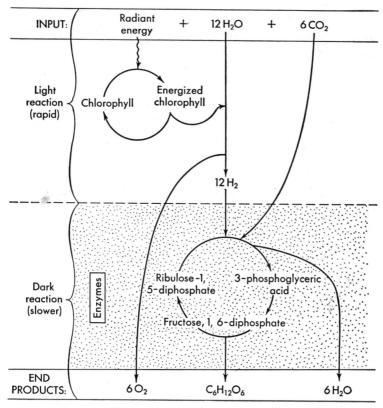

Figure 59 Diagram illustrating some major steps involved in the light and dark reactions of photosynthesis.

In brief, photosynthesis is viewed at present as a complex of processes in which water is decomposed and one molecule of hydrogen reacts with CO_2 to remove one oxygen atom as H_2O, and the other molecule of hydrogen reacts with CO to form (CH_2O). This may be illustrated as follows:

$$CO_2 + 2\,H_2O^* + \text{Energy} \longrightarrow (CH_2O) + H_2O + O_2^*$$

That the basic reaction is in reality one involving only hydrogen and carbon dioxide is further shown by van Niel who demonstrated that in the photosynthesis of green sulfur bacteria, hydrogen is derived from hydrogen sulfide rather than water as shown by the following equation:

$$CO_2 + 2H_2S + \text{Energy} \longrightarrow (CH_2O) + H_2O + 2S$$

A further simplification is indicated as follows:

$$CO_2 + 2H_2 + \text{Energy} \longrightarrow (CH_2O) + H_2O$$

Photosynthesis may be classified therefore as an oxidation-reduction process in which water or some other hydrogen donor is oxidized and carbon dioxide is reduced.

Methods of Measuring Photosynthesis.

Information on the nature of the photosynthetic process and how such factors as light intensity affect its rate has been obtained by various investigators. These scientists have devised methodology for the determination of CO_2 used, O_2 released, and chemical constituents formed. As has been shown, CO_2 is used and O_2 is released in photosynthesis. This enables one to measure the rate of photosynthesis as indicated by the change in pressure or concentration of the gases exchanged during the process. Instrumentation, then, involves an apparatus for determining changes in gas pressure or in concentration. However, only within the last decade has determination of the chemical constituents formed during photosynthesis yielded information of value to the understanding of the photosynthetic mechanism. This has come about through the utilization of radioactive C^{14} and separation of the tagged organic molecules by means of paper chromatography.

Gaseous exchange determinations have been made by means of the manometric method which can best be carried out on algal suspensions in small enclosed vessels attached to manometers. The change in pressure in the vessels as a result of O_2 evolution is measured on the attached manometers. One design for such vessels along with a contant temperature water bath and shaking mechanism is shown in Figure 60. The vessels are immersed in the constant temperature water bath to enable the

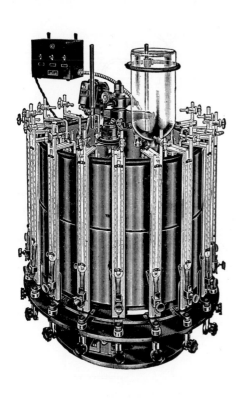

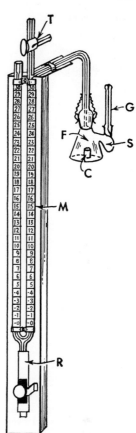

Figure 60 Circular bath, shaking mechanism, and manometer supports for micro-respirometer flasks. The water bath by means of temperature controls is used to maintain a constant temperature of the water in which the flasks are submerged. The figure to the right shows the constant volume respirometer in greater detail. *(From Umbreit, W.W. et al. 1949, Manometric Techniques and Tissue Metabolism. Burgess Publishing Co. Minneapolis. Water bath photograph courtesy of American Instrument Co., Silver Spring, Maryland.)*

investigator to control temperature. Thus if light intensity is being studied, temperature can be held constant; or if desired, the effect of temperature can be determined by altering temperatures of the water bath. The shaking mechanism keeps the vessels in rotation so as to assure a quick release of the O_2 from water to air as well as for maintaining CO_2 constant in the water. Manometric techniques, however, are seldom used for the study of gaseous exchange in land plants. Instead, rates of CO_2 absorption are measured by determining the difference in CO_2 con-

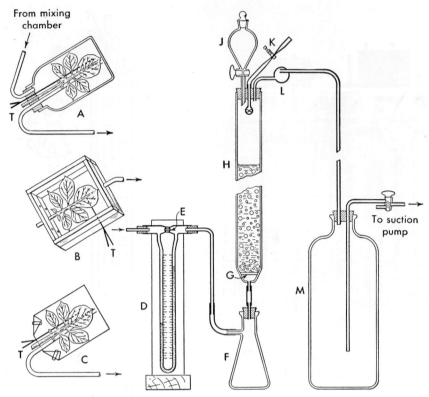

Figure 61 A gas steam apparatus used for measuring photosynthesis by passage of air over enclosed leaves. *(From Chapman, H.W. and W.E. Loomis,* Plant Physiology. *28:703–716, 1953.)*

tent between a measured stream of air not in contact with a leaf and an equal volume of similar air that has been drawn over an enclosed illuminated leaf. Such an apparatus is diagrammed in Figure 61. The CO_2 content of the air stream is determined by passage of the air through KOH solution in the absorption tower H.

Analytical investigations using radioactive C^{14} involve the use of algal cells which are grown in nutrient solutions in especially designed glass vessels under artificial illumination (Figure 62). Aliquots of these liquid algal cultures are then placed in small flasks into which is introduced radioactive carbon in the form of sodium carbonate (Figure 63). The algae, after a certain length of time, are then killed and fractionated into a soluble extract, a portion of which is placed in the corner of a large piece of filter paper (Figure 64). The filter paper is then placed in chromatographic chambers where, by allowing the paper to be en-

Figure 62 Apparatus used to culture algae for photosynthesis studies. *(From Calvin, Melvin. The Path of Carbon in Photosynthesis. University of Notre Dame Press, 1949.)*

Figure 63 A flask containing algae cells into which radioactive carbon is being introduced for tracer studies. *(From Calvin, Melvin. The Path of Carbon in Photosynthesis. University of Notre Dame Press, 1949.)*

Figure 64 Placing a small aliquot of the algae extract in the corner of large piece of filter paper in preparation for paper chromatography. *(From Calvin, Melvin. The Path of Carbon in Photosynthesis. University of Notre Dame Press, 1949.)*

veloped in special solvents, the various compounds from the algae will be separated on the paper into several spots. Such a separation is shown in Figure 65 after the filter paper is exposed to X-ray film. The radioactive compounds which are separated into spots will then develop an identifiable pattern.

The following outline summarizes some of the fundamental features of photosynthesis:

1. Photosynthesis is the reduction of CO_2 and the oxidation of H_2O resulting in the accumulation of energy in organic molecules (sugar).
2. The raw materials used in the process are carbon dioxide from the atmosphere (directly or dissolved in water) and water from the soil (or a water medium).
3. The end products formed are sugar, water, and oxygen. The oxygen released in the process is that which was originally a part of the water molecules, whereas the hydrogen originally in the water becomes united with the carbon dioxide in the synthesis of the carbohydrate molecule.
4. The process requires light as a source of energy. It occurs in the chloroplasts of higher green plants and in the unorganized chlorophyll of blue-

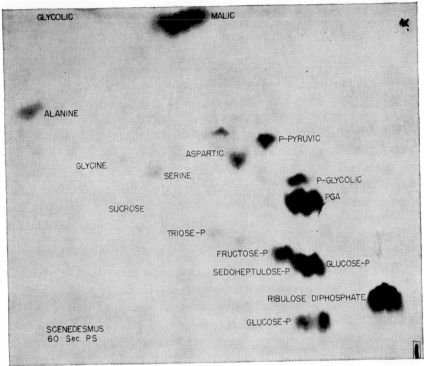

Figure 65   Radiogram of a paper chromatograph of an algae extract showing the pathway of radioactive carbon into early products of photosynthesis. (*From Calvin, Melvin.* The Path of Carbon in Photosynthesis. *University of Notre Dame Press, 1949.*)

green algae. Sugar is also made photosynthetically by certain bacteria which contain carotenoid-like pigments.

5. A part of the light energy absorbed by green cells is transformed into the chemical energy of the sugar molecules.

6. Other factors essential for photosynthesis are a suitable temperature, chlorophyll, and the presence of certain enzymes.

7. Generalized word equation:
   Carbon Dioxide + Water + Light + Suitable temperature + Chlorophyll + Enzymes → Sugar + Water + Oxygen

8. Chemical equation:
   $6CO_2 + 12H_2O$ + Light + Suitable temperature + Chlorophyll + Enzymes → $C_6H_{12}O_6 + 6H_2O + 6O_2$

9. Photosynthesis consists of a series of complex intermediate steps many of which are not well understood at present.

11.
RESPIRATION

In photosynthesis light energy is changed to chemical energy which becomes a part of the sugar which is synthesized in the process. The conversion of sugar into other organic compounds requires energy. Sugar, however, is usually not utilized directly as such, but it is first broken down into simpler organic molecules and these may then be synthesized into foods or assimilation products. Both these other organic molecules and the energy used in food synthesis and assimilation result from a complex of reactions collectively known as respiration. In an effort to portray simply what takes place in respiration, teachers often represent this process by the following brief but really fallacious equation:

$$C_6H_{12}O_6 + 6O_2 \longrightarrow 6CO_2 + 6H_2O + \text{Energy (673 Kg. Cal.)}$$

This equation represents a direct oxidation process. If it occurred in living cells, such a reaction would result in a release of all the chemical energy in a single combustion-like process. Release of energy in this manner would cause a rise in temperature sufficient to kill living protoplasm. Even if the protoplasm were not destroyed, no energy would be left for cell metabolism. Of course, this does not happen as a single, direct chemical reaction.

On the contrary, the sugar is gradually broken down in a series of reactions which involve the release of energy, and which may ultimately result in the formation of CO_2 and H_2O. For these reactions to occur, cell catalysts called enzymes must be present to serve a two-fold purpose. First, they are instrumental in splitting the more complex organic molecules into simpler ones. Second, and perhaps more importantly, these enzymes facilitate the transfer of energy to energy-rich phosphate bonds in organic phosphate molecules, as will be described later. The energy which is gained by these molecules during respiration may subsequently be used in other essential metabolic processes in living cells. Since it is so important, the role which enzymes play in respiration must be considered in some detail.

Enzymes.

Enzymes influence the rate of various cellular reactions. Furthermore, enzymes are specific in action, each cellular reaction being catalyzed by a particular enzyme or group of related enzymes. A small number of enzyme particles can speed up the reaction of a large number of reacting molecules. The enzyme, however, is not consumed during these cellular reactions.

Enzymes have been isolated in pure form from plant cells and in all cases have been found to be proteins. Some enzymes are protein molecules only, while other enzymes have a nonprotein portion. The nonprotein portion is designated as the prosthetic group or coenzyme. Without the prosthetic group, the protein portion of an enzyme is enzymatically inert. A prosthetic group may consist of a single atom (usually a metal), or prosthetic groups may be complex organic molecules which are often vitamins. Cellular enzymes occur in the living protoplasm and are found in the soluble portion of cytoplasm, in the chloroplasts, in chondriosomes, and in the nucleus.

The activity of enzymes is influenced by temperature, pH, hydration, activators, and inhibitors. If these factors are at an optimum for enzyme activation, the actual reaction will depend on the concentration of the molecules which are being enzymatically catalyzed together with the concentration of the enzyme molecules.

Whereas enzymes which are involved in the various respiratory reactions attract our immediate interest, it is well to remember that almost all other cellular reactions are likewise catalyzed by enzymes. Examples of the various kinds of enzymes in respect to their substrates (molecules which are being acted upon catalytically) and end products formed are given in Table 22.

The Mechanism of Respiration.

For an understanding of the many integrated reactions in respiration, it is first necessary to establish that the living cells of some species of plants have respiratory reactions which do not require utilization of free oxygen. The best known example of such a species is common yeast in which the following respiratory reaction occurs:

$$C_6H_{12}O_6 \longrightarrow 2C_2H_5OH + 2CO_2$$

The end products of this reaction are ethyl alcohol and carbon dioxide; whereas in the utilization of free O_2 in respiration, carbon dioxide and water are the end products. Many living cells, for example yeast, have both aerobic and anaerobic respiratory systems. The kind of respiratory reactions that occur is generally dependent on whether free oxygen is present or not. Some species of bacteria are known that cannot live in the presence of free oxygen. They are called obligate anaerobes. In both aerobic and anaerobic respiration, the end products are formed only after a series of intermediate reactions. In the past twenty years biochemical research has shown that in these two kinds of respiration, the intermediate reactions are the same. The intermediate reactions common to aerobic and anaerobic respiration are called glycolysis and do not utilize or require free oxygen.

Table 22 A list of some of the enzymes involved in various cellular reactions and their activities.

ENZYME	SUBSTRATE	END PRODUCTS
Sucrase *	Sucrose	Glucose + fructose
α Amylase *	Starch	Dextrins
Cellulase *	Cellulose	Cellobiose
Lipase *	Fats	Glycerol + fatty acids
Proteases *	Proteins	Peptones, polypeptides + amino acids
Phosphorylase *	Glucose-1-phosphate	Amylose + H_3PO_4
Glutamic dehydrogenase **	α Ketoglutaric acid + NH_3	Glutamic acid
Hexokinase **	Glucose	Glucose-6-phosphate
Aldolase **	Fructose-1, 6-diphosphate	Phosphoglyceraldehyde + dihydroxyacetone phosphate
Phosphotransferase **	Phosphoenolpyruvic acid	Pyruvic acid
Malic dehydrogenase **	Malic acid	Oxalacetic acid
Succinic dehydrogenase **	Succinic acid	Fumaric acid
Pyruvic acid carboxylase **	Pyruvic acid	Acetaldehyde + carbon dioxide
Alcohol dehydrogenase **	Acetaldehyde	Alcohol

* Enzymes which catalyze hydrolytic reactions.
** Enzymes which catalyze respiratory reactions.

The central feature of the initial breakdown by glycolysis is the conversion of hexose sugar to pyruvic acid through a series of reactions which involve phosphorylated derivatives of hexose sugar or other carbohydrates. Each step involves the action of a specific phosphorylase enzyme; these steps may be summarized as follows (the enzyme names rest on the arrows):

1. Glucose $\xrightarrow{\text{Hexokinase + ATP}}$ Glucose-6-phosphate

2. Glucose-6-phosphate $\xrightarrow{\text{Phosphohexoisomerase}}$ Fructose-6-phosphate

3. Fructose-6-phosphate $\xrightarrow{\text{Phosphohexokinase + ATP}}$ Fructose-1, 6-diphosphate

4. Fructose-1, 6-diphosphate $\xrightarrow{\text{Aldolase}}$ Dihydroxyacetone phosphate + 3-phosphoglyceraldehyde

5. 3-phosphoglyceraldehyde $\xrightarrow{\text{Triosephosphate dehydrogenase + ADP}}$

6. 3-phosphoglyceric acid $\xrightarrow{\text{Phosphoglycero mutase}}$

7. 2-phosphoglyceric acid $\xrightarrow{\text{Enolase}}$

8. Phosphoenolpyruvic acid $\xrightarrow{\text{Phosphotransferase}}$ Pyruvic acid

With the formation of pyruvic acid, the initial and intermediate steps common to aerobic and anaerobic respiration end. The fate of pyruvic acid is different in the two kinds of respiration. In one type of anaerobic respiration the following reactions occur:

$$\text{Pyruvic acid} \xrightarrow{\text{Carboxylase}} \text{Acetaldehyde} + CO_2$$

$$\text{Acetaldehyde} \xrightarrow{\text{Alcohol dehydrogenase}} \text{Ethyl alcohol} + CO_2$$

In aerobic respiration pyruvic acid is converted to $CO_2 + H_2O$ by a series of reactions known collectively as the Krebs cycle. This cycle involves two kinds of enzymes: dehydrogenases which remove hydrogen, and carboxylases which remove CO_2. The dehydrogenases, in turn, release the hydrogen to the terminal oxidases which combine the hydrogen with free oxygen in forming H_2O. Thus the end products of aerobic respiration (H_2O and CO_2) are the final products of pyruvic acid oxidation.

The Krebs cycle may be summarized by the following steps:

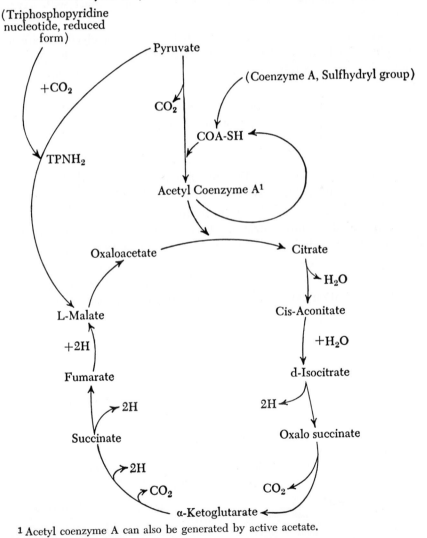

[1] Acetyl coenzyme A can also be generated by active acetate.

By the addition of the pyruvate (3 carbon compound) to oxaloacetate (4 carbon compound) and by passage through the Krebs cycle, three molecules of CO_2 are split off from different intermediates and sufficient hydrogen transferred to oxygen to yield 3 molecules of H_2O. In the formation of citric acid (6 carbon compound) from oxaloacetate plus pyruvate, one molecule of CO_2 is liberated. The citric acid is then degraded via the Krebs cycle with the loss of two additional molecules of CO_2. This results in the regeneration of the 4-carbon compound, oxaloacetate. The cycle is then repeated by adding another molecule of pyruvate. During the cycle in addition to the CO_2 formed, some of the intermediate compounds are oxidized by the removal of hydrogen. The hydrogen by means of certain enzyme systems may react with oxygen to form H_2O.

All of the molecules of pyruvate that result from glycolysis are not decarboxylated and oxidized to CO_2 and H_2O. Some of the pyruvate molecules have the following fates: 1. participation in the formation of high phosphate bond energy enzymes; 2. as intermediate compounds in amino acid synthesis; 3. as precursors via acetyl coenzyme A for the synthesis of fatty acids; and 4. as other precursors for the biosyntheses of assimilation products.

Unless some of the pyruvate molecules are utilized in the above mentioned metabolic pathways, the integrated metabolism that results in life would cease. As far as is known this holds true for most living cells.

The formation of L-malate from pyruvate by the addition of CO_2 that is accompanied by the oxidization of $TPNH_2$ is known as carbon dioxide fixation or carboxylation. This mechanism is similar to but distinct from CO_2 fixation in photosynthesis. The principal difference appears to be the specific kind of organic molecule that acts as the CO_2 acceptor. Aerobic respiration can be summarized in its entire reactions as follows:

Phosphorylases

Glucose ———————→ Fructose diphosphate
(1 molecule)   (1 molecule)
2-Phosphoglyceric acid
(2 molecules)

            Dehydrogenase   Oxidase
            ———————→ $4H$ + Carrier ——————→ O_2

Pyruvic acid $2H_2O$
(2 molecules)

$6H_2O$ →
            Dehydrogenase   Oxidase
            ———————→ 2 OH + Carrier ——————→ $5O_2$

$6CO_2$ $10H_2O$

In the above series of reactions in the respiratory process, sugar is broken down by means of a step by step oxidation resulting in a loss of energy at each step. Some of this energy is dissipated, for example, as heat energy. More important, however, is the energy which is transferred to the phosphate enzymes and which is subsequently released in various biosyntheses or which is the source of energy for these reactions. This transfer of energy is not shown in the previously discussed reactions because such energy transfer involves additional reactions.

The key phosphate enzymes are the three adenine derivatives. The adenine derivatives are molecules composed of adenine, ribose, and phosphate groups. The phosphate groups contain the stored energy. Adenosine diphosphate (ADP) has two phosphate groups, while adenosine triphosphate (ATP) has three groups. Each phosphate group has 12,000 calories of energy. It is only recently that the mechanism of the adenosine formation has been understood in its relationship to respiration. For example, during glycolysis ADP and ATP are formed when phosphoglyceraldehyde is converted to 3-phosphoglyceric acid. This may be shown as follows:

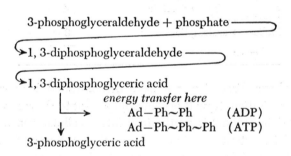

The above transfer of energy-rich phosphate bonds (Ph~Ph) can count for only a small portion of the energy which is stored as such bonds. Research has shown that the oxidation of one mol of hexose to CO_2 and H_2O should release 680,000 cal. Actual measurements show that approximately 290,000 cal. are not released but are stored in the form of phosphate bond energy. The question of how the remaining energy is transferred to storage is not entirely clear, but it is thought that ATP is generated during the Krebs cycle or pyruvic acid oxidation. Biochemists now are of the opinion that, during the splitting off of hydrogen and carbon dioxide, these reactions involve the taking up of phosphate and the formation of organic phosphate intermediates which, in turn, release the energy-rich phosphate bonds to ATP. The transfer of energy can occur at any of the steps in the Krebs cycle and may be illustrated at the pyruvic to acetic acid step as follows:

$$\text{Pyruvic acid} + \text{phosphate} \xrightarrow{\text{CoI}} \text{Acetyl phosphate}$$
$$+ CO_2 + H_2O \qquad\qquad\qquad \downarrow \text{ADP}$$
$$\text{Acetic acid}$$
$$+ \text{Ad}-\text{Ph}\sim\text{Ph}\sim\text{Ph}$$
$$\text{(ATP)}$$

A summary of these reactions is given in Table 23 with the number of phosphate high energy bonds yielded. The 16 bonds yield 184,000 cal. out of the 274,000 cal. released by oxidation of pyruvic acid or an energy capture of 67 per cent.

Table 23   The reactions in the Krebs citric acid cycle and the number of energy-rich phosphate bonds of the various intermediate reactions.

REACTION	NUMBER OF ENERGY-RICH BONDS
Pyruvic ⟶ acetic	4
Isocitric ⟶ α ketoglutaric	3
α Ketoglutaric ⟶ succinic	4
Succinic ⟶ fumaric	2
Malic ⟶ oxaloacetic	3
Total	16

In the above discussion, we have demonstrated how energy was captured in respiration. Now it becomes important to show how a respiratory intermediate product is synthesized into a cellular constituent. This is the second important function of respiration in terms of metabolism, since CO_2, H_2O, and dissipated energy are useless. α Ketoglutaric acid, a respiratory intermediate, is the raw material for the amino acid, glutamic acid. This synthesis occurs as follows:

$$\alpha \text{ Ketoglutaric acid} + NH_3 \xrightarrow[\substack{\text{glutamic} \\ \text{dehydrogenase}}]{\text{DPN}} \text{glutamic acid}$$

Factors Affecting the Rate of Respiration.

From the previous discussion on the nature of the respiratory mechanism, it should be evident that respiration involves an extremely complicated series of biochemical reactions which are intimately tied up with all living processes. If this were not true, methods used for the measurement of respiration would be far more accurate than they are at present. Respiration usually has been measured by the gas exchange technique which has already been described for the measurement of photosynthesis (review chapter 10). If one is investigating the rate of aerobic respiration as it is affected by a certain factor, the oxygen used or carbon dioxide involved is measured per weight of tissue. The gas exchange technique thus operates on the assumption that respiration is a complete oxidation of sugar in which one hexose molecule is oxidized by six O_2 molecules and six CO_2 molecules are released. Hence, the ratio of the volume of CO_2 evolved to the volume of O_2 used is equal to unity. This ratio is called the respiratory quotient (CO_2/O_2). But as our discussion of the respiratory mechanism indicated, each molecule of hexose sugar does not always end up as CO_2 and H_2O. Therefore, the rate of respiration as measured by CO_2 evolution may be far from a completely accurate index of the respiratory intensity. However, in the development of our present knowledge of factors which affect the rate of respiration, it was necessary to evaluate respiration by gas exchange because better methods were not available to the investigators who obtained the data. It is well to remember, therefore, that such data do not constitute an absolute indicator of respiratory intensity, but are rather an approximation or what might be called an apparent respiration rate.

The rate of respiration is influenced by a complex of interrelated factors, that is, respiration intensity is dependent on conditions within the living cell and environmental factors. The role of the living cell in regulating respiratory intensity is illustrated by differences in rate of respiration between species of plants, between organs of the same species, and by age of the organ. Such differences are comparable only if environmental factors are the same. These differences are substantiated by experimental data presented in Tables 24 and 25.

Table 24 The rate of respiration of various plant species. (*From Stiles, Walter. An Introduction to the Principles of Plant Physiology. Methuen and Co., 1950.*)

SPECIES	DESCRIPTION	TEMPERATURE	INTENSITY OF RESPIRATION
		°C	cc. $O_2/hr./g.$ fresh wt.
Cactus (*Cereus*)	Herbaceous perennial	12	3.00
Ecuador cholla	Herbaceous perennial	13	6.80
Prickly pear (*Opuntia*)	Herbaceous perennial	13	11.40
Stone crop	Herbaceous perennial	13	16.60
Norway spruce	Tree	15	44.10
Common snowdrop	Perennial bulb	13	77.60
Broad bean	Herbaceous annual	12	96.60
Four-o'clock	Herbaceous perennial	15	120.00
Wheat	Annual	13	291.00

Table 25   The rate of respiration of various plant organs. *(From Stiles, Walter, and William Leach. Respiration In Plants. Methuen and Co., 1952.)*

SPECIES	TEMPERA-TURE	RESPIRATORY INTENSITY, CC. CO_2/HR./G. FRESH WT.				
		SEPALS	PETALS	STAMENS	PISTIL	LEAVES
	°C.					
Mullein	23.0	0.747	0.177	0.761	0.815	0.382
Beard-tongue	23.5	0.571	0.398	0.602	0.689	0.300
Poppy	22.0	0.390	0.367	1.041	0.690	0.332
Tree-mallow	22.0	0.615	0.303	0.576	0.894	0.394

These data show that at approximately equal temperatures, respiratory intensity varies with species of plant and with various plant organs or parts of plant organs of the same species.

The question now to be answered, as far as can be determined from present information, is why do differences in respiration intensity occur? Excluding environmental factors, the answer is found in the intracellular factors which control the many reactions of respiration. These are concentration of substrate such as sugar, concentration of enzymes, enzyme activators, enzyme inhibitors, and the degree of cell hydration. How these factors affect respiratory intensity can be seen by examination of some experimental data. The effect of concentration of substrate is illustrated by the data in Figure 66. These data show that as sugar substrates are exhausted, rate of respiration decreases (as measured by CO_2 evolution). On the other hand, the effect of decreasing cellular water content in soybean seed on the rate of respiration is shown in Figure 67.

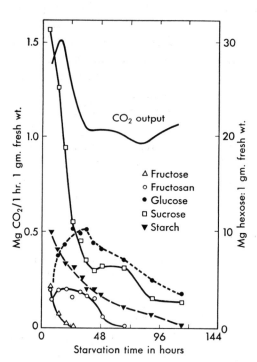

Figure 66   The association of the rate of respiration as measured by CO_2 evolution with changes in the concentration of carbohydrates in barley leaves kept in the dark. *(From Yemm, E.W. Proc. Roy. Soc. London B 117:483, 1935.)*

Research on fruit has demonstrated that time is an important factor in respiratory intensity. The time effect as related to age of fruit is illustrated by the data on several varieties of apples (Figure 68). These data show that as the apples reach maturity, the rate of respiration is increased. Other data show that this peak of respiratory intensity (climacteric) does not continue, but rapidly falls off to a steady state.

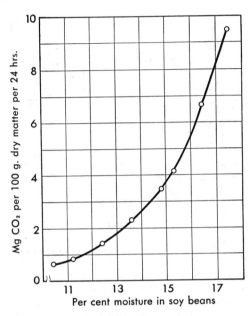

Figure 67   The association of the rate of respiration as measured by CO_2 evolution with the moisture content of soybean seed. (*From Ramstad, P.E. and W.F. Geddes,* The Respiration and Storage Behavior of Soybeans. *Minn. Agr. Exp. Sta. Tech. Bull. 156, 1942.*)

The major environmental factors which affect the rate of respiration are temperature, oxygen concentration, carbon dioxide concentration, and light. Respiration is a chemical reaction and thus temperature should increase the rate two to three times for each 10 degrees centigrade rise in temperature. This rate of increase of the process is expressed by the symbol Q_{10} and is called the temperature coefficient. Between 0°C. and 35°C., the Q_{10} for most kinds of plant tissue is 2.0 to 2.5.

Above 35°C., the rate of respiration can be shown to increase for short periods of time; but from 40°C. to 45°C., the rate rapidly falls to less than rates at 30°C. This is thought to be due to enzyme inactivation and failure to maintain a supply of substrate. However, it should be pointed out that at 35°C., time may affect the respiratory intensity of some kinds of plant organs. The effects of temperature and time on the rate of respiration of plums are graphically presented in Figure 69.

When food production is compared with food use, it is interesting to note that the maximum rate of photosynthesis occurs at lower temperatures than the maximum rate of respiration (Figure 70). This means that during exteremely hot daylight hours of summer, the rate at which food is made by photosynthesis may barely equal the rate at which food is used in respiration. When it is recalled that respiration goes on continuously day and night and that photosynthesis occurs only during the hours of daylight, it is evident that, if such conditions persisted for a very long period, use (respiratory decomposition) would greatly exceed the production of food, growth would cease, and the plant would succumb.

The considerations relative to factors affecting respiratory intensity

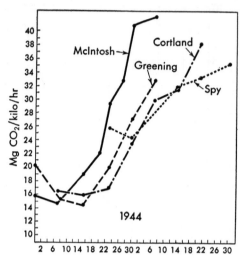

Figure 68   The effect of age of fruit (as denoted by harvest date) on the rate of respiration as measured by CO_2 evolution of several varieties of apples. (*From Smock, R.M. and C.R. Gross, Cornell Univ. Agr. Exp. Sta. Memoir 297, 1950.*)

are applicable to both aerobic and anaerobic respiration. As previously indicated, the rate of aerobic respiration is affected by the concentration of oxygen as well as by other factors. In closed chambers containing plant material on which respiration is being determined, unless the oxygen used is replaced, the air in the chambers becomes progressively lower in oxygen and higher in carbon dioxide. The rate of respiration is decreased under such conditions. Is such a decrease the result of CO_2 toxicity or lack of oxygen? It is difficult to draw inferences from the data obtained. The direct effect of oxygen concentration can be determined only under experimental conditions where oxygen is the variable and CO_2 is kept at the normal atmospheric level. Claypool and Allen (32) studied the effect of oxygen concentration on plum fruit respiration under such experimental conditions, and the data obtained at 86°F. are presented in Figure 71. These data show that with increasing oxygen concentrations from 1 per cent to 50 per cent, accelerated rates of respiration were obtained which maintained a fairly constant rate with time. At oxygen concentrations above 50 per cent, respiratory intensity is accelerated for a short period of time but then falls off.

The direct inhibitory effect of increasing concentrations of carbon dioxide on respiration is shown by the data on germinating mustard seed in Table 26. It should be pointed out that increasing CO_2 concentration does not always have a direct inhibition effect on respiration. Leaves in light placed in higher concentrations of CO_2 have higher rates of respiration because the increased photosynthetic rate results in more sugar substrate for respiration.

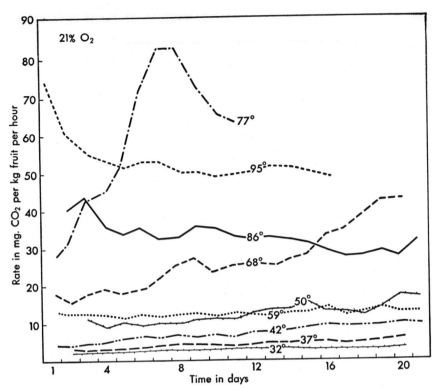

Figure 69 The effect of temperature on the rate of respiration as measured by CO_2 evolution of Wickson plums. *(From Claypool, L.I. and F.W. Allen, Hilgardia 21:129–160, 1951.)*

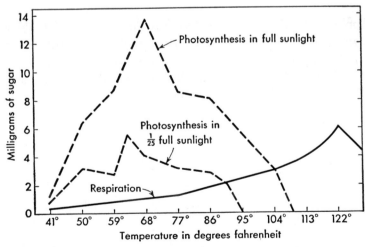

Figure 70 Relative rates of photosynthesis and respiration in potato leaves during 10-minute exposures to different temperatures in shade and in full sunlight. *Recalculated from data by H.S. Lundegardh. (From Transeau, E.N., Sampson, H.C., and Tiffany, L.H. Textbook of Botany. Harper & Brothers, 1953.)*

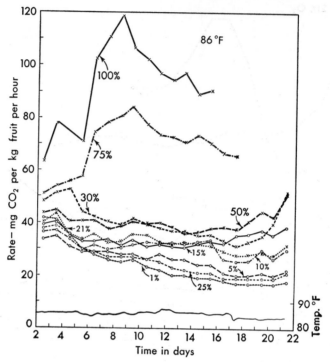

Figure 71   The effect of oxygen concentration on the rate of respiration as measured by CO_2 evolution of Wickson plums. *(From Claypool, L.I. and F.W. Allen,* Hilgardia *21:129–160, 1951.)*

Applications of Respiration Research To Agricultural Problems.

Data from respiratory research have enabled scientists to recommend methods whereby various food products may be transported and stored with a minimum loss of quality. Fruit and vegetables are kept at high quality for shipment and storage by refrigeration. The reason

Table 26   The effect of various concentrations of CO_2 on the respiratory intensity of germinating mustard seed. *(From Kidd, F. London. Proc. Roy. Soc. B89: 136–156. 1915.)*

CONCENTRATION	O_2 USED	CO_2 EVOLVED
%	$ml./O_2/hr.$	$ml./CO_2/hr.$
0	5.1	4.1
10	4.1	3.4
20	3.4	2.7
30	3.2	2.4
40	2.7	1.9
80	2.3	1.2

back of refrigeration is that low temperature causes minimum respiration rate (review Figure 69). Deterioration in quality occurs at the higher temperatures because of factors associated with high rates of respiration. Deterioration is also held to a minimum by the maintenance of high CO_2 concentrations and low oxygen concentrations in storage structures, but refrigeration is the most widely used method.

Unlike fruits and vegetables, seeds which are to be stored for food or planting purposes can be kept at high germinability and low deterioration by removing moisture in the seeds to a level where the rate of respiration is at a minimum (review Figure 67). Maintenance of germinability and prevention of loss in quality of stored seeds is now being carried out on a large scale by removing moisture from seeds to a safe storage moisture content. Moisture removal is accomplished either by natural curing in environments of high evaporation or by artificial drying in humid environments. The safe storage moisture contents of several kinds of seeds are shown in Table 27. It will be noted that a considerable variation exists in safe storage moisture contents among the different kinds of seeds. The reason is that safe storage moisture content for a seed is the moisture content which will be in equilibrium with relative humidities of less than 75 per cent so as to prevent or check microbial deterioration. The equilibrium moisture of a particular kind of seed at relative humidities of less than 75 per cent will depend on the chemical constituents of the seed. Seeds high in hydrophilic colloids (proteins and starch) will have higher safe storage moisture contents than those seeds low in hydrophilic colloids (oil seeds). The same principles are also applicable to the storage of hay crops.

In our discussion of temperature effects on the rate of respiration, the interrelationship between photosynthesis and respiration as influenced by temperature was briefly mentioned (review Figure 70). This interrelationship is important in crop yields. The light intensity at which the rates of respiration and photosynthesis are equal is called the compensation point. If light intensities are sufficient to increase photosynthesis rates as rapidly as increases in temperature cause acceleration in respiration, the compensation point changes. However, before growth can occur in plant parts such as stems, roots, bulbs, fuits, and seeds, the rate of photosynthesis must exceed the rate of respiration so that sufficient sugar remains for leaf respiration at night and for translocation to storage organs. Thus two considerations are involved: 1. amount of sugar not used in light, and, 2. rate of night respiration which is generally controlled by night temperatures. A well known example illustrating

Table 27   The safe storage moisture contents of various kinds of seeds for maintenance of high germinability and low deterioration. (*From various sources in the literature.*)

KIND OF SEED	SAFE STORAGE MOISTURE CONTENT [1]
	per cent
Barley	12.0
Buckwheat	12.5
Blue lupine *	11.0
Corn	12.0
Crimson clover *	10.0
Flaxseed	7.9
Oats	11.8
Peanuts *	6.0
Rice	12.5
Rye	12.2
Sericea lespediza *	8.5
Sorghum	11.9
Soybeans	9.3
Watermelon *	8.4
Wheat	12.0

[1] On a basis of wet weight.
* Determined by Agricultural Experiment Station, Ala. Poly. Inst.

these considerations has to do with the size of Irish potato tubers under different conditions. Warm nights, by causing a comparatively high rate of respiration, leave too little sugar for growth of the tubers and as a result small potatoes are formed. On the other hand, cool nights facilitate yields of large potatoes. Thus in open habitats, night temperatures are very important in the growth and development of storage organs.

The fundamental features of respiration are summarized below:

1. The process of respiration is not an oxidative combustion process, but it is rather a slow breakdown of sugar by a complicated series of enzymatically controlled intermediate reactions.
2. Enzymatically controlled reactions result in the formation of several kinds of end products depending on whether the cells are in an oxygen environment (aerobic respiration) or in an oxygen deficient environment (anaerobic respiration).
3. The intermediate steps which are the same in both aerobic and anaerobic respiration, are called glycolysis, are catalyzed by the phospholase enzymes, and result in the end product pyruvic acid.
4. Under anaerobic respiration conditions, pyruvic acid is converted to various kinds of organic acids plus CO_2 or to ethyl alcohol plus CO_2.
5. Aerobic respiration uses O_2 and results in a conversion of pyruvic acid by what is known as the Krebs organic acid cycle to $CO_2 + H_2O$.
6. Aerobic and anaerobic respiration cause a part of the chemical energy in

sugar to be released, some of the energy being transferred to phosphate enzymes (ATP and ADP) where the energy is then available for use in the synthesis of foods and assimilation products.

7. Many of the organic acids and phosphorylated sugars are the raw materials from which foods and assimilation products are synthesized.

8. Enzymes are the cellular catalytic molecules and aggregates and consist largely of protein-type particles.

9. Many enzymes have attachments which consist of either a simple metallic atom or a more complex molecule, and these attachments are called prosthetic groups or coenzymes.

10. The activity of enzymes can be controlled by cellular factors such as inhibitors, pH, hydration, activators, and the number of enzyme molecules. Enzyme activity may also be influenced by environmental factors.

11. Rate of respiration under constant environmental conditions is dependent on the following cellular factors: 1. activation and number of enzyme particles, 2. concentration of substrate molecules, 3. cell hydration, and 4. age of cell.

12. The principal environmental factors which affect the rate of respiration are: 1. temperature, 2. oxygen concentration, 3. carbon dioxide concentration, and, 4. light.

13. Respiratory activity is an important plant process which must be considered in the artificial storage of fruits, vegetables, seeds, and hay if high quality is to be maintained.

14. Growth of plants, either shoot and root growth or storage organs, is dependent in a large measure upon the balance between rate of photosynthesis and rate of respiration.

12.
PLANT BIOSYNTHESES

STARCH SYNTHESIS AND STARCH DIGESTION

Starch is a complex carbohydrate made from glucose in plants. It is now known that starch synthesis proceeds along rather definite pathways and results, 1. from the conversion of glucose-1-phosphate to amylose by the enzymes phosphorylase, and, 2. from the conversion of glucose-1-phosphate to amylopectin by the Q-enzymes. The amylose and amylopectins are then combined to form starch. Starch synthesis may be represented by the following diagram:

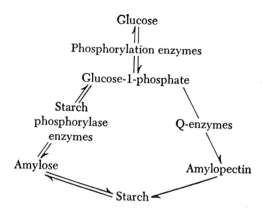

Q-enzymes are not now thought to cause starch digestion; however, starch decomposition may be brought about by hydrolytic cleavages facilitated by enzymes as follows:

$$(C_6H_{10}O_5)_n \xrightarrow{\alpha \text{ Amylase}} (C_6H_{10}O_5)_n \xrightarrow{\beta \text{ Amylase}} C_{12}H_{22}O_{11} \xrightarrow{\text{Maltase}} C_6H_{12}O_6$$

Starch   Dextrin   Maltose   Glucose

As indicated by the above diagram, starch consists of two components which differ in physical properties, namely, amylose (a linear unbranched compound) and amylopectin (a branched chain molecule). The two constituents are composed of from 200 to 700 units of glucose residues. In leaves the proportions of amylose and amylopectin are 18 per cent and 82 per cent respectively. With the iodine test, amylose gives a blue coloration, while amylopectin gives a reddish-brown color.

Both conditions within the cell and environmental factors play important roles in determining whether starch synthesis or starch digestion will predominate in a living plant cell. Within a living plant cell, a low inorganic phosphate level and a low acidity (pH 5.7) are conducive to starch synthesis. Conversely, greater acidity and a high inorganic phosphate level favor starch digestion in living plant cells. Flaccidity resulting from decreased water content causes starch hydrolysis in the cells of leaves. However, seeds differ from leaves in that an increase in water content (rather than a reduction) causes starch digestion in seeds. Temperatures above 10°C. favor starch synthesis, whereas lower temperatures cause the conversion of starch into sugar as shown by potatoes in storage.

Starch is synthesized in the chloroplasts of chlorenchyma and in the leucoplasts of non-green cells. As previously explained, these plastids serve as centers around or in which starch grains are formed. The synthesis of starch from sugar is apparently controlled by conditions present in the amyloplasts. As yet man has been unable to duplicate this process artificially.

Starch is insoluble in water and cannot diffuse from cell to cell. Therefore, the presence of starch grains in a cell means that the starch was synthesized in that cell from soluble carbohydrates which were originally produced in the chlorenchyma and translocated to that cell. The starch contains the energy which was in the sugar. Conceivably, starch synthesis could occur in any living plant cell containing amyloplasts, an ample supply of glucose, favorable acidity, and the proper enzymes. However, sugars are generally used up so rapidly in active meristems that little or no accumulation of starch occurs in these regions of cell division. The chief areas of starch accumulation in plants are seeds, certain fruits, the cortical tissues of roots, underground and aerial stems, and the mesophyll of some leafy vegetables. The parenchymatous cells of these tissues are sometimes called "food accumulation cells" to distinguish them from other living cells in which little or no food accumulates. Starch accumulation in most leaves is only temporary, however. When more sugar is made in the leaves during the day than can be used or translocated, the excess may be momentarily converted to starch in the chloroplasts. Subsequently during the night, the starch is usually digested to simpler soluble carbohydrates which move out of the leaves into other parts of the plant.

Starch synthesis and photosynthesis are two different and distinct processes. Whereas photosynthesis requires chlorophyll and the radiant energy of light, starch synthesis can take place in both light and darkness and in either green or non-green tisuues of plants. That starch synthesis is a separate process is shown also by the fact that starch does not accumulate in the mesophyll cells of several plants, yet photosynthesis does occur in these cells. Absence of starch in the mesophyll is characteristic of onions, certain species of lilies, and several other plants. Although of wide occurrence, starch synthesis therefore is not a necessary process in all green plants.

Starch extracted from plants is made into many important commercial products such as adhesives, sizing, dextrin, glucose, and alcohol. Starches are also used extensively in the compounding of pharmaceutical preparations. Since the size, shape and markings of starch grains are characteristic for many plants, these features may be used in determining the nature and purity of certain drugs and food products.

Dextrins, Glycogen, and Inulin.

Dextrins are intermediate products between starch and sugar and may occur naturally either when sugar is changed to starch or when starch is digested to sugar. Commercial dextrin is prepared by heating starch under controlled conditions.

Glycogen, like starch, is also formed from glucose. It is of wide occurrence in the animal kingdom, but in plants it has been found only in certain lower forms such as fungi, bacteria, and algae.

Inulin, made from fructose, occurs in many plants. It is especially abundant in certain organs of dandelion, salsify, and Jerusalem artichoke.

Sugars, starches, dextrin, glycogen, and inulin are all carbohydrates, that is, they are compounds composed of carbon, hydrogen, and oxygen atoms in which the proportion of hydrogen to oxygen occurs in a ratio of 2:1.

The following outline summarizes some of the fundamental features of starch synthesis and starch digestion:

I. STARCH SYNTHESIS:

1. Starch synthesis is a combination of biochemical reactions.
2. The source material used in this process is glucose.

3. The end product formed is insoluble starch.
4. Starch may be synthesized from glucose in the plastids of both green and non-green tissues of plants, and in both light and darkness, if the proper enzymes and inorganic phosphorus are present, and if other conditions such as acidity, water content, and temperature are favorable. Vegetable starch is not synthesized in animals. However, a starch-like product, called glycogen or "animal starch," may be formed in certain animals and a few species of lower plants.
5. Most of the energy of the numerous glucose molecules which are combined in the production of starch is transferred to and becomes a part of the starch.
6. Starch synthesis involves a series of complex intermediate steps.

II. STARCH DIGESTION:

1. Starch digestion is a hydrolytic process.
2. The materials used are starch and water.
3. The product formed is maltose or glucose, which then contains most of the energy formerly in the starch.
4. Starch digestion may occur in both plants and animals, and in both light and darkness. The amylase enzymes are instrumental in starch digestion.
5. Starch digestion may be illustrated by the following chemical equation:

$$\underset{\text{Starch}}{(C_6H_{10}O_5)_n} \xrightarrow{\alpha \text{ Amylase}} \underset{\text{Dextrin}}{(C_6H_{10}O_5)_n} \xrightarrow{\beta \text{ Amylase}} \underset{\text{Maltose}}{C_{12}H_{22}O_{11}} \xrightarrow{\text{Maltase}} \underset{\text{Glucose}}{C_6H_{12}O_6}$$

6. Starch digestion, like starch synthesis, consists of a series of complex intermediate steps.

FAT SYNTHESIS AND FAT DIGESTION

Like starches, fats are made from sugar and are compounds composed entirely of carbon, hydrogen, and oxygen atoms. However, fats are not carbohydrates. The ratio of hydrogen to oxygen in the fat molecule is not 2:1, as is illustrated by the chemical formula for the fat tripalmitin, $C_3H_5(C_{15}H_{31}CO_2)_3$. In other words, fat molecules contain much less oxygen than do carbohydrate molecules. Fats differ from sugars and starches also in that fats can be synthesized in both plants and animals, whereas sugars and starches are produced only in plants. Furthermore, fats are greasy and when rubbed on paper, they cause the paper to become more translucent.

Fats and oils are referred to collectively as lipids. A lipid which is fluid at room temperature is commonly known as an oil; if it is more or less solid at this temperature, it is called a fat. Waxes, cutin, suberin, and similar substances are designated as lipoidal (fat-like) compounds. Several lipoidal compounds are made by plants. As previously pointed out, these compounds render cell walls in which they occur almost impermeable to water. They are also constituents of cytoplasmic membranes, and are thus important in membrane permeability and absorbtion phenomena.

Both fats and oils occur in the protoplasm of plant cells, frequently in the form of emulsions. The protoplasm of any living cell apparently possesses the ability to convert carbohydrates to fats and oils. This transformation may take place in either light or darkness if other conditions are favorable such as ample food and the presence of the proper enzymes (lipases).

Fat synthesis is an entirely different process from either photosynthesis or starch synthesis. In fat synthesis some of the sugar (or a closely related product of photosynthesis) is changed by enzymes to glycerol and another part of the sugar is converted to fatty acids. This initial series of biochemical reactions involves a number of intermediate steps and includes the production of several relatively unstable compounds. The second major process, which usually follows immediately, involves the combination of 1 molecule of glycerol with 3 molecules of fatty acids and results in the synthesis of a fat or an oil with the elimination of 3 molecules of water. This second process also consists of a series of biochemical reactions including condensation and requires the catalytic activity of enzymes. Many of the intermediate reactions are not fully understood at present.

Fats and oils, like starches, are insoluble in water and do not diffuse from cell to cell. Therefore, the presence of fats in a cell means that the fats were synthesized in that cell either from glycerol and fatty acids in the cell or from soluble carbohydrates which moved into the cell.

Fat digestion involves the hydrolytic decomposition of the more complex fat molecule to the simpler molecules of glycerol and fatty acids which were originally combined in forming the fat. This is frequently as far as the digestion of a fat proceeds. The same glycerol thus liberated or another may immediately recombine with the same or other fatty acids in the resynthesis of the same or a different fat. For example, a mouse eats corn and transforms the corn fat to mouse fat; a pig eats the mouse and the mouse fat is digested and changed to pig fat; man eats the pig and converts the pig fat to human fat. The corn fat is not the same as mouse fat; the mouse fat is different from the pig fat; and human fat is unlike pig fat. The formation of these various kinds of fats is due principally to different inherent enzyme systems in corn, mouse, pig, and man.

Whether synthesis exceeds digestion or the reverse is primarily dependent upon the water content of the cell. An ample supply of carbohydrates
and a comparatively low water content constitute two of the principal
conditions conducive to fat synthesis in plant cells. The greatest amount
of fat is produced in the seeds of certain commercially important plants
when these plants are grown in relatively dry climates where there are
many clear, bright days. As most seeds mature, the water content of
their cells decreases and an accumulation of fat occurs in the cells. Conversely, fat digestion in germinating seeds occurs when the water content of the cells is increased. It should be pointed out, moreover, that
during germination, the fats and oils in seeds may first be digested to
glycerol and fatty acids and these, in turn, may be broken down into
soluble, transportable carbohydrates.

Plants produce many kinds of fatty acids. Three of the more common of these are $C_{15}H_{31}COOH$ (palmitic), $C_{17}H_{35}COOH$ (stearic), and
$C_{17}H_{33}COOH$ (oleic). Since numerous combinations are possible in the
union of 1 molecule of glycerol with 3 molecules of fatty acids, it is
obvious that many different kinds of fats may be synthesized in plants.

Comparison of the chemical formulas of a simple sugar ($C_6H_{12}O_6$)
with that of a fatty acid ($C_{15}H_{31}COOH$) will reveal differences in the
arrangement and in the number of the carbon, hydrogen, and oxygen
atoms in the two kinds of molecules. This is apparent in the proportion of
carbon to oxygen atoms in the fatty acid molecule as compared with that
of the sugar molecule. Such a comparison will also show that oxygen
is eliminated in the transformation of the sugar to the fatty acid, that is,
the conversion involves reduction or the accumulation of energy in the
fatty acid. The energy required to bring about this reduction becomes
available through the oxidation of other sugars in the cell. Thus both
oxidation and reduction are involved and the reaction is spoken of collectively as an oxidation-reduction process. There is more than twice as
much energy per unit weight in fat than there is in sugar. This fact
can be demonstrated by separately burning equal weights of these two
kinds of foods and comparing the amounts of energy released from each.

Fats are especially abundant in many kinds of seeds. A few commercially important fats and oils extracted from plants are peanut, cot-
tonseed, tung, corn, castor, pea, olive, soybean, linseed, coconut, and
cocoa. Fats obtained from plants are used in soaps, paints, lubricants,
medicinal preparations, cooking oils, salad oils, and many other products.

The following outline summarizes some of the fundamental features of fat synthesis and fat digestion:

I. FAT SYNTHESIS:

1. Fat synthesis involves a series of biochemical reactions many of which are not completely understood at present.
2. The material used is a product of photosynthesis or digestion.
3. The source of the energy in the fat molecule is energy previously bound in the organic molecules from which the fat is synthesized.
4. Fats contain approximately 2¼ times as much energy per unit weight as sugar.
5. Enzymes are necessary before fat synthesis will occur. These enzymes apparently function in energy transformations.
6. Fat synthesis consists of two broad steps. The first step (a) involves the production of glycerol and fatty acids. The second step (b) involves the formation of fat and water from the reactions of the glycerol and fatty acids. Many intermediate biosyntheses precede each major step.
7. Generalized word equation:

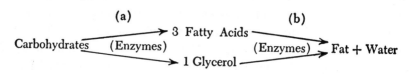

8. This process can take place in all living cells, both plant and animal, and in either light or darkness.

II. FAT DIGESTION:

1. Fat digestion is the hydrolytic decomposition of fat.
2. Fat digestion is a chemical process in which fat is changed to fatty acids and glycerol. There is no major change in energy values in this transformation.
3. Generalized word equation:

$$\text{Fat} + \text{Water} \xrightarrow{\text{Enzymes}} 3 \text{ Fatty Acids} + 1 \text{ Glycerol}$$

4. As indicated, this process requires the action of enzymes.
5. It may occur in every living cell, both plant and animal, and in either light or darkness.
6. Various recombinations of fatty acids and glycerol may result in the formation of different kinds of fats, or the fatty acids and glycerol may be further broken down into soluble carbohydrates.

PROTEIN SYNTHESIS AND PROTEIN DIGESTION

Proteins are the most complex foods. Protein synthesis, like fat synthesis, consists of two broad major steps. The first step is the synthesis of amino acids from sugar, nitrogen, and in at least one instance, sulfur also. The second broad step is the conversion of amino acids to proteins with the elimination of water. Also like fat synthesis, protein synthesis involves many complicated intermediate reactions and the production of a series of relatively unstable products. Not all these intermediate biosyntheses and products are known at present.

Although certain broad similarities exist among them, protein synthesis in detail is different from photosynthesis, starch synthesis, or fat synthesis. In addition to carbon, hydrogen and oxygen atoms, there must also be present nitrogen and, in cystine, sulfur, as may be seen in the chemical formulas of the four following amino acids: glycocol $C_2H_5O_2N$; lysine $C_6H_{14}O_2N_4$; tryptophane $C_{11}H_{12}O_2N_2$; and cystine $C_6H_{12}O_4N_2S_2$. When amino acids are converted to proteins, phosphorus may also be added, as in casein of milk $C_{708}H_{1130}O_{224}N_{180}S_4P_4$.

Several facts are illustrated by the formula for casein. It will be observed that the casein molecule is extremely large, being composed of 2,250 atoms of six different elements, as compared to only 24 atoms of three different elements in glucose. The relatively large amount of nitrogen in comparison to the amount of sulfur which is characteristic of protein molecules is also evident in casein. Moreover, it is seen that the proportion of carbon to oxygen is greater than in sugar, and that the ratio of hydrogen to oxygen is not 2:1 as it is in carbohydrates. Whereas sugar or a closely related product of photosynthesis is the direct source of carbon, hydrogen, and oxygen in proteins, nitrogen, sulfur, and phosphorus must be obtained from the soil. Many proteins do not contain phosphorus, however, as is shown by zein of corn $C_{736}H_{1161}O_{208}N_{184}S_3$ and gliadin of wheat $C_{685}H_{1068}O_{211}N_{196}S_5$.

With the exception of aquatic forms, most plants obtain nitrogen, sulfur, and phosphorus from the soil. One of the ironical facts of nature is that the large amount of nitrogen in the atmosphere (approximately 78 per cent) is not directly available to plants, except to nitrogen-fixing bacteria and a few other lower plants. In other words to higher plants the nitrogen of the air is an inert gas which becomes useful only when made available in some other manner such as naturally through the metabolic activity of lower organisms, or artificially by means of nitrate salts in fertilizers. Various salts of sulfur, such as ammonium sulfate $(NH_4)_2SO_4$, constitute the major source of sulfur for most plants. The major source of phosphorus is soil phosphate salts such as calcium superphosphate $CaH_4(PO_4)_2$ or $Ca_2H_2(PO_4)_2$. The salts of nitrogen, sulfur, and phosphorus are soluble in soil moisture and dissociate releasing the anions NO_3^-, SO_4^{--}, and PO_4^{---} which enter into and are utilized by plants. It is evident, therefore, that the amounts of available nitrogen, sulfur, and phosphorus in the substrate may materially affect the rate of growth of plants through their effects on the synthesis of proteins.

Amino Acid Synthesis.

As previously mentioned, the first broad step in the formation of proteins is the synthesis of amino acids from carbohydrates and inorganic salts of nitrogen and sulfur. This synthesis may occur in all living cells of plants and animals and in either light or darkness. To date some 30 amino acids have been discovered in plant tissues. Man can synthesize 15 amino acids in his own body, but other amino acids essential for his health must be obtained from plants or from other animals. All plants, except certain fungi and bacteria, synthesize all the amino acids required for their own metabolism; but any one plant, such as corn or wheat, may not produce all the amino acids essential for man and other animals.

Thus it is seen that amino acids are the building blocks from which proteins are made. Amino acid synthesis proceeds along several basic pathways; however, it is generally agreed that the first step is the reduction of the nitrate ion to ammonia in case ammonia is not the original source of nitrogen. An organic acid (which results as an intermediate product of respiration) is then combined with the ammonia in the formation of an amino acid as shown by the following equation:

$$\text{Organic acid} + NH_3 \xrightarrow{\text{Enzymes}} \text{Aspartic acid}$$

It is also known that amino acids may be synthesized from amides such as asparagine and glutamine. Furthermore, amino acids may be synthesized from other amino acids through the transfer of the amino group by suitable enzymes to another organic acid molecule.

As explained, nitrogen is chemically reduced in the process of amino acid synthesis. This means that per unit weight, amino acids contain more energy than sugar. The energy necessary for the reduction process is most frequently obtained through the oxidation of sugar; however, other products of photosynthesis or some of the products resulting from digestion or respiration may serve as the source of energy utilized in the reduction of the nitrogen. Hence it is evident that amino acid synthesis involves both reduction and oxidation and is therefore spoken of as an oxidation-reduction process. Other conditions necessary for amino acid synthesis include a plentiful supply of food, a high rate of respiration, available water, suitable temperature, favorable acidity, and the activity of complex enzymes in the living cells.

Protein Synthesis.

Protein synthesis consists of a series of complex biochemical reactions and involves the formation of several intermediate and relatively unstable compounds. Many of these reactions and the products resulting therefrom are unknown at present. The final step is a condensation resulting in the formation of a protein with the elimination of water. Proteins are constructed of amino acid residues bound together by the linkage,

$$-NH-\overset{\displaystyle O}{\overset{\displaystyle \|}{C}}-$$

, which is called a peptide bond. A protein molecule is a chain of amino acids linked by peptide bonds. It is these bonds that are broken by enzymatic hydrolysis (digestion) of proteins with a subsequent split of a protein molecule into its individual amino acid components.

Comparison of an amino acid $(C_6H_{12}O_4N_2S_2)$ with a protein $(C_{685}H_{1068}O_{211}N_{196}S_5)$ shows that more than 100 amino acid molecules may become joined in one large molecule of protein. It bears repeating that if phosphorus is present as a part of a protein molecule, the phosphorus must have been added as the amino acids were converted to the protein, since phosphorus is not present in amino acids. It should also be kept in mind that since the organic matter in protoplasm is made up largely of proteins or closely related nitrogenous compounds, the conversion of amino acids to proteins must occur in all physiologically active cells of both plants and animals.

It is doubtful that proteins move from cell to cell since all protoplasmic proteins are apparently insoluble in water. It seems more likely that the proteins in a cell are synthesized in that cell from amino acids which may be produced elsewhere in the plant and then move into the cell. For example, it has been shown that in woody species, amino acids are produced in the dark in the roots; whereas in grasses, such as wheat, amino acids are produced in light in the leaves. Although they may be found in all plant organs, proteins occur in highest percentages in certain seeds such as soybean and the common bean, and in grains such as wheat, corn, and rice.

Digestion of Proteins.

The digestion of proteins to amino acids is the reverse of protein synthesis. The same enzymes which catalyze the synthesis of a protein may under different conditions facilitate the digestion of that protein. The amino acids liberated by digestion may be converted to organic acids and ammonia, and the organic acids may then be oxidized to simpler compounds such as CO_2 and H_2O. More often, however, the amino acids resulting from protein digestion are resynthesized to other proteins in both plants and animals. The relinkage of the numerous possible amino acids may result in the synthesis of an entirely different kind of protein. That the number of possible proteins is enormous is apparent when it is recalled that there are some 30 different kinds of amino acids, and that more than 100 amino acid molecules may be combined in the formation of a protein molecule. Although evidence is available to show that there may be definite limitations to the number of proteins a given organism can synthesize, it is apparent that the protein content of the protoplasms of different organisms varies considerably. To the extent that this occurs, it would mean that the protoplasms of different organisms are somewhat different. Yet for any particular species the synthesis of proteins follows a rather specific pattern. This is especially true regarding the hereditary structures of protoplasm, the chromosomes and the genes, which remain constant from generation to generation unless altered by abnormal causes. Proteins and their derivatives appear to be the primary chemical bases of different protoplasms, different hereditary units, and different species of plants and animals. The specificity of organic synthesis in plants and animals and its constancy in repetition, cell after cell and generation after generation, are among the most important facts of nature.

The following outline summarizes some of the fundamental features of protein synthesis and protein digestion:

I. PROTEIN SYNTHESIS:

1. Protein synthesis is a combination of biochemical reactions.
2. Protein synthesis is the process in which a product of either photosynthesis, digestion, or respiration and certain mineral salts constitute the materials used, and protein and water are the end products.
3. Protein synthesis involves both amino acid synthesis and amino acid linkages to form proteins. It can be most easily illustrated as two major processes:

A. **Amino acid synthesis:**
  (1) Generalized word equation:

$$\text{Carbohydrate} + \text{Nitrogen} + (\text{Sulfur}) \xrightarrow{\text{Enzymes}} \text{Amino Acids.}$$

  (2) A complex of enzymes is required for this process.
  (3) At present some 30 amino acids have been discovered in plant tissues. Man can produce 15 amino acids in his body, but others must be obtained from the food he eats. Higher green plants can make all of the amino acids essential for them, but a single kind of green plant may not supply all the amino acids which are essential for man or other animals.

B. **Protein synthesis:**
  (1) Generalized word equation:

$$\text{Amino Acids} + \text{Phosphorus (in some cases)} \xrightarrow{\text{Enzymes}} \text{Protein} + \text{Water}$$

  (2) Many enzymes are required for this process.
  (3) Protein synthesis can occur in all living cells, both plant and animal, and in both light and darkness.
4. Proteins, like fats, have more energy per unit weight than sugar.
5. This energy is obtained from the combined amino acids.
6. The protein molecule is very large and complex. The number of possible kinds of protein molecules is enormous.

II. PROTEIN DIGESTION:

1. Protein digestion is a hydrolytic process.
2. Generalized word equation:

$$\text{Protein} + \text{Water} \xrightarrow{\text{Enzymes}} \text{Amino Acids} + \text{Phosphorus (in some cases)}$$

3. This process may occur in every living cell, both plant and animal, and in both light and darkness.
4. Enzymes are necessary for protein digestion.
5. There is no significant change in the bound energy in this process.
6. Under varying conditions, the amino acids resulting from digestion may be resynthesized into other proteins.

ASSIMILATION

The term assimilation has a vague meaning. In a general sense assimilation has been defined as a process, or a series of processes, by means of which foods are converted or changed by living protoplasm into more protoplasm, into cell wall materials, and into numerous organic substances (other than foods) found in cells, such as pigments, resins, gums, latex, and tannins. Hence assimilation has been considered a phase of growth.

On the other hand, Loomis (55) states, "If we divide the total development of plants into growth and differentiation, growth will include the processes of cell division and enlargement which result in increases in the size and green weight of the plant, while differentiation can be thought of as including all of the irreversible or semi-irreversible changes which may occur in the wall, the protoplast, or the inclusions of the undifferentiated cell." According to this view, a part of what has been called assimilation is growth (cell division and enlargement including the production of protoplasm and primary cell wall materials), whereas another part is referred to as differentiation (production of secondary cell wall materials, resins, latex, tannins).

The validity of the term assimilation in the sense that it refers to the conversion of foods to cell constituents is further challenged by recent research. The rapidly expanding knowledge of biochemistry in plants has strongly indicated that at least some of the intermediate products of respiration may serve as the "raw materials" in the so-called process of assimilation (31). In fact, there are those who believe this is generally, if not universally, the case. This, of course, raises a question as to what is a food. Are the intermediate products of respiration modified foods, or should they be considered something else?

Regardless of whether foods are transformed directly into cell constituents or the materials used are intermediate products of respiration, such end products as resins, latex, and tannins cannot be considered foods in the same sense as sugars, starches, fats, and proteins. That is to say, food synthesis and assimilation (or growth and differentiation) are different kinds of biochemical processes.

Until our knowledge of what is actually involved here is clarified, we shall, for convenience, refer to such cell materials as lignin, suberin, cutin, resins, latex, and tannins as products of assimilation, and feel at liberty to group into this category all those organic end products found in cells which are not generally recognized as foods. Therefore, it seems appropriate at this point to catalog some of the materials of importance in or to plants into the following categories:

	FOODS	
RAW MATERIALS [1] ⟶	AND FOOD INTERMEDIATES [2] ⟶	PRODUCTS OF ASSIMILATION [3]
Water	Sugars	Protoplasm
Carbon dioxide	Starches	Pectic compounds
Oxygen	Dextrin	Cellulose
Minerals	Inulin	Hemicellulose
Nitrates	Fatty acids	Lignin
Sulfates	Glycerol	Suberin
Phosphates	Fats or oils	Cutin
Calcium	Amino acids	Wax

RAW MATERIALS [1] $\longrightarrow$	FOODS AND FOOD INTERMEDIATES [2] $\longrightarrow$	PRODUCTS OF ASSIMILATION [3]
Potassium	Proteins	Callose
Magnesium	Intermediate products of	Chlorophylls
Iron	respiration	Carotenoids
Manganese		Anthocyanins
Zinc		Resins
Copper		Gums
Boron		Mucilages
Molybdenum		Tannins
Chlorine		Latex
		Essential oils
		Alkaloids
		Antibiotics
		Other drugs
		Poisons
		Vitamins
		Enzymes
		Hormones

[1] Obtained primarily from external sources.
[2] Synthesized within living plant cells.
[3] Transformed in living cells.

All plants contain a variety of organic substances made from foods. As has been seen, some of these are important constituents of cell structures; others, such as enzymes and the chlorophyll pigments, are essential for plant processes; while still others, on the basis of present knowledge, appear to be neither of value nor detrimental to the plant. Regardless, we should never lose sight of the important facts that foods are the building materials as well as the immediate source of chemically bound energy, and that all organic compounds of which cells are composed are made directly or indirectly from foods.

The products of assimilation associated with protoplasm (itself an assimilation product) and cell walls (pectic compounds, cellulose, lignin, etc.) were discussed in Chapter 4. Attention will now be given to some other important organic materials in plants which are generally considered to be products of assimilation.

Pigments.

Although the chemical and physical nature of the chlorophyll pigments and carotenoids was discussed in Chapter 9 (particularly in relation to photosynthesis), a few additional facts regarding these and one other group of pigments, the anthocyanins, will be considered here. Some interesting comparisons and relationships are brought out by what is commonly called autumnal coloration of the leaves and young stems of many plants due to physiological changes occasioned by a combination of internal conditions and environmental factors. As summer, with its longer days, more intense light, and higher temperatures shifts to the shorter periods of daylight and cooler weather of autumn, chemical changes become evident in plants and plant parts, especially the leaves of many deciduous woody and herbaceous species. Unless disease or injury interfere with the normal physiological activity of the leaves, the carotenoids which are present in the chloroplasts with the chlorophylls are obscured by the green pigments during the summer months. As the autumn advances, however, the chlorophyll pigments in many species disappear and the carotenoids, which are less sensitive to environmental change, become conspicuous. The disappearance of the chlorophyll pigments in the autumn is attributed to a number of factors. Whereas in most species light is necessary for the formation of chlorophyll, there is much evidence to show that continued exposure to sunlight will also bring about the destruction of chlorophyll. Therefore, if a leaf is to remain green, new chlorophyll must be made constantly. This means that the conditions necessary for chlorophyll synthesis must be favorable. Included in these conditions are adequate supplies of water and minerals. Due to the loss of vitality as autumn approaches plus the development of certain morphological obstructions, the leaves may become deficient in both water and minerals. As a result, chlorophyll synthesis is retarded and eventually stopped. Hence the green color occasioned by the chlorophylls gradually gives way to the yellow pigments.

In the leaves of certain maples, oaks and other species, there may also occur the formation of other pigments which range in color from red to purple. It appears that these colors are more intense in leaves containing an abundance of sugar. For this and other reasons which will be discussed subsequently, the red and purple colors are believed to be caused primarily by another complex group of pigments known collectively as anthocyanins. As winter comes on, however, both the carotenoids and anthocyanins may also disintegrate and be replaced by substances such as tannins which impart a tan or brownish coloration to the leaves. When the autumn is characterized by bright days and moderately cool weather, coloration is most brilliant. On the contrary, when heavy frosts occur early in the season or when the weather is wet and cloudy, the formation of anthocyanins is greatly retarded and the less spectacular yellow and brown colors are dominant. Thus we have further evidence which illustrates how changing environmental factors and internal conditions may initiate and control physiological processes in living plants.

All investigations to date indicate that the carotenoids are always present in the chloroplasts of chlorenchyma. However, the carotenoids may occur separately in the chromoplasts of many plant parts. For example, the yellow or orange colors of the flowers of goldenrods and sunflowers, of the fruits of lemons, oranges, and certain varieties of corn and tomatoes, of the seeds of peas, clovers and others, and of the roots of carrots, are due principally to carotenoids. On the other hand, the color of certain leaves, such as variegated and purple coleus, and the under surface of the leaves of wandering Jew, result from a combination of the chlorophylls, carotenoids and anthocyanins. Usually the anthocyanins occur in the vacuoles of the epidermis, whereas the chlorophylls and carotenoids are confined to the chloroplasts of the mesophyll cells. The anthocyanins, being water soluble, may be removed by placing such leaves in hot water. This treatment will make the chlorophylls and carotenoids more conspicuous in the leaves since these pigments are not soluble in water. When cows, chickens, and certain other animals eat plant parts containing carotenoids, these pigments may reappear in cream, butter, fat, and egg yolks. Carotenoids also lend color to the eyes, feathers, and scales of certain animals. Carotene has been shown to be the precursor of vitamin A. For this reason carrots and leafy vegetables in general are dietary sources of this important vitamin.

Anthocyanins are complex substances formed from various sugars, anthocyanidins, and other organic compounds. Chemically anthocyanins are glucosides; that is, they are compounds which, when decomposed, yield sugar among other substances. There are many kinds of anthocyanins and their occurrence may vary in different species, no doubt as a result of heredity. It is possible for more than one kind of anthocyanin to be present in a single species. As previously explained, anthocyanins occur in the cell sap solutions of vacuoles, not in plastids, and they play no known role in photosynthesis. That they may be present in various tissues and organs is shown by their occurrence in red, blue and purple flowers, in purple cabbage, in certain varieties of potatoes and popcorn, and in beets.

The roots of some plants such as beets and radishes, become red in the dark; whereas light (particularly blue and violet light) is necessary for the formation of anthocyanins in most leaves and fruits. Intensity of color of anthocyanins in aerial organs is increased by abundance of light, cool weather, and low nitrate concentrations. These factors apparently influence anthocyanin synthesis indirectly by affecting the quantity of available sugars in the cells, since a high sugar content appears to be a necessary prerequisite for anthocyanin formation. It is a matter of common knowledge that many fruits, such as apples and peaches, when exposed to full sunlight are redder than those growing in less intense light. These fruits also differ in color when grown in different localities under different climatic and soil conditions. In case of apples, low temperatures, especially at night, are also important to the accumulation of sugar and the formation of anthocyanins. Low temperatures likewise favor the formation of anthocyanins in some evergreen plants, such as certain varieties of juniper and arbor vitae, and in many heaths. On the other hand anthocyanin color of some flowers is more directly related to pH than to either light intensity or temperature. For example, the flowers of the French hydrangea are bluish when the plants grow in acid soils containing available salts of aluminum, and reddish when the plants grow in alkaline soils in which aluminum is rendered insoluble by calcium. Conversely, if a red geranium flower is exposed to ammonia, it will turn blue. Replacing the ammonia vapor with the fumes of an acid will restore to the flower its previous red color. This change may be hastened by crushing the petals of the flowers on a blotter or piece of filter paper and then alternately exposing the wet surface as explained. The presence of certain ions, such as potassium, will prevent this color change. The major economic importance of anthocyanins lies in their ability to impart colors to flowers, fruits, vegetables, shrubbery and trees.

Resins, Gums, and Mucilages.

Resins, gums, and mucilages are also produced in plants mainly from carbohydrates by a combination of biochemical processes. These products may be either general or localized in distribution within the plant, and they may vary considerably in chemical and physical properties.

Being insoluble in water, resins render cell walls practically impermeable to water. However, resins are soluble in alcohol, certain oils, and other organic solvents. Commercially resins are used in the preparation of varnishes, soaps, dyes, medicines, and plastics. Certain resins are also used as ingredients in tobacco flavoring and in incense. Unrefined resin (rosin) is a hard, amber-colored to almost black material which is left as a residue after distilling off the volatile oil of turpentine. Rosin is used in the manufacture of linoleum, oil cloth, printer's ink, roofing compounds, paper sizing, and in many other industrial products. The substances which are poisonous to animals in mountain laurel and water hemlock are basically resins. Resin is one of the important products of the pine forests of the southeastern United States, many of the so-called "naval stores" being made from it.

Gums and mucilages are alike in that both are insoluble in alcohol, but become sticky and assume a more or less jelly-like consistency in water. Since they adsorb water greatly, they are considered to be important in holding water in plant tissues in which they occur. Certain plant gums, such as gum arabic, swell in water, forming viscous liquids used in the manufacture of chewing gum, mucilages and other adhesives, as stabilizers in ice creams and candies, and as soothing agents in cough syrups.

Tannins.

The bark and heartwood of several trees, the galls occurring in oak leaves, and certain unripe fruits, such as persimmon, contain bitter astringent substances called tannins which are generally considered to be metabolic waste products. These substances change (coagulate) proteins to insoluble compounds. The coagulation of proteins in raw hides is a basic process in the tanning of leather. Tannins react with the proteins of animal skins in such manner that the skins become soft and pliable. When mixed with soluble iron salts, tannins become black or green and for this reason they have been used in the manufacture of inks and dyes. Freshly cut surfaces of many fruits and vegetables become dark because of the oxidation of tannic acid, especially in the presence of iron from a knife. Tannic acids are used also in pharmacy and in compounds applied in the treatment of burns. Tannins are obtained in commercial quantities from the bark and wood of hemlock, certain oaks, and some tropical trees, from the leaves of sumac and other species, and from other plant parts.

Latex.

Many plants, such as milkweeds, euphorbias, figs, dandelion, guayule, and rubber plants, contain a milky colloidal fluid called latex which may be made up of a complex mixture of sugars, lipids, proteins, mineral salts, alkaloids, terpene derivatives, gums, tannins and enzymes. Rubber, guttapercha, balata, and chicle are the chief commercial products made from latex. The numerous products manufactured from rubber are widely known, such as tires, inner tubes, hose, appliances, toys, and cements.

Rubber is used where a combination of elasticity, flexibility and resilience is desired or required. Most of the latex used in rubber comes from the Para rubber tree, originally a native of Brazil, but now extensively grown in the East Indies, Malaya, and Africa. Gutta-percha, obtained from several species of Asiatic trees, differs from rubber in that it is only slightly elastic. It is pliable and resilient, however, and is used in the manufacture of golf balls, insulation and other electrical and telephonic materials and equipment, and in dentistry. Balata, which is produced by a tree species native to the northern part of South America, is frequently substituted for gutta-percha, and is used also in golf balls, in machine belting, in gaskets, and to some extent as insulation. Chicle, produced by trees which grow in southern Mexico, Central America, and parts of northern South America, is the principal constituent of chewing gum.

Essential Oils.

Essential oils, being generally regarded as metabolic by-products, are chemically very different from edible fats and oils, and are of no importance as food. They are greatly desired, however, as flavors and perfumes. Essential oils, which are aromatic compounds, include such products as oils of menthol, camphor, turpentine, mint, wintergreen, pine, juniper or "cedar," geranium, lemon, orange, ginger, anise, cloves, sage, citronella, sassafras, pennyroyal, hops, wormwood, lavender, jasmine, carnation, rose, bergamot, bitter almonds, cinnamon, nutmeg, and vanilla. The many uses of these products in cooking, confections, pharmacy, paints and varnishes, cosmetics and perfumes, beverages, deodorants, incense, insect-repellents, and in many other ways are well known. The characteristic odors and flavors of onion, garlic, watercress, radishes, and many kinds of mustard are due mainly to essential oils containing sulfur.

The fragrance of flowers and the odors and flavors of fruits and vegetables are in large measure due to essential oils. Many plants, such as sweet corn, are delicious when first harvested. Much of the flavor is soon lost, however, due in part to the fact that most of the essential oils are highly volatile and evaporate rapidly from plants, and in part as a result of the oxidation of sugar and the rapid change of sugar to starch after the fruits or vegetables are removed from the plants on which they grew. Loss of odor and/or flavor can be reduced by refrigeration since these changes occur more slowly in low temperatures.

Most essential oils are terpenes. Chemically the terpenes are considered to be derivatives of the C_5H_8 compound isoprene. Many of the essential oils are composed of two or more simpler types of terpenes.

Alkaloids.

These products of assimilation are of no known value to the plants that produce them, but they are of great economic and medicinal importance. They are organic compounds containing nitrogen and are derived from proteins. Usually they have no odor, but are bitter to the taste. Alkaloids definitely affect the physiology of animals, and are extensively used as stimulants and narcotics. In large dosages they may cause death. Perhaps the most familiar alkaloids are caffeine from coffee and cacao seeds, nicotine from tobacco, atropin from the deadly nightshade, strychnine and brucine from strychnos, cocaine from cocoa leaves, quinine from cinchona bark, and morphine and codeine from the Oriental poppy. The poisonous principles in certain plants are alkaloids which cause chronic nervous disorders or death when these plants are eaten by cattle, horses, and sheep.

Alkaloids, as the name implies are basic in reaction, and only slightly soluble in water. Present information indicates that most of them are physiologically unimportant by-products of the nitrogen metabolism in a relatively limited number of species.

Antibiotics.

In recent years there has been a renewed interest in the search for plant products of medicinal value. The importance of the rapidly increasing use of antibiotics assimilated by fungi is well known. Antibiotics are substances which are assimilated by one kind of organism and which inhibit the growth of or destroy other kinds of organisms. Penicillin, streptomycin, aureomycin, and terramycin are four of the more widely used antibiotics in the treatment of diseases and infections. Extensive research in this field is being carried on by many chemical and pharmaceutical companies in which the chemist, the bacteriologist, and the botanist join hands in the endless fight against disease.

Other Drugs.

The list of drug products obtained from plants is much too long to include here. Suffice it to say that various species of algae, fungi, mosses, ferns, gymnosperms, and angiosperms produce substances extensively used in the compounding of medicines. In some instances the entire plant is used; in other species the root, stem, leaf, flowers, fruit or seed, or certain tissues thereof, contain the important pharmaceutical material. Some of these have already been named; others include such products as digitalis, a valuable drug in certain types of heart disease; ephedrine, an important ingredient in nasal jellies and sprays; cascara and senna, which are gentle laxatives; and balsams, used as soothing and healing agents.

Poisons.

Although apparently harmless to the plants that produce them, several products of assimilation are toxic to animals. Most familiar of these are the volatile oils produced by poison ivy and poison sumac, hydrocyanic (prussic) acid produced by wild cherry and sorghums, glucosides produced by oleander, resins produced by mountain laurel and water hemlock, and belladonna produced by the deadly nightshade. Because of the disease or death of animals which eat them, such plants are receiving increasing attention in agriculture and veterinary science. For example, the fatal effect of HCN in wild cherry leaves and in many other plants or plant parts is of grave concern to stock raisers. It is now known that certain grasses, such as Sudan and Johnson grass, build up high glucoside contents when growth is retarded by drought, rusts, insect attack, or cold weather. Under such conditions, hydrocyanic acid is formed which makes these grasses poisonous to livestock.

Numerous other organic substances occur in the living cells of plants as a result of assimilation including those important regulators of physiological processes, namely, the enzymes, hormones (auxins), and vitamins. These last three will be discussed in detail in connection with growth in Chapter 13.

ACCUMULATION

The foods which are made by plants and not used by them in respiration or assimilation accumulate in plant parts where conditions are favorable for such accumulation. The latter is what the farmer generally refers to when he speaks of yield. Increased yield per acre, moreover, is the ultimate aim of most, if not all, applied plant science, and it involves much of the important research carried on by the agronomist, plant breeder, plant pathologist, horticulturist, and forester.

The foods which accumulate in plants may be used by them, or they may be consumed by non-green plants and animals. Consequently, the amount of food available to humans depends on the quantity synthesized by green plants in excess of that which they use or is used by non-green plants and animals other than man. It is evident that unless photosynthesis exceeds respiration and assimilation, no food will accumulate in plants. It has also been pointed out that man may obtain much more food per acre by eating plants directly than by eating animals which feed on plants, since most of the food eaten by animals is oxidized in respiration. However, there are animals that feed, either directly or indirectly, on plants in which the food is unavailable to man. Animals which live in fresh or salt water, such as fish, oysters, clams and shrimp, convert large amounts of the food in aquatic plants into food that is

Table 28 The per cent protein, fat, and carbohydrate content of various kinds of storage organs.

KIND OF PLANT ORGAN	DRY MATTER	PROTEIN	FAT	CARBOHYDRATE
	per cent [1]	per cent [1]	per cent [1]	per cent [1]
Seeds:				
Beans	88.2	22.9	1.4	56.1
Cottonseed	93.6	39.0	33.2	14.8
Flaxseed	93.6	23.5	36.4	24.2
Pea	89.2	25.3	1.7	53.6
Peanut	94.7	30.5	47.7	11.7
Pecans	97.0	9.7	75.2	13.4
Soybean	90.2	36.9	17.2	26.3
Sunflower	95.5	27.7	41.4	16.3
Walnuts	96.7	15.5	66.6	16.1
Fruits:				
Apple	15.9	1.8	2.5	93.7
Avocado	34.6	4.9	76.3	14.7
Banana	25.2	4.8	0.8	91.2
Barley	90.2	11.6	2.0	72.1
Corn	90.7	11.5	7.9	67.2
Grape	18.1	7.7	7.7	82.3
Oats	91.7	16.2	6.4	65.3
Orange	12.8	7.0	1.6	87.5
Rice	90.2	8.9	2.0	77.2
Strawberry	10.1	7.9	4.9	82.1
Wheat	89.6	13.5	2.1	69.8
Stems:				
Asparagus	7.0	31.4	2.8	55.7
Onion	12.4	8.1	1.6	85.5
Potatoes, Irish	22.2	9.0	4.5	86.0
Leaves:				
Brussel sprouts	15.1	29.1	3.3	59.0
Cabbage	7.6	18.0	2.6	69.7
Celery	6.3	20.6	3.1	58.7
Lettuce	5.2	23.1	3.8	55.8
Roots:				
Beet, garden	12.4	12.9	0.8	77.4
Carrot	11.8	10.1	2.5	78.8
Radish	6.4	18.7	1.6	65.6
Turnip	9.1	12.1	2.2	78.0
Sweet potato	31.5	5.7	2.2	88.6

[1] Per cent of dry weight basis.

Starch accumulation
in chloroplasts in cells
of a leaf of aloe

Starch grains and a
protein crystal in a
cell of potato tuber

Inulin crystals
in the cells of
dandelion root

Cell from the endosperm
of a castor bean with
aleurone grains (mainly
proteins) imbedded in the
granular matrix of the
cell containing both
proteins and oil

Oil globules in
a portion of a
fungus cell

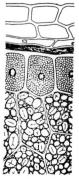

Small portion of a section of a
potato tuber containing starch
grains and protein crystals

Small portion of a section
of a wheat grain containing
starch and protein

Oil globules
in a cell of
coconut seed

Figure 72   Illustrations of various foods which accumulate in plant
cells. (*From Sampson, H.C. Work Book in General Botany. Harper &
Brothers.*)

available to man. Cattle, sheep, and some of the wild animals which
graze on the open range and forest reserves may be considered gatherers
and converters of food in plants which otherwise is not available to man.

Inheritance and environment combine in the determination of the
kinds and amounts of food which accumulate in various plants or plant
parts. For example, much of the excess food accumulates in the roots of

sweet potatoes, carrots, turnips, radishes and beets; in the underground stems (tubers) of Irish potatoes and the above-ground stems of asparagus and sugar cane; in the leaves of cabbage, lettuce and onions; and in the fruits and seeds of corn, beans, peas, wheat, rice, apples, peaches, bananas, peanuts, walnuts and pecans. That plants contain varying amounts of the three basic foods is shown by Table 28 and in Figure 72. The data in Table 28 also shows that seeds have the highest dry matter content or the lowest moisture content, followed by fruits, while stems, leaves, and roots have the least dry matter and the highest moisture content. Another interesting fact is seeds and fruits are the principal storage organs that accumulate fats and proteins in large quantities. Stems, leaves, and roots accumulate mainly carbohydrates.

13.
DYNAMICS OF GROWTH

Preceding chapters have included discussions of several processes which occur in rooted-green plants, including water absorption, mineral nutrition, photosynthesis, respiration, food synthesis, and assimilation. Now we shall consider how all these and other processes work together in a plant as a whole and result in an extremely complex phenomenon called growth. It is growth which causes a plant to increase in size, and for growth to occur all plant parts must play an interrelated role. For instance, roots absorb water and minerals and leaves furnish sugar and other organic materials used in the development of stems, flowers, and other plant parts. In addition growth is regulated by minute quantities of organic substances called plant hormones which will be discussed later. It is evident that growth involves a coordination of both hereditary and environmental factors. So far research in plant physiology has been able to explain plant behavior, including growth, only in part, many problems remaining unsolved. As an example, how does the genetic constitution of a plant exert an influence upon physiological processes? To date the effects of environmental factors and the chemistry of the physiological processes of growth are better understood than are the effects of genes. However, as in all plant processes, it is clear that growth is controlled by and is a result of the interaction of the genes and the environment.

Before progressing with our study of growth, we need to set forth certain definitions. The term growth has been given a variety of meanings, often being used synonymously with yield in agricultural literature. Whereas the end product sought by the practical agriculturist is yield (whether that be grain, forage and pasture herbage, board feet or cords of wood, ornamental shrubs, flowers, vegetables, or fruit), yield is not growth *per se*. Instead yield is a result of growth; more properly in physiology the term yield is used to designate the accumulation of photosynthate not used in growth. An example will help to clarify this point. A corn plant grown under optimum conditions is characterized by more and larger leaves than a corn plant grown in a suboptimum environment. Growth, then, would result in the capacity for increased photosynthate which could be transformed into bigger ears with larger grains. Therefore, growth can better be defined in terms of the production of more protoplasm and new cells which elongate and differentiate. Growth in its broadest sense is thus concerned with all three phases of cellular development, namely, cell division, elongation, and differentiation. Nevertheless, in present day plant physiology, growth is often limited to cell division and more particularly to cell elongation. These processes bring about what has been defined as an irreversible increase in volume. The nature of the cellular processes of these phases of growth will be one of the several topics which will follow. To limit discussion of growth to cell division and enlargement, however, would result in an incomplete presentation of the total manifestation of growth in a rooted-green plant. Differentiation is also important, and the development of a plant as a whole in terms of vegetative organ growth and reproductive organ growth is an intricate result of all these processes. Thus we need to examine growth both at the cellular level and in terms of the plant as a whole organism, including the development of plant parts.

DIFFERENTIATION

Originally the term differentiation was often used in a somewhat restricted sense to describe the morphological changes in cells as they grew older or approached maturity. For example, those tissues in stem and root tips in which cells began to differ in size and shape were commonly referred to as the regions of cell differentiation. Later as knowledge of developmental anatomy increased, the term differentiation was broadened to include shifts in physiological activity such as the change of parenchyma to meristematic tissue, e.g., the differentiation of certain cortical cells to cork cambium, the change of ray cells to interfascicular cambium, and the development of secondary roots by the pericyclic tissue of primary roots. More recently the term differentiation has been further broadened to cover virtually any kind of a change in a cell, either morphological or physiological or both, occurring after the cell ceases its elongating. Thus the change which occurs in stem tips when the cells produced by the terminal meristem cease developing into vegetative tissues and begin forming flower primordia is interpreted as a kind of differentiation. In this regard, Loomis (55) states, "Sexual reproduction in the seed plants, and probably in lower plants as well, is basically similar to vegetative development in its dependence upon growth and differentiation. It varies in being initiated by a different reaction, the flower-bud differentiation of the horticulturists, which is frequently assumed to be the formation of a specific flowering substance or hormone." Moreover as explained in Chapter 12, the term differentiation is used currently to designate the formation of cell substances and structures which were previously thought of as products of assimilation by some students.

If we restrict our definition of growth to cell division and enlargement, it seems appropriate at this point that we turn our attention to those plant tissues in which these phenomena occur and to the processes which happen in them.

MERISTEMS

Meristems are tissues in which the cells are capable of indefinite division and hence are frequently called regions of cell division. Two general types of meristematic tissues are usually recognized: those occurring at the tips of stems and roots; and those which occur laterally. However, most tissues composed primarily of living parenchymatous cells may become meristematic, especially if they are injured or subjected to other abnormal conditions.

Terminal or Apical Meristems.

These tissues, often referred to as growing points, in general have several well defined characteristics (Figures 41, 42, 73, and 74). The cells which compose them are immature and have primary walls consisting of a middle lamella and only a few thin layers of cellulose. There is no secondary wall thickening. In each cell the nucleus is large in comparison to the total volume of the cell. The remainder of the cell is almost completely filled with dense cytoplasm, the vacuoles present at this stage being small and scattered. The cells of terminal meristems are essentially isodiametric, that is, they have approximately the same length, width, and depth. There are few, if any, intercellular spaces among these cells. Most important, however, is the fact that under favorable conditions, such cells are capable of repeated divisions.

There is considerable evidence to indicate that terminal meristematic cells of stems possess potentialities for the production of both vegetative and reproductive structures. The differentiation of either vegetative or floral structures depends upon internal conditions, including heredity, and/or environmental factors. This fact is of great importance in regard to the time of flower formation, and in many plants it is intimately associated with photoperiods and/or temperature. Important growth regulating substances known as hormones also are produced in these meristems.

Terminal meristems, as this name implies, are found at the apices of both stems and roots. Although the shape of terminal meristematic cells may vary somewhat (they sometimes appear more cubical in root tips than in stem tips), they are similar in all other respects. These meristems produce the cells

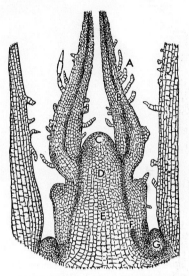

Figure 73 Longitudinal section of the terminal bud of *Coleus* showing features of a stem tip: A, epidermal hairs. B, young leaf. C, terminal meristem (region of cell division). D, region of cell elongation. E, region of cell differentiation. F, provascular strand. G, axillary bud. (*From Sampson, H.C.* Workbook in General Botany. *Harper & Brothers, 1949.*)

which account for the increase in length of roots and stems. The terminal meristem of a root also produces the cells which form the root cap, whereas its counterpart in a stem tip produces the young cell groups (primordia) which give rise to new branches, leaves, or flowers.

Lateral Meristems—Vascular Cambium.

The meristematic tissue between the xylem and phloem of many stems is called the vascular cambium (Figures 75 and 76). This tissue consists of a single layer of cells which by division cut off new cells on the inner side, some of which form the so-called water conducting tissue (secondary xylem), and other daughter cells on the outer side, some of which form the food conducting tissue (secondary phloem). Since this

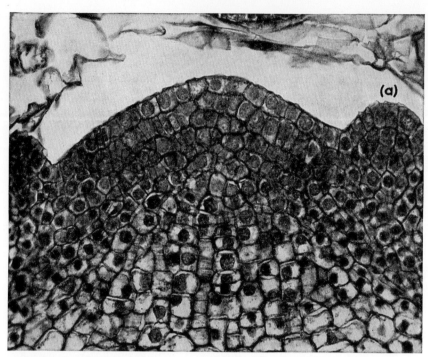

Figure 74 Terminal meristem of the stem tip of *Chrysanthemum morifolium* showing leaf primordia (a). *(Photomicrograph courtesy of R.A. Popham and A.P. Chan.)*

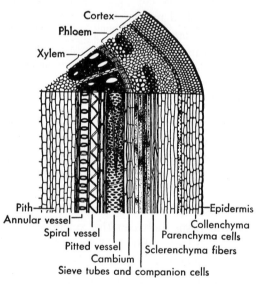

Cortex—
Phloem—
Xylem—

Pith—
Annular vessel—
Spiral vessel
Pitted vessel
Cambium
Sieve tubes and companion cells

—Epidermis
Collenchyma
Parenchyma cells
Sclerenchyma fibers

Figure 75 Diagrammatic three-dimensional view of a dicto herbaceous stem. *(From* College Botany, *Revised Edition, by Harry J. Fuller and Oswald Tippo. By permission of Henry Holt and Company, Inc., Copyright 1949, 1954.)*

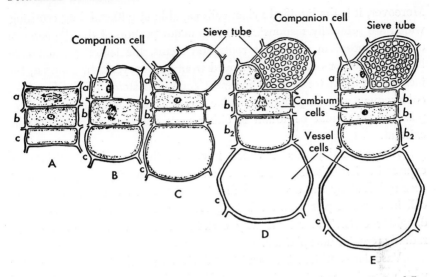

Figure 76 Diagram illustrating the division of the vascular cambium and the differentiation of phloem and xylem. (*From Holman and Robbins. Textbook of General Botany. John Wiley and Sons, Inc.*)

meristem consists of but one layer of cells, it is obvious that as each mother vascular cambium cell divides tangentially, one of the daughter cells remains meristematic. The other daughter cell, if on the inner side, may be referred to as a xylem initial, which differentiates and forms one or the other of the different types of xylem cells (Figure 76 c). If on the outer side, the daughter cell may be a phloem initial which will mature into one of the various kinds of phloem cells (Figure 76 a). Although apparently connected with the physiological activity of the protoplasm in response to different conditions, the production sometimes of xylem cells and at other times of phloem cells by the vascular cambium is not well understood. There is some speculation to the effect that when the vascular cambium is acid, xylem initials are produced; that when it is otherwise, phloem initials are produced. Regardless of the cause, it appears evident that during the growing season, more xylem cells are produced than phloem. It is also apparent that the potentialities for the development of the various kinds of xylem and phloem cells reside in the protoplasm of the vascular cambial cells, and that for reasons not clearly understood, certain of these potentialities may be dominant at one time while others determine the direction of growth at another time or under another set of conditions. At any rate, it is the vascular cambium which produces the cells which account mainly for the increase in diameter of gymnosperm and dicot roots and stems.

Moreover, it is the lignified xylem cells capable of withstanding crushing, which are primarily responsible for the major portion of the diameter of older gymnosperm and dicot roots and stems, the softer phloem cells being crushed or otherwise destroyed from year to year. In contrast, the increase in diameter of most monocot roots and stems results from the enlargement of cells produced in the terminal meristems, since in these plants the vascular cambium is either very poorly developed or non-existent.

In perennial plants in which it occurs, the vascular cambium increases in circumference as a root or stem enlarges in diameter. This is accomplished by the occasional division of a vascular cambium mother cell in a radial plane and the tangential enlargement of the resultant daughter cells. The reason why certain vascular cambial cells divide radially remains unexplained.

Vascular cambium is a persistent derivative of the terminal meristem which remains meristematic and by division forms secondary xylem and phloem. Vascular cambial cells are similar to terminal meristematic cells in practically all respects except that they are not isodiametric, the longitudinal diameter exceeding the others (Figure 75).

Cork Cambium.

This meristematic tissue develops between the younger phloem and the outer surface of the plant organ in which it occurs, and results from further differentiation of other cells in this area (Figures 77 and 78). Usually in perennials the cork cambium originates during the first growing season in cortical cells just below the surface of a stem or root, but it may develop from the epidermis, as in the apple, or within the pericycle, as in the currant. In some species such as beech, birch, cork oak, and certain cherries, the original cork cambium remains active for many years and continues to form new cork cells annually. However, in most species, the cork cambium progressively develops more deeply each year, until frequently it extends as far inward as the youngest phloem cells, but never to the vascular cambium (Figure 77 E). The formation of the deeper layers may vary somewhat from the manner in which the original cork cambial tissue was formed, the available oxygen apparently exerting considerable influence. Smith et al (62) state that the first-formed cork cambium is usually a thin cylinder which completely encircles the stem. The successive cork cambiums, which develop centripetally, frequently take the form of concave, trough-like strips, their edges abutting upon previously formed strips. In cross section they appear as small intersecting arcs.

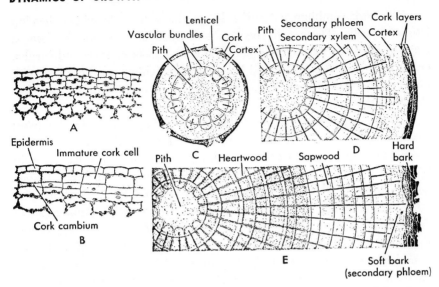

Figure 77   A, cells of the outermost cortical layer are differentiating and forming a cork cambium. B, a later stage, cork forming on the outer face of the cork cambium and parenchyma on its inner face. C, development of the first layer of cork. D and E, formation of later layers of cork. In E the epidermis, cortex, pericycle, and primary phloem have died and sloughed off. *(From Smith et al.* A Textbook of General Botany. *The Macmillan Company, 1942.)*

Figure 78   Portion of a cross section of a young stem of elder, *Sambucus canadensis,* showing a lenticel in relation to the cork cambium and other tissues. A, collenchyma. B, epidermis. C, lenticel. D, cork. E, cork cambium. F, cortex. G, pericycle fibers (sclerenchyma). H, phloem. I, vascular cambium. J, xylem. K, ray. *(Courtesy Geo. H. Conant, Triarch Products.)*

The cork cambium cuts off cells on the outer side which develop into cork cells. These cells become suberized and commonly form a major part of the bark of the older stems and roots of trees and shrubs. Other cells may also be formed by the cork cambium on the inner side, but these are usually soft, thin-walled living cells which differ considerably from the cork cells.

Mature cork cells are dead. When the suberin produced by the living protoplasm becomes infiltrated into the cell walls, they are rendered practically impervious to water and food. Suberization results not only in the death of the cork cells, but the epidermis and all other tissues exterior to the cork, being cut off from water and food, also die. The subsequent increase in circumference of the root or stem usually causes the dead tissues to crack and crumble or flake off. This splitting brings about the formation of furrows of varying depth and is thus instrumental in the development of bark patterns which are consistently characteristic for many species. In fact, an experienced woodsman can accurately classify many trees in winter condition by merely observing their bark.

Several shrubs and trees, such as sweetgum and certain species of euonymus and elm, frequently develop conspicuous flanges of cork projecting from the surface of the twigs and smaller branches. These are of no known physiological benefit to the species that produce them.

Potential Meristematic Areas.

As previously mentioned, most if not all tissues composed primarily of living parenchymatous cells may become meristematic under certain conditions. A few of the more common meristems are listed in the following table:

Meristems

Name	Occurrence	Function
1. Terminal (apical) meristems	1. Tips of roots, stems, inflorescences, etc.	1. Cause growth in length.
2. Lateral meristems	2. Along sides of roots and stems.	2. Cause growth crosswise.
a. vascular cambium	a. usually between xylem and phloem of roots and stems	a. causes growth in diameter of roots and stems
b. cork cambium	b. formed between phloem and surface tissue of roots and stems	b. produces cork cells on surface of organs

Name	Occurrence	Function
c. pericycle	c. formed inside of root endodermis from parenchymatous cells	c. produces branch roots
3. Intercalary meristems	3. Masses of meristematic cells separated by masses of fully matured cells, esp. at nodes and in leaf sheaths of grasses and other monocots. Also, growth of flowers and fruits may be regarded as intercalary growth.	3. Produces limited growth in length of stems and leaves, also growth of flowers and fruits.

DYNAMICS OF GROWTH

The Growth Pattern.

Before initiating a discussion of growth in relation to its physiological mechanisms, let us examine growth in a more general way. Living organisms, whether they are simple one-celled individuals or more complex organisms made up of millions of cells, increase in number and in size by a series of interrelated processes, common to all living matter, which is recognized as some form of growth. Although it is an attribute of all living organisms and has been observed by man since antiquity, growth is only partially understood by modern scientists.

Growth of a colony of microorganisms, higher plants, animals, or populations of nations can be expressed quantitatively. Such data have been treated mathematically and, if plotted, show a curve whose shape is typical of all kinds of growth. If growth be expressed by measuring such

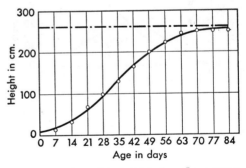

Figure 79 Growth in height of sunflower stem. (From Odum, E.P. Fundamentals of Ecology. W.B. Saunders Co., 1953.)

things as numbers of bacteria, height of man, length of stem, or weight in relation to time, the expression in a graph is usually an S-shaped curve (Figure 79). These curves show that all life is characterized by three stages of growth: an early period of slow growth; a central period of rapid growth; and a final period of slow growth. Thus the characteristic form of the S-shaped curve shows that growth is marked by a period of increasing velocity (the nearly straight line portion of the curve) followed by decreasing velocity. The search for answers as to

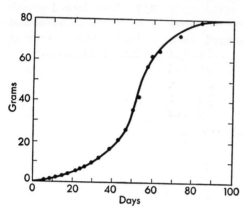

Figure 80   Growth of entire corn plant as measured by increase in dry weight. From Gustav Backman, after Stefanowska. *(From Thompson, D'Arcy W. On Growth and Form. University Press Cambridge, 1942.)*

why growth is so characterized is occupying the attention of many biological scientists. However, mathematical treatment of such data is not necessary for biological interpretation of growth. Modern physiology suggests that hormone activity is one of the important factors in controlling growth at the cellular level in a constant environment. Therefore, growth rates do not continue at a constant velocity, because of hormone inactivation or inhibition. Another cause which has been recently postulated as influencing the rate of growth is an inactivation of the phosphate energy transferring enzyme systems. Shift in growth from production of vegetative parts to the production of reproductive parts usually results in reduction or cessation of vegetative growth. This is thought to result in part from competition for available photosynthate in which the reproductive parts win out.

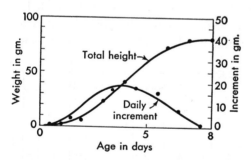

Figure 81   Growth in height of a bean stem as measured by increase in dry weight. Data from Sach. *(From Thompson, D'Arcy W. On Growth and Form. University Press Cambridge, 1942.)*

S-shaped curves are indicative of the growth of entire plants or of plant parts separately. A curve for one measurement of growth of a corn plant as a whole is shown in Figure 80. Curves for the growth of a bean stem (Figure 81) and for the growth of a leaf (Figure 82) are characteristically S-shaped. The daily increment is an expression of growth on a day to day basis. Growth can be illustrated also by means of a series of time photographs which show the striking increase in size of a plant part. Often this increase in size (or rate of relative growth) is extremely rapid, as is demonstrated by fruit growth of squash (Figure 83). Giant bamboo in tropical environments has been shown to increase its stem length at a rate of 60 centimeters per day.

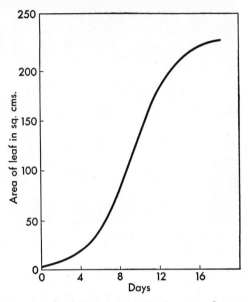

Figure 82   Growth of a leaf of a cucumber as measured by increase in area. (From Gregory, F.G. Annals of Botany, 1921, 35, 93.)

Not only is the growth of plant parts or of entire plants characterized by S-shaped curves, but an individual plant cell, from daughter cell to maturity, also goes through the same pattern as is shown by increases in cell volume in the pea root (Figure 84).

Annual plants complete their growth cycle in a single growing season, while perennials may exhibit differential growth of their parts during certain seasons of the year. In some trees, height growth is limited to several weeks of the spring (white ash, oak, and walnut), while in other trees (yellow poplar and pines) height growth occurs during the entire summer (Figure 85). Plant physiologists would like to know why height growth ceases long before the favorable seasonal environment is terminated for such trees as ash, while other trees such as yellow poplar continue to grow in length. Answers to such questions could bring about a new approach to tree production.

Patterns of growth in plants are accompanied by certain gross changes in the proportions of the main chemical constituents of the plant parts. These gross changes, expressed as percentages of dry weight, are primarily shifts in protoplasmic constituents from a high level in rapidly growing tissues to lower levels as these tissues cease growth and their cells differentiate secondary wall materials. In the management of forage crops, grown for the purpose of producing the maximum rate of growth in animals, such plants are maintained in a state of active growth as long as possible by certain fertilizer, irrigational, and grazing practices.

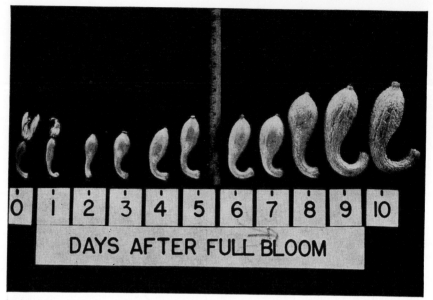

Figure 83 Growth of fruit of summer Crookneck squash. *(From Lorenz, A. Calif. Agr. 5:6–12, 1951.)*

This is because a cessation of growth in such herbage results in a decrease in protein and fat and a large increase in cellulose and lignin (Figure 86).

DORMANCY AND QUIESCENCE

Dormancy.

As illustrated by the growth curves of perennial woody plants (Figure 85), such plants are not in a continuous state of growth. Cessation of growth in meristems (as in buds) may be due to temporary conditions such as water deficits or other external causes. This is called quiescence. When the inhibiting causes are internal and growth cannot be renewed by subjection to a favorable environment, meristematic tissues are said to be in a state of dormancy. Dormancy occurs in buds, seeds, bulbs, tubers, and corms. Roots, however, do not appear to exhibit dormancy.

Dormancy in seeds has been carefully studied by Crocker and his associates (43). Causes of dormancy in seeds are: 1. impermeability of seed coats to water and/or oxygen; 2. rudimentary embryos; 3. certain biochemical features of embryos; 4. light; and 5. restriction of embryo growth by encasing structures. Of these five causes, the term true dormancy should probably be restricted to that resulting from rudimentary embryos and dormant embryos. In the other cases, an embryo will initiate growth without internal physiological changes. When seeds are dormant because of internal conditions, dormancy can be broken by exposing the seeds to certain environments. In such environments, rudimentary embryos will complete their development, and dormant embryos will undergo certain biochemical changes which will permit such embryos to initiate growth.

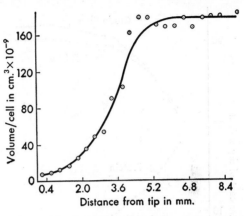

Figure 84   Average cell volume at increasing distances from tip of the pea root. (*From Brown, R. et al. Symposia of the Society for Exp. Biol. 6. Academic Press, Inc., 1952.*)

The biochemical changes which occur during the breaking of dormancy are thought to be either the result of the formation of growth-promoting substances or the destruction of an inhibitor of growth. In either case, this period of breaking of dormancy or afterripening is accompanied by

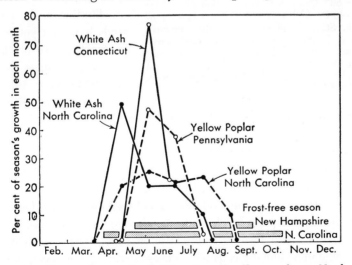

Figure 85   Height growth of white ash and yellow poplar in North Carolina, Connecticut, and Pennsylvania as per cent of season's growth in each month. (*From Kramer, P.J.* Plant Physiol. *18:239–251, 1943.*)

changes in pH, enzyme activity, and in the rate and course of respiration.

Afterripening can occur in several kinds of environments and is specific for certain species. Low temperature (about 41°F.), moisture, and oxygen for one to six months suffice for many seeds. This is sometimes referred to as stratification. Other seeds require moist storage at a temperature of 34°F. Alternating temperatures are required by some seeds such as between 80°F. and 40°F. in some species, or between 60°F. and 104°F. in others. All seeds do not afterripen in moist storage, but instead they require dry storage at either high or low temperatures. Some examples of seeds and their requirements for the breaking of dormancy are shown in Table 30.

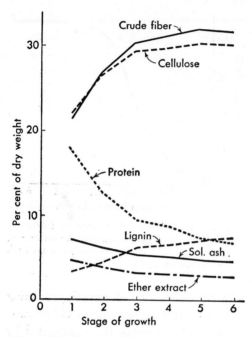

Figure 86 Changes in composition of pasture grasses in Pennsylvania with changes in stage of growth. Stage 1 refers to vegetative growth; stages 2, 3, and 4 refer to macroscopic flower bud and opening of flower stages; stages 5 and 6 refer to growth and development of fruit and seed. (*From Phillips, T.G. et al.* Agron. Jour. *46:361–369, 1954.*)

Studies on dormancy in seeds have not yet revealed its exact nature or the biochemical changes involved, but some very interesting facts have been discovered.

In some embryos, dormancy is restricted only to the epicotyl, while in others dormancy is restricted to the radicle or to the hypocotyl. Removal and growth of embryos which have not been afterripened will produce abnormally dwarfed seedlings. Partial completion of afterripening will give various degrees of abnormal growth.

The causes of dormancy in buds are not well understood. Quiescence, due to lowering of auxin level, may precede dormancy. As is shown later, a decrease in auxin level is found also in cells which stop elongating and in some meristematic cells which cease dividing. However, dormancy has not been shown to be regulated by auxin level. Causes for bud meristems becoming dormant also are not well understood. In some woody

Table 30   Afterripening or breaking of dormancy requirements of various kinds of seeds. (From Crocker, W. and L. V. Barton, *Physiology of Seeds. Waltham, Mass.: Chronica Botanica Co.* 1953.)

| KIND OF SEED | TREATMENT IN STORAGE | | TIME IN STORAGE |
	TEMPERATURE °C	TYPE	
Maple	5	moisture	3 months
Birch	0–10	moisture	2 months
Hawthorn	5– 6	moisture	3 months
Pines	5	moisture	1–3 months
Cherry	3	moisture	3 months
Peach	3	moisture	2.5 months
Apple	5–10	moisture	2.5 months
Ragweed	5	dry	3 months
Oats	40	dry	8 days
Wheat	5	dry	2–4 days

species, it is thought that photoperiods and/or temperature may cause dormancy. Regardless, it is recognized that buds have three states of dormancy or rest. These are preliminary rest, mid rest, and after rest. Dormancy is most easily broken in the preliminary and after rest states.

Dormancy in buds can be broken by cold temperatures, high temperatures, wounding, and chemicals. Under natural conditions, dormancy is usually broken by low temperature of proper duration. Initiation of growth from buds which have undergone partial breaking of dormancy will produce shoots which are abnormal in appearance.

Studies on buds which are in a state of dormancy have revealed that their cells are more opaque, the protoplasm has contracted, and the plasmodesms are ruptured. As dormancy is broken, respiration of an anaerobic nature is increased and the glutathione (a tripeptide) level rises. As a result of breaking of dormancy, an unknown chemical stimulus is formed which is translocatable. This stimulus, which has been transmitted by grafting experiments, will break dormancy in buds. Breaking of dormancy is accompanied by a rise in auxin level.

As pointed out previously, the dormancy of buds is usually broken in nature by the low temperatures of the winter months. In the southern states, some winters pass without sufficient cold weather to break dormancy. When this happens, growth of vegetative shoots the following spring are abnormal and flowering is irregular. Because of this, considerable research effort has been directed toward chemical methods of breaking dormancy. Ethylene chlorohydrin, thiocynates, thiourea, benzotriazole, dinitrocresol, dinitrophenol, and mineral oils have been used to break dormancy. Chemical treatment, however, has not been successful on all species.

Initiation of bud growth prior to the last killing frost is, of course, undesirable. Sprouting of potatoes and onions is also undesirable during storage. Prolongation of dormancy by chemicals has been most successfully accomplished with potatoes and onions, and some control has been obtained on fruit tree buds. The chemicals used to prolong dormancy are naphthalene acetic acid and maleic hydrazide.

PLANT GROWTH REGULATORS

During the past 20 years, plant physiologists have definitely established that growth is controlled in plants by small quantities of certain organic compounds. Many names have been given to these compounds, such as hormones, growth substances, phytohormones, and auxins. Whereas some of these compounds are synthesized in living cells, a large number of organic compounds which do not occur naturally in plants have been found to cause growth responses in plants. In order to have a terminology which could bring order to this confusion of terms, the American Society of Plant Physiologists has proposed the following nomenclature (69):

1. Plant Regulators are organic compounds, other than nutrients, which in small amounts promote, inhibit or otherwise modify any physiological process in plants.

2. Growth Regulators (Synonym: Growth substances) are regulators which affect growth.

3. Flowering Regulators are regulators which affect flowering.

4. Plant Hormones (Synonym: Phytohormones) are regulators produced by plants, which in low concentrations regulate plant physiological processes. Hormones usually move within the plant from a site of production to a site of action.

5. Growth Hormones are hormones which regulate growth.

6. Flowering Hormones are hormones which initiate the formation of floral primordia, or promote their development.

7. Auxin is a generic term for compounds characterized by their capacity to induce elongation in shoot cells. They resemble indole-3-acetic acid in physiological action.

Auxins may, and generally do, affect other processes besides elongation, but elongation is considered critical. Auxins are generally acids with an unsaturated cyclic nucleus or their derivatives.

8. Auxin Precursors are compounds which in the plant can be converted into auxins.

9. Anti-Auxins are compounds which inhibit competitively the action of auxins.

The existence of hormones in plants was discovered through studies of the bending of cereal coleoptiles in unilateral light. Darwin in 1881 and Boysen-Jensen in 1913 demonstrated that some unknown chemical substance, diffusing from the coleoptile tip, caused phototropic response in the region of cell elongation. Further proof that a chemical regulator was involved and that it was synthesized in the coleoptile tip came from the studies of F. W. Went in 1928. He found that he could collect this hormone in agar blocks. This hormone, because it was shown to be necessary for cell elongation, has been called auxin, a term which is based on the Greek word *auxe* meaning grow.

In 1934, biochemists in Holland isolated a growth-promoting compound from plant tissues, a compound named indoleacetic acid:

$$\text{CH}_2 \text{COOH}$$

Indoleacetic acid is now accepted as being the naturally occurring auxin of plants. Some investigators believe that other auxins occur in plants, but the status of these is uncertain.

It is recognized that indoleacetic acid causes a multiplicity of effects on plant growth. Some of these involve a stimulation of growth, while others involve inhibition of growth. Among these effects are:

1. Cell elongation responses in oat coleoptiles, stems, veins, and petioles of leaves.
2. Cell division responses in adventitious roots, parthenocarpic fruit, callus tissues, and cambial growth.
3. Inhibition of growth in root elongation, apical dominance, and suppression of abscission layer separation.

How auxin could both inhibit and stimulate growth was explained by Thimann in 1937 on a basis of effective concentration in the tissue. Ranges of growth responses of various plant organs to indoleacetic acid are shown in Figure 87. From these curves it is seen that 0.0001 mg. per liter is optimum for root growth, whereas 1.0 mg. per liter is optimum for stem growth.

Auxin cannot be quantitatively analyzed in plant tissues by usual chemical methods because of its very low concentration. It has been estimated that 10,000 coleoptile tips will yield only 1 microgram of indoleacetic acid. Therefore, in order to analyze auxin in plant tissues, bioassay methods are employed. The three most widely used methods are the Avena (oat) curvature test, the Avena straight growth test, and the split pea test. A diagrammatic summary of these three techniques is presented in Figure 88. The two Avena tests are carried out on oat coleoptiles which have had their auxin levels reduced to a minimum by removal of a few millimeters of the tips. The rate of cell elongation of these decapitated coleoptiles may then be controlled through external applications of auxins by means of several auxin assay methods. These assay methods can be used to quantitatively evaluate auxin concentration. In the curvature test, unequal rates of

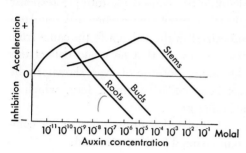

Figure 87 Inhibition and growth promotion effect of indolacetic acid on roots, buds, and stems. (*From Thimann, K.V. The Action of Hormones in Plants and Invertebrates. Academic Press, Inc., 1952.*)

elongation of the coleoptile are effected by placing agar blocks containing auxin on one side of the tip. In the straight growth test, entire pieces of coleoptile are placed in auxin solution, and permitted to elongate.

Oat seedlings are grown under controlled environmental conditions which consist of initial growth in darkness followed by exposure to red light for two to four hours prior to decapitation in order to prevent excessive elongation of the first internode. The curvature test is carried out in a room with a temperature maintained at 25°C., a relative humidity of 85 per cent, and exposure to red light.

In the split pea test, advantage is taken of the response of plant tissues which are low in native auxin by treating them with external auxin concentrations. The epidermal cells of the split pea stem elongate more rapidly under the influence of auxin than do the inner cortical cells and, as a result, the split halves curve inward. The degree of curvature is proportional to the auxin concentrations of the solutions into which the split sections are placed. The split stem sections are obtained from the third internode of pea seedlings which have been grown in darkness and then exposed to red light for four hours prior to treatment.

A less commonly used technique for auxin assay, known as the cress root growth inhibition test, is shown at the bottom of Figure 88. In this test inhibition of growth instead of promotion of growth is used as a criterion of auxin concentrations. For a more detailed treatment of the auxin assay methods, consult the recent book by Leopold (53).

The Occurrence, Production, and Inactivation of Auxin.

Meristematic tissues are generally the sites of auxin synthesis as well as the areas of highest concentration of these substances. In addition to meristems, enlarging organs such as leaves, flowers, fruits, nodules, and tumors produce large amounts of auxin. Auxin, which is synthesized in stem apices, diffuses down the stem via the parenchyma tissue. The distribution in oat and pea seedlings is shown in Table 31. Some auxin concentrations in various plant parts and species of plants are given in Table 32.

Table 31   The distribution of auxin in the oat coleoptile and in bean seedlings.

DISTANCE FROM APEX	AUXIN DISTRIBUTION IN OAT COLEOPTILE	PART OF SEEDLING	AUXIN DISTRIBUTION IN BEAN SEEDLING
mm.	A.E./mm.[1]		R. U.[2]
2	0.28	Apical bud	12.0
5	0.18	Youngest leaf	2.2
8	0.13	Second leaf	1,5
13	0.10	Third leaf	0.3
		Fourth leaf	0.4

[1] Arbitrary units.
[2] Relative units.

Various extraction and long term diffusion experiments have demonstrated that all the auxin in plant tissues does not occur in the same form. Auxin exists in the free and bound states. Free auxin is the form which is translocated through the parenchymatous tissue, and which diffuses easily from plant tissues placed in contact with an agar block,

Table 32   The distribution of indoleacetic acid in various species and plant tissues. (*From Leopold, A.C.* Auxins and Plant Growth. *Univ. of Calif. Press. 1955.*)

SPECIES	ORGAN OR TISSUE	INDOLEACETIC ACID CONCENTRATION
		µg/kg fresh wt.
Corn	endosperm	105,000
Lily	stem tip	83,900
Wheat	endosperm	22,000
Oat	grain	1,000
Rice	endosperm	250
Turnip	seed	250
Sunflower	stem	74
Beet	seed	50
Pineapple	young leaf	11
Bean	young leaf	8
Giant kelp	terminal blade	0.5

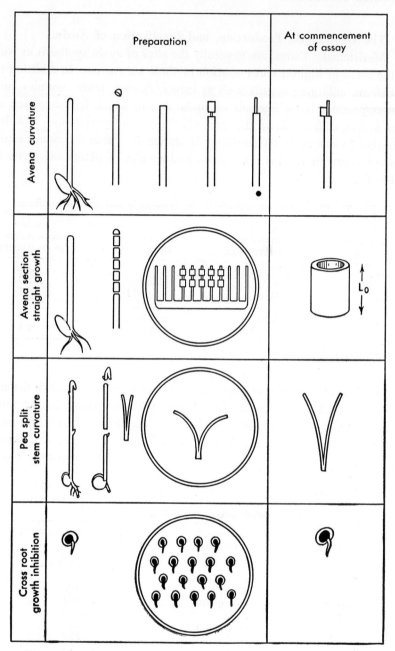

Figure 88 The four methods of auxin assay and effect of auxin concentration on response. *(From Andus, L.J.* Plant Growth Substances. *Leonard Hill (Books) Ltd., 1953.)*

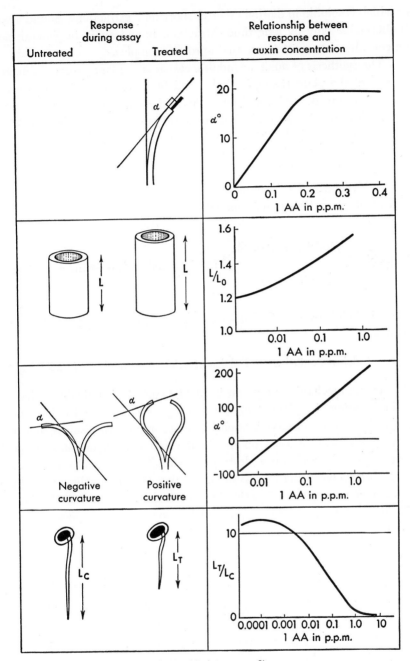

Figure 88 (*Continued*)

or which is soluble in diethyl ether in short time extractions. Bound auxin is obtainable only by long time extraction. Bound auxin in general may be considered to exist in an auxin-protein complex.

The synthesis of auxin or indoleacetic acid in plant tissues is affected by age of the plant tissue, by light, and by zinc. The apices of tomato plants reach peak auxin production in 40 days. Auxin levels will gradually be lowered in the dark, but the level rises again when tissues are again exposed to light. Zinc deficiencies will prevent auxin formation by retarding the synthesis of tryptophan, the auxin precursor.

The pathways of auxin synthesis in living plant cells involve several steps with intermediate products, all of which originate from the amino acid tryptophan. These are summarized as follows:

$$\text{Tryptophan} \begin{array}{c} \nearrow \text{Indolepyruvic acid} \searrow \\ \searrow \text{Tryptamine} \nearrow \end{array} \text{Indoleacetaldehyde} \longrightarrow \text{Indoleacetic acid}$$

Recently indoleacetonitrile has been found to be another possible source of auxin:

$$\text{Indoleacetonitrile} \longrightarrow \text{Indoleacetamide} \longrightarrow \text{Indoleacetic acid}$$

Several mechanisms operate in plant tissues to inactivate or destroy auxin. Bending of a plant stem which is exposed to unequal light intensities has long been observed. Such bending, or phototropism, is due to a lower auxin concentration on the light exposed side, or because some light activated mechanism destroys auxin. Such a mechanism would probably involve a pigment system. Studies of the wavelength of light which can cause auxin inactivation show the greatest inactivation at 450 mμ, that is, in the blue region of the spectrum. The pigments riboflavin and β-carotene probably are active in absorbing this light. The following reaction has been suggested for auxin destruction:

$$\text{Indoleacetic acid} + O_2 \longrightarrow \text{Indolealdehyde} + CO_2$$

This reaction may be catalyzed by the enzyme indoleacetic acid oxidase which is light activatable. However, Galston and Dalberg (45) have shown recently that light is not necessary for indoleacetic acid oxidase activation. According to their concept, the indoleacetic acid oxidase enzyme has its concentration increased by a rise in the level of indoleacetic acid. A plant cell as it undergoes elongation is accompanied by an increase in the indoleacetic acid level, and this results in a corresponding rise in the indoleacetic acid oxidase enzyme. The result is destruction of indoleacetic acid and a cessation of cell elongation.

The naturally occurring auxin, indoleacetic acid, can be both inhibited and promoted in its effect on growth by certain kinds of chemical substances. Substances that promote growth in the presence of auxin more than auxin alone are called auxin synergists. Some examples are 2,3,5-triiodobenzoic acid, chelidonic acid, and phthalamic acid. Conversely, if the auxin synergist compound concentration is too high in proportion to the auxin concentration, an inhibition of growth will result. Other compounds inhibit growth by competing with the auxin molecules for the binding sites of the receptor. These are called anti-auxins. The anti-auxin molecules on being bound to the receptor yield a complex that is unable to initiate the growth process. The inhibiting effects are decreased by increasing the ratio of auxin to anti-auxin molecules. The chemical structure of anti-auxins is very similar to auxins, but they differ in one of the three requirements of ring structure, acid group, or configuration. Some examples of anti-auxins are phenylbutyric acid, transcinnamic acid, 2,4,6-trichlorophenoxyacetic acid, and 2,4-dichloroanisole. In contrast with the anti-auxin type of inhibition, other kinds of chemical substances continue to inhibit growth in the presence of increasing concentrations of auxins. These are growth inhibitors and probably affect the growth process other than via the auxin-receptor complex. Some examples are maleic hydrazide, commarin, and other unsaturated lactones.

Other Plant Growth Regulators.

Although indoleacetic acid is indispensable for plant growth, several other growth regulators have been demonstrated to be needed for the growth of various plant parts. One group of compounds of unknown chemical constitution is called the calines. Rhizocaline is thought to be needed along with auxin for root initiation of woody cuttings. It is believed to be synthesized in the leaves. Caulocaline is synthesized in the roots and is needed for stem growth. Phyllocaline is required for mesophyll growth in leaves.

Tissue culture techniques have shown that excised roots grow only if supplied with an external source of certain vitamins. These vitamins are thiamin (B_1), pyridoxine (B_6), and nicotinic acid. The requirements of roots of different plant species for these three vitamins vary considerably. The majority need thiamin. In intact plants, these vitamins are synthesized in the leaves and translocated to the roots. The essentiality of the B-vitamins for the growth of excised tomato roots by means of the tissue culture technique is illustrated in Figure 89.

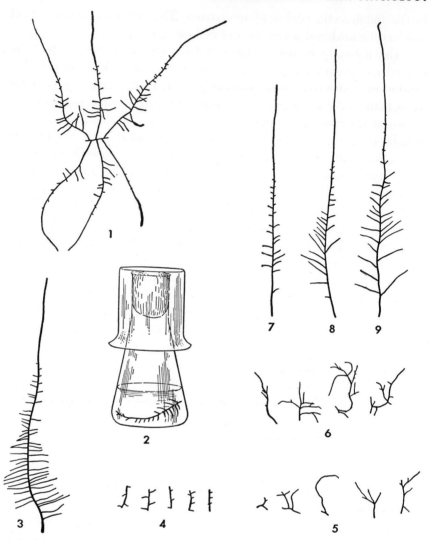

Figure 89 Effect of B-vitamins on tomato root growth. 1–3. All vitamins and glycine.
4. B₆, nicotinic acid, and glycine, 2nd passage. 5. B₁, 4th passage. 6. B₁ and nicotinic
acid, 7th passage. 7. B₁ and B₆, 7th passage. 8. B₁, B₆, and nicotinic acid, 7th passage.
9. B₁, B₆, nicotinic acid, and glycine, 7th passage. (*Courtesy of H.E. Street and
Leonard Hill (Books) Ltd.*)

    Another plant growth regulator is synthesized in living plant cells
as the result of wounding. The cells near the wound which are fully
mature resume cell division and produce wound callus. A specific growth
regulator other than indoleacetic acid was shown to be necessary to

cause resumption of growth. This specific wound growth regulator has been isolated and shown to be a dibasic acid, $C_{10}H_{18}(COOH)_2$, called traumatic acid.

As mentioned previously, mesophyll tissue of leaves is not controlled in its growth by indoleacetic acid. Some recent research has shown that mesophyll tissue growth may be stimulated by a purine called adenine, which is found in many living plant cells. This very interesting substance has been shown by Skoog (60) to have other functions in plant cellular growth. Adenine at a concentration of 40 mg. per liter was shown to cause bud differentiation of tobacco stem segments in tissue cultures.

Research with tissue cultures has demonstrated that additional, unknown growth regulators are yet to be identified. One such unknown substance can be demonstrated by the effect of the addition of coconut milk on the growth of carrot discs. This effect of coconut milk is illustrated by the data in Figure 90.

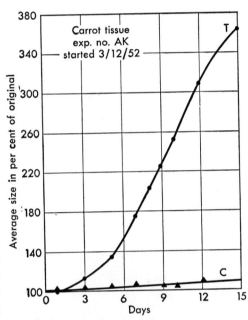

Figure 90   The effect of coconut concentrate on the growth of carrot callus fragments. C-control and T- with coconut concentrate. (*From Skoog, Folke*. Dynamics of Growth Processes. *Princeton University Press, 1954.*)

In the last five years American and European scientists have been investigating a potent growth regulator known as the gibberellins. Application of such low concentrations as 0.0001 to 10 micrograms on a single plant will cause marked increases in the rate of growth (Figure 90-A). With some dwarf mutants, application of gibberellins will cause the dwarfed plants to grow to the same size as the normal plants. The gibberellins are synthesized by the fungus, *Gibberella fujikuroi*, which causes the foolish seedling disease of rice. For 25 years prior to its study by Western scientists, the growth regulator effects of the filtrate from the fungus were extensively investigated by the Japanese.

Figure 90-A Comparative growth of bush bean variety Contender 31 days after treatment with 20 micrograms of gibberellins. Plant at left untreated and plant at right treated with gibberellins. (*From Wittwer, S.H. and M.J. Bukovac, Michigan State Univ. Agr. Exp. Sta., Quarterly Bulletin, Vol. 39. No. 3:3–28, 1957.*)

Chemists have shown that the gibberellins are a mixture of closely related chemicals. One of these is a tetracyclic dihydroxlactonic acid ($C_{19}H_{22}O_6$) and is called gibberellic acid. The filtrate containing the gibberellins is now available on a commercial scale. Since 1956, many plant scientists have studied their growth regulator effects on higher plants. Although an increase in cell elongation is the most often noted response to the giberrellins, many other interesting effects on growth have been reported. These are promotion of cell division in callus tissues, leaf expansion (substitutes for red light), overcoming dwarf growth of seedlings from partially broken dormant embryos, germination of lettuce seed (substitutes for red light), flowering of biennials (substitutes for cold period), flowering of long day plants in short day environments, and breaking of dormancy in buds.

Application of the gibberellins on a commercial scale may not be advisable until more research results are obtained. In many instances, increased growth has resulted without an increase in dry weight. Such plants are easily lodged and sometimes chlorotic. Breaking of dormancy and induction of flowering would seem to be a more useful application.

Are the gibberellins synthesized by the higher plants in which they cause such a diversity of growth responses? At present the gibberellins have not been isolated from higher plants. Some indirect evidence with decapitated pea plants indicates that the gibberellins are synthesized in terminal bud meristems. When gibberellins were applied to the decapitated pea plants, these grew normally. Many of the growth promoting effects of the gibberellins are similar to those caused by indoleacetic acid.

In addition to the naturally occurring plant growth regulators, a large number of synthetic organic compounds have been shown to affect plant growth. Research dealing with these synthetic organic substances has been concerned with hundreds of compounds and has been one of the principal fields of plant growth regulator studies. The exhibition of growth activity is the property of diverse molecular structures and has led to the study of the relationship of molecular structure to this activity. As early as 1938, Koepfli, Thimann, and Went (48) listed the basic molecular requirements for growth activity as follows:

1. An unsaturated ring.
2. An acid side-chain.
3. A particular spatial arrangement between the ring and the side-chain.

Since 1938 a large number of synthetic organic compounds have been tested to determine if the above basic molecular requirements are necessary for activity. Compounds investigated generally were in the following series: indole derivatives, naphthalene derivatives, phenoxyacetic acid derivatives, substituted benzoic acid, and phenylacetic acid. Examples of these compounds are shown on page 212.

Indole derivative:

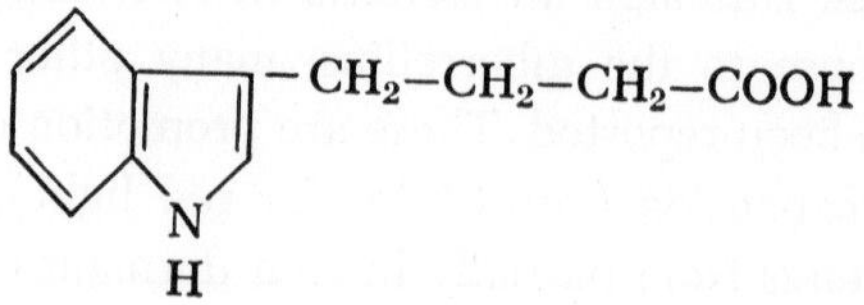

Indolebutyric acid

Naphthalene derivative:

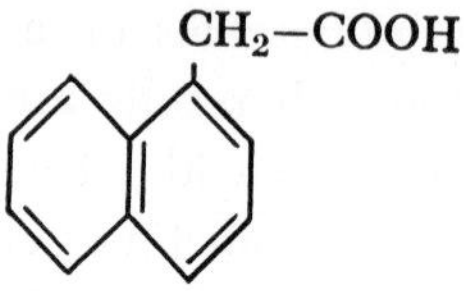

α-Naphthaleneacetic acid

Phenoxyacetic acid derivative:

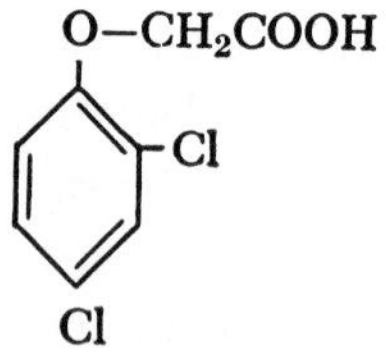

2,4-Dichlorophenoxyacetic acid

Substituted benzoic acid:

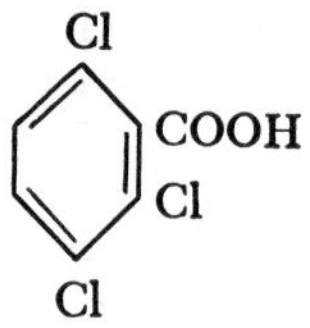

2,3,6-Trichlorobenzoic acid

Phenylacetic acid:

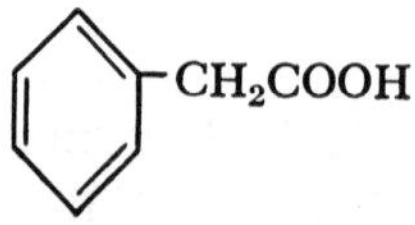

Many other compounds in the above classes, as well as compounds in other classes, have been tested. Many of these substances were found to have some growth promoting activity, but not all were tested by the specific assay methodology, i.e., by the Avena coleoptile section test. Because all compounds were not subjected to an assay test, difficulty has been encountered in the interpretation of many results. At present it would seem that all the compounds which are active in one of the assay tests possess a double bond in the ring and have an acid group on the side-chain. Plant physiologists had expected that research with these growth regulators would lead to an understanding of how growth regulators function in the cellular growth process. However, as pointed out by Bonner and Bandurski (40), no new concepts have resulted from this research.

It now appears that there are many chemical regulators which can affect plant growth. Many of these compounds are of synthetic origin and do not occur in plant cells, but are still to be considered by definition as plant growth regulators. On the other hand, indoleacetic acid, calines, vitamins B_1, B_6 and nicotinic acid, and traumatic acid are synthesized in plant cells and by definition are called plant hormones.

Agricultural Applications of Growth Regulators.

The discovery in 1935 that several of the synthetic growth regulators would cause an increase both in number and in rate of development of roots of woody cuttings initiated the entrance of growth regulators into the field of agriculture. During the 23 years which followed, research on use of growth regulators has resulted in the production of many agricultural chemicals which have assumed an importance comparable to that of fertilizers, insecticides, and fungicides. The possibilities of development in the field of growth regulators as an important part of agricultural chemistry are unlimited. The synthetic growth regulators are manufactured at a lower cost than the hormone indoleacetic acid, and many of the synthetic products cause physiological action at lower concentrations than does indoleacetic acid. This is particularly true of the phenoxyacetic acid derivatives.

Application of growth regulators to hasten the rooting of woody cuttings, however, has not enabled horticultural workers to bring about root development on woody cuttings of species which do not initiate roots naturally. The growth regulators cause only an acceleration of rooting and, in some species, result in larger, more vigorous roots. Moreover, growth regulators do not substitute for the essentiality of sugar and soluble nitrogen which are furnished by the leaves. The most successful growth regulator so far discovered for rooting of cuttings is indolebutyric acid, although alpha-2,4,5-trichlorophenoxypropionic acid and alpha naphthalenebutyric acid are also used. In some species better root development results from treatment with a combination of these growth regulators. The effect of indolebutyric acid on the rooting of apple and plum cuttings is shown in Figure 91.

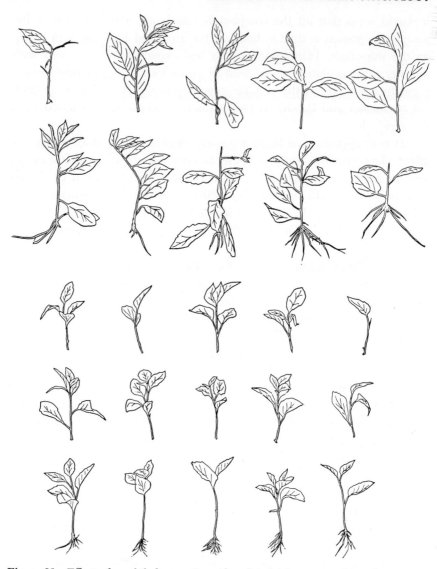

Figure 91 Effect of naphthaleneacetic acid and indolebutyric acid on the rooting of apple and plum cuttings. Top row—Control. 2nd row—30 ppm. Napthaleneacetic Acid. 3rd row—Poor Source. 4th row—Control. 5th row—20 ppm. indolebutyric acid. (*From Andus, L.J.* Plant Growth Substances. *Leonard Hill (Books) Ltd., 1953.*)

In 1936 Gustafson found that application of indolebutyric acid and other regulators to stigmas of flowers of tomato, pepper, squash, and other species would cause the formation of seedless fruits (parthenocarpy). Further research showed that many other species, such as watermelon, cucumber, holly, and citrus fruits, could be induced with growth regulator chemicals applied to their pistils to form seedless fruit. Wide use of growth regulator chemicals to produce seedless fruit, however, has not been employed with crops, except for tomatoes, holly, and figs. Figure 92 shows a seedless tomato which resulted from treatment with indolebutyric acid. Growth regulators used for the production of seedless fruit are naphthaleneacetic acid, para-chlorophenoxyacetic acid, 2,4,5-trichlorophenoxyacetic acid, and β-naphthoxyacetic acid.

In order to obtain larger fruit, commercial growers either remove some of the flowers or some of the young fruits from plants. In 1941 it was found that naphthaleneacetic acid could be used to thin flowers, and later this chemical proved effective in fruit thinning. Other plant growth regulators which have been used for this effect are 2,4,5-trichlorophenoxyacetic acid and 2,4,5-trichlorophenoxypropionic acid.

Growth regulator chemicals have also been used for the prevention of sprouting in potatoes, onions, and nursery stock of trees and shrubs. Naphthaleneacetic acid was first employed in 1939 to prevent sprouting of potatoes during storage at warm temperatures; more recently maleic hydrazide has been used to prevent such sprouting during storage.

In horticulture one of the most widely adopted uses of chemical growth regulators has been for the prevention of preharvest fruit drop. In 1940 α-naphthaleneacetic acid was used successfully to prevent preharvest fruit drop of apples, and this compound is still the most widely used chemical in commercial practice for this purpose. More recently 2,4-dichlorophenoxyacetic acid, 2,4,5-trichlorophenoxyacetic acid, and 2,4,5-trichlorophenoxypropionic acid have been used to some extent. The inhibition of preharvest drop has been successful with apples, pears, and citrus fruits, but not with peaches and grapes.

Application of chemical growth regulators to fruit both at preharvest and at postharvest times has been successful in both delaying maturity and in the hastening of ripening. 2,4-dichlorophenoxyacetic acid and 2,4,5-trichlorophenoxyacetic acid have been most widely used for both delaying maturity and for the acceleration of ripening of fruit. Preharvest spraying is used for delaying maturity, while for hastening ripening, the fruits are dipped in the chemical. Application to citrus fruit has been done on a commercial basis, the growth regulator being applied as a preharvest spray.

So far the use of chemical growth regulators to induce flowering has not been generally successful, except in pineapples. Naphthaleneacetic acid is used on a commercial scale to induce pineapple flowering. At present, research on the effects of various chemical growth regulators in inducing flowering has shown that these chemicals will not cause floral initiation in most species of plants. On the contrary, when applied to most species, growth regulators will inhibit flowering. On the other hand anti-

Figure 92   Production of parthenocarpic tomato fruit by treatment of the cut style with 2 per cent indolebutyric acid in lanolin. Top illustration, tagged fruits-treated and untagged-normal pollination. Lower illustration, a cross section of treated fruit. (*From Gustafson, F.G.* Plant Growth Substances. *University of Wisconsin Press, 1951.*)

auxins such as 2,3,5-triiodobenzoic acid and 2,4-dichloroanisole have been found to induce flowering. These chemicals are still being tried on an experimental basis, and as yet have not been used commercially. Since chemical growth regulators inhibit flowering, they can be used to prevent the production of flowers in crops whose flowering is undesirable, such as leafy vegetables and sugar beets.

Use of chemical growth regulators in such diverse ways as rooting of cuttings and the prevention of fruit drop are of importance in their areas of application, but they do not entirely account for the large scale commercial production of chemical regulators. Another use has stimulated the manufacture of large amounts of these chemicals for use in agriculture, specifically the control of weeds or as herbicides. This field of application has developed mainly since 1945. Slade in England in 1940 first demonstrated that a growth regulator, naphthaleneacetic acid, could be used as a herbicide. He observed a rather remarkable property of naphthaleneacetic acid, namely, that it would kill broad-leaved weeds but would not harm grain crops. Such a chemical regulator is called a selective herbicide. In both England and in the United States research workers have found that the phenoxyacetic acid derivatives exhibit selective herbicidal properties, and at much lower concentrations than did naphthaleneacetic acid. Furthermore, these phenoxyacetic acid derivatives can be produced cheaply on a commercial scale. 2,4-dichlorophenoxyacetic acid (2,4-D) is the principal selective herbicide used in the United States, while 2-methyl, 4-chlorophenoxyacetic acid (MCPA) is widely used in England.

Another phenoxyacetic acid derivative which is used as a herbicide with woody plants is 2,4,5-trichlorophenoxyacetic acid (2,4,5-T). 2,4-D and 2,4,5-T are often more effective when used together. These compounds are applied in several ways to kill weeds. They may be applied in the form of sprays directly on the plants, or they may be applied to soils (pre-emergence treatment). When applied to the soil, they kill the weeds as soon as seed germination occurs.

Selectivity, low concentration, and low cost of production are important characteristics of the phenoxyacetic acid derivatives. A very important additional characteristic of these chemicals is their rapid translocation within plant bodies. For example, when applied to leaves as a spray, 2,4-D will move to the roots and kill them,—a very important consideration in the control of many weeds. Movement out of the leaves is dependent on adequate sugar being present in the leaves, since 2,4-D is translocated only when sugar is being translocated. Thus, for maximum lethal effects on weeds, herbicides should be sprayed on plants during a sunny day when maximum photosynthesis is occurring. Other factors also will affect the maximum toxic action of herbicides, such as stage of growth and soil moisture. Weeds are most easily killed during rapid vegetative growth and when soil moisture is near field capacity.

One effect of 2,4-D on plants is known as epinastic response which is a bending and twisting of the petioles and stem. This effect on tomatoes

Figure 93 Effect of 2,4-D applied at various concentrations by four methods on the tomato plant. A, applied to one leaflet. B, applied to petiole in lanolin. C, sprayed on entire plant. D, applied to the soil. (*From Hitchcock, A.E. and P.W. Zimmerman. Contributions from Boyce Thompson Institute. 16:209–214, 1951.*)

is shown in Figure 93. Another effect is an inhibition of terminal bud growth, which is illustrated by bean plants in Figure 94. In each case illustrated, 2,4-D was applied to the leaves. Application to the bean

Figure 94   Ten micrograms of 2,4-D when applied to both primary leaves of bean seedlings caused a reduction in stem growth of plants that were placed in the sunlight but had no effect on bean seedlings kept in the shade. Bending of stems often results from 2,4-D application. Plant on the extreme left is bean seedling as it appeared prior to 2,4-D application. The two adjacent plants were grown in the shade. The three plants on the right were grown in sunlight. All bean seedlings except one on extreme left photographed after 3 weeks of growth. (*From Mitchell, John W. and J.W. Brown. Botanical Gazette. 107:393–407, 1946.*)

leaf of a drop of water which contains 10 micrograms of 2,4-D is sufficient to cause diffusion into the leaf tissues and subsequent translocation to the terminal bud.

The property of selectivity by the phenoxyacetic acid herbicides is not simply a matter of their toxicity to dicotyledenous plants and nontoxicity at the same concentrations to monocotyledenous plants. Selective toxicity varies also among species of both classes of plants. Furthermore, application of a herbicide to kill weeds may have a toxic effect on an otherwise resistant crop plant if the herbicide is applied at a particular stage of growth of the crop plant. Toxic reactions of winter wheat to the application of 2,4-D during various stages of growth are shown in Figure 95. These illustrations show the effects of the application of 2,4-D which caused a more toxic effect during the reproductive growth of the plant than during vegetative growth. This is often seen in other plants such as cotton and corn, and the 2,4-D may persist in the seed

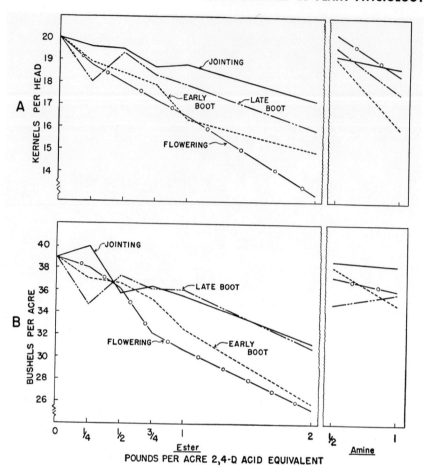

Figure 95 Three-year average number of kernels per head (A) and yield in bushels per acre (B) of Pawnee wheat as affected by 2,4-D applications at four stages of growth. *(From Klingman, D.L. Agronomy Journal. 45:606–610, 1953.)*

and cause abnormal growth of subsequently developed young plants. Response to 2,4-D injury has been demonstrated to differ also among varieties of crop plants. Data on the response of the roots of various varieties of oats illustrate these varietal differences as shown in Figure 96.

The nature of selective toxic action of the phenoxyacetic acid derivatives has not been fully explained. It is possible that it is not due to any single cause, but to a combination of several factors. One of these is the morphological characteristics of the epidermal tissue of the leaves. The cutin of some species permits an easy penetration of the 2,4-D molecules, while the cuticles of other species are not so easily penetrated.

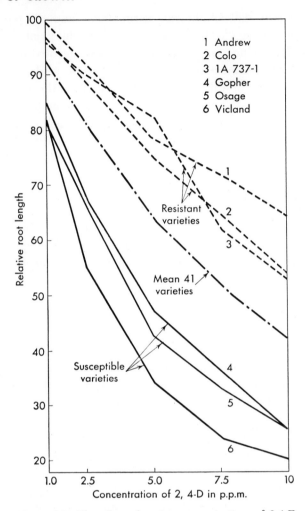

100

90

80

Relative root length

70

60

50

40

30

20

1   Andrew
2   Colo
3   1A 737-1
4   Gopher
5   Osage
6   Vicland

Resistant
varieties

Mean 41
varieties

Susceptible
varieties

1

2

3

4

5

6

1.0   2.5   5.0   7.5   10

Concentration of 2, 4-D in p.p.m.

Figure 96   The effect of various concentrations of 2,4-D
on the relative root growth of three tolerant and three
susceptible oat varieties. *(From Williams, J.H. Agronomy
Journal. 45:293–297, 1953.)*

Some leaves are ridged and do not allow the spray to accumulate and
spread. Another explanation is based on the concentration differences
required to produce a toxic effect at the cellular level. Thus a herbicide
may be absorbed and translocated by two different species, but the concentration will cause a toxic effect in one while in the other no toxic effect
occurs. Moreover, in the same species selective toxic action is often manifested in different organs due to the concentration differences required
to cause toxicity. For example, in water cress, 1 p.p.m. will inhibit root

growth, 10 p.p.m. will inhibit seed germination, and 100 p.p.m. are required to cause toxic effects on the leaf parts of the plant.

A considerable amount of research has been devoted to determining the cause of the toxic action of the phenoxyacetic acids on susceptible plants. As a result of this research, the following theories have been advanced: 1. phenoxyacetic acid molecules inhibit or block the master biochemical reaction of growth; 2. phenoxyacetic acid molecules cause a depletion of food reserves and increase protein hydrolysis; 3. energy transfer via the phosphorylated enzyme system is blocked by interference with respiration; and 4. abnormal metabolic processes result in the accumulation of an inhibitor of growth. Whatever the exact mechanism, herbicides do cause abnormal behavior such as epinastic responses and stimulated growth of such tissues as pericycle, phloem, and endodermis. This disorganized proliferation of growth results in the splitting of the root tissues and the blocking of phloem translocation. In comparison with money spent on screening new compounds and empirical field studies, the amount expended on basic research directed toward discovering the nature of toxicity of herbicides is very small, and for this reason progress has been slow.

Many herbicides of a selective nature now available are not classed as growth regulators. Some of these are the carbamates, trichloroacetates, phenylmercuric acetate, 3-(p-chlorophenyl)-1, 1-dimethyl urea, and nitrated phenols and creosols.

The above discussion on plant growth regulators does not begin to cover the information accumulated in this field of plant physiology. Plant growth regulator research has been the most prolific area of study by plant physiologists during the past 20 years, and published papers in this field far outnumber those in other fields of plant physiological research. For more detailed reviews, it is suggested that the books by Thimann (64), Audus (38), and Leopold (53) be consulted. A book by Tukey (68) covers agricultural applications of this field of work.

NATURE OF THE GROWTH PROCESS

As was pointed out in the discussion on plant growth regulators, the plant hormone and auxin, indoleacetic acid, controls growth in a multiplicity of ways. Just how the naturally occurring auxin is thought to affect growth will now be discussed along with other facts which have been discovered about growth in recent years. Within the last decade, new methods of analytical chemistry have enabled biochemists to measure some of the very complex chemical processes which occur during growth. These interesting data, however, do not as yet offer a complete explanation of the growth mechanism. A great deal of emphasis has been placed on research which deals with the biochemistry of growth because of its promise in discovering a cure for cancer.

Before dealing with some of the more recent research, we shall consider how the growth mechanism was explained not more than ten years ago and see how present ideas differ from earlier concepts. Most investigators have studied growth mainly during the cell elongation stage. Cell elongation was originally considered to be the result of two principal processes. First, it was thought that, as a result of a greater DPD in the cell, water diffused inward and caused TP to develop on the primary cell wall which, in turn, caused the wall to stretch. The cell wall was viewed as a plastic structure,—elasticity being the result of the presence of the naturally occurring auxin in high concentrations during the cell elongation phase. It was believed that, as the auxin level decreased, plasticity of the primary cell wall ceased and with it cell elongation. It is now known that this purely physical mechanism of cell elongation is impossible because of the very nature of the cell wall. Furthermore, auxin has been shown to be associated with many biochemical processes in cells during elongation.

The recent studies by Frey-Wyssling and his associates have demonstrated that the primary wall consists of a closely woven textile structure. Such a wall could no more be stretched than could a piece of cloth. The electron microscope has revealed also that the primary cell wall is made up of a woven texture of dispersed cellulose microfibrils. An electron microscopic picture of a small portion of a primary cell wall is shown in Figure 97. Any theory of cell elongation must take into account the structure of the primary cell wall. In this regard, two theories have been advanced, both of which hold that the cell wall increases in area by the addition of new cellulose microfibrils as the result of the extension of the cytoplasm into the microfibrial framework. One theory postulates a loosening of the microfibrils in the primary wall with the addition of more microfibrils along the entire wall area. Examination of microfibrial network by the electron microscope has not substantiated this theory. Furthermore, the studies of Frey-Wyssling (44) show that a definite microfibrial framework does not form at the tips of elongating plant cells. Therefore, it is thought that a cell wall lengthens by the bipolar addition of parallelized microfibrils which are formed by the living cytoplasm. Frey-Wyssling has called this bipolar tip growth.

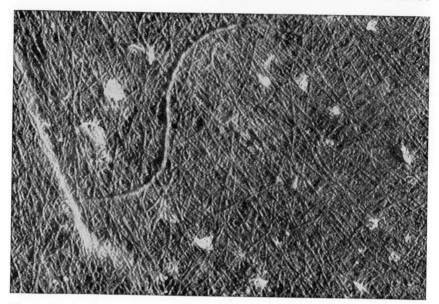

Figure 97 An electron microscopic view of the primary wall of an onion root cell fragment in the region of cell elongation showing the arrangement of the microfibrils. Enlarged 26,000 times. *(From Scott, Flora Murray, et al. American Journal of Botany. 43:313–324, 1956.)*

It would seem, then, that any theory of plant cell growth must explain growth of the primary cell wall as resulting from metabolic processes in living cytoplasm. As previously pointed out, there is evidence that cell elongation does not occur unless auxin is present at an optimum concentration in the cell. Thus auxin must play a role in cell wall growth. The exact steps in this bio-process or the manner in which auxin plays a role are not definitely known. At present one can say only that auxin acts as a coenzyme in cellulose microfibrial synthesis. This concept and other possible roles of auxin in growth are summarized in an article by Thimann (65).

At the same time that growth in area of the primary cell wall is taking place, diffusion of water into the vacuole is occurring. The rate of diffusion of water into the vacuole keeps pace with the growing cell wall. At one time considerable emphasis was placed on the role of auxin as a regulator of this water absorption (non-osmotic diffusion). This concept does not stand up either against experimental evidence or in light of theoretical treatment of water influx. Inward diffusion of water is viewed as a result of osmotic forces.

A large number of studies (53) show that auxin is a regulator of many metabolic processes during cell elongation as well as cell differentiation. During cell elongation, auxin controls the rate of organic acid metabolism, increases the rate of respiration, regulates the activation of several kinds of enzymes, and affects the kinds and amounts of many plant constituents. These studies indicate that probably the most important effects of auxin are the regulating of phosphate enzyme energy transfers and the rate of synthesis of ribose-nucleic acids and desoxyribose nucleic acids. Skoog (61) is of the opinion that the latter relation is the most logical approach to the role of auxin in the cellular growth process. With molecular structural configurations known for the naturally occurring auxin as well as many different kinds of synthetic chemical regulators, it was hoped that the exact role of auxin in the growth mechanism could be postulated. However, to date these studies have not revealed the exact role of auxin. At present considerable information is available on auxin effects in cellular growth, but the exact role of auxin in these various metabolic processes is yet to be elucidated.

The studies of Skoog (61) have revealed that auxin regulates differentiation of a cluster of cells. His studies have been concerned with bud differentiation of isolated fragments of tissue, such as tobacco pith, which were grown in nutrient culture. Results show that auxin concentration controlled bud differentiation. A very low concentration of auxin in combination with adenine caused bud differentiation, i.e., the auxin/adenine ratio controlled differentiation of buds. Higher auxin concentrations also stimulated root initiation and growth. These results can be summarized by the data presented in Figure 98.

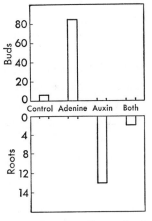

Figure 98 The effects of adenine, naphthaleneacetic acid, and both on the formation of buds and roots on tobacco stem segments in tissue cultures. (*From Leopold, A.C. Auxins and Plant Growth. University of California Press, 1955.*)

The relationships between auxin and growth by no means constitute the entire picture in the physiology of a growing plant cell. Recently microchemical and chromatographic analyses have revealed interesting shifts in the concentrations of various amino acids during cell division and cell elongation (63). Cells in the meristem are high in arginine, lysine, glutamine, and glutamic acid, while older elongating cells are high in asparagine and aspartic acid. Furthermore, as young cells undergo elongation, their protein nitrogen increases, which may indicate an actual increase in the total protoplasm as the cell elongates. Dry weight and protein increase in parallel fashion until cell elongation ceases. During cell differentiation, however, protein decreases. These relationships are brought out by data from studies on growth of various regions of pea roots (Figure 99).

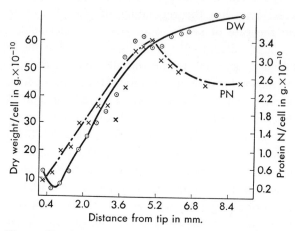

Figure 99 Average dry weight (DW) and protein nitrogen (PN) of cells at various distances from the root tip of the pea. *(From Brown, R. et al. Symposia of the Society for Experimental Biology. No. 6, 1952.)*

From the same studies, trends in respiration and enzyme activity are shown in Figures 100 and 101.

In summary one can begin to postulate some concepts in a generalized manner regarding the mechanisms of growth in the plant cell. In such concepts auxin would be viewed as a "trigger agent" which acts through an unknown enzyme system in regulating a highly active and dynamic metabolic system in living cells. A simplified scheme might be:

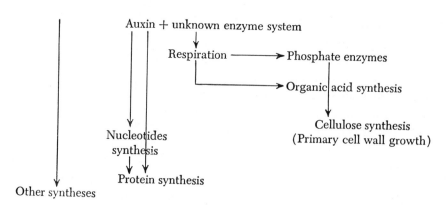

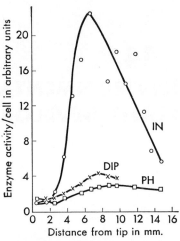

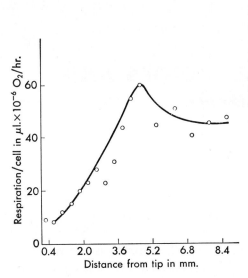

Figure 100 Average respiration per cell at various distances from the root tip of the pea. *(From Brown, R. et al. Symposia of the Society for Experimental Biology. No. 6, 1952.)*

Figure 101 Average activity per cell of invertase (IN), dipeptidase (DIP), and phosphotase (PH) at various distances from the root tip of pea. *(From Brown, R. et al. Symposia of the Society for Experimental Biology. No. 6, 1952.)*

In all probability, primary cell wall growth is a special metabolic pathway of the over-all growth mechanism in plant cells. It would seem, moreover, that the main metabolic system is one common to all living protoplasm, plant and animal, with hormones and enzyme systems being different but having in common a similar biochemical process which features an interlocking respiration-protein metabolism accompanied by carbohydrate and lipid degradation.

14.
ENVIRONMENTAL FACTORS AND PLANT DEVELOPMENT

As has been previously pointed out, plant growth is controlled by the interaction of genetic and environmental factors. It was emphasized also that growth involves most of the bioprocesses occurring within the living cell and is regulated by plant hormones. The basic pattern of growth, we may say, is determined by the heredity of a plant, and the detailed expression of that pattern is influenced by such environmental factors as light, temperature, water, essential minerals, CO_2, and O_2. Water, essential minerals, CO_2, and O_2 have already been discussed in relationship to growth (see Chapters 5, 6, and 11). Light and temperature will be examined in some detail in this chapter because so far only brief mention has been made of these two very important factors.

Light.

Intensity, quality, and duration of light (length of light and dark periods during a 24 hour day) all affect plant growth. The main effect of light intensity on plant growth is an indirect one. Intensity, or the total energy of the various parts of the spectrum which reach the earth's surface, may vary not only in different parts of the world, but also at different times. Such variations may exert direct effects on plant growth. These changes in solar radiation have not been studied sufficiently to learn exactly how they affect growth.

The indirect effect of light intensity on plant growth comes about in large degree through the relationship of light intensity to the rate of photosynthesis. Light intensity must be high enough to cause an excess of sugar in the leaves above that used by the various bioprocesses in the

228

living leaf cells. This accumulated sugar which is available for translocation to the various growing areas of the plant is called photosynthate.
The best way to understand how available photosynthate affects growth
is to study data which various
investigators have obtained.
F. W. Went has shown that
the rate of stem elongation of
the tomato plant during the
night hours is related to the
light intensity of the light
period (Figure 102). The
English plant physiologist,
Blackman, has shown interesting relationships among
growth, leaf area, and light
intensity for sunflower, buckwheat, peas, tomato, clover,

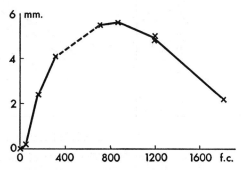

Figure 102 Stem growth in darkness of tomato plants after exposure to various intensities
of light for 6 hours. (*From Went, F.W.* American Journal of Botany. *31:597–618, 1944.*)

and several native species. By means of statistical treatment of his data,
Blackman expressed the relationship of light to growth by the following
interactions:

1. Net assimilation rate (NAR) = rate of increase in total plant weight/
   leaf area/week
2. Leaf area ratio (LAR) = total leaf area/total plant weight
3. Relative growth rate (RGR) = (NAR) × (LAR)

These relationships for tomato are illustrated in Figure 103. These
data show that plant growth increases with the log. of light intensity.
Since growth is related logarithmically to light intensity, one must increase light intensity tenfold to obtain corresponding increases in growth.
Thus these data should present sufficient evidence to the student that
photosynthate is one of the principal factors controlling growth and
that photosynthate concentration, in turn, is dependent on leaf area
and incident light intensity.

The above relationships are based upon recent studies, yet the
original experimental evidence can easily be established from one of the
oldest investigations in plant physiology. Van Helmont (1577–1644)
showed that the bulk of the dry matter in green plants did not originate
from the soil minerals (review Figure 23). Despite this long-established
fact as to the origin of dry matter in green plants, some persons still hold
the idea that plant yield is the result of food that comes from the soil.

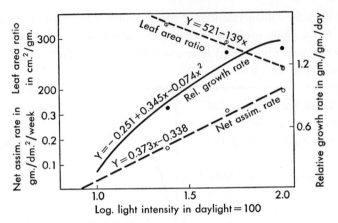

Figure 103 The effects of various light intensities on the net assimilation rate, leaf-area ratio, and the relative growth rate. *(From Blackman, G.E. and G.L. Wilson. Annals of Botany, New Series 1951. 15:373–408.)*

Of course, a deficiency of any of the essential minerals will limit yield, but so will inadequate light, water, oxygen, carbon dioxide, and unfavorable temperature. Data obtained from a study of the effects of nitrate level and light intensity on the yield of vegetative parts and bolls of cotton plants (Table 33) clearly show that increasing nitrate level will not cause boll growth when light intensity is low (1,000 foot candles).

Table 33 Effects of various levels of nitrate and low and high light intensities on the yield of vegetative parts and bolls of the cotton plant. *(From Eaton, F. M. and N. E. Rigler. Plant Physiol. 20:380–411. 1945.)*

NITRATE IN NUTRIENT SOLUTION	Low light STEMS AND LEAVES	BOLLS	High light STEMS AND LEAVES	BOLLS
m.e./l.	gm.	gm.	gm.	gm.
1	128	117	107	170
4	319	153	382	458
16	328	150	367	468
64	239	142	252	370

The relationship of light intensity to boll growth is but one of many examples which can be shown between available photosynthate and growth. Others will be considered later when growth correlations are discussed.

In addition to indirectly affecting growth through control of available photosynthate, light has important direct effects on plant growth.

These can be discussed as photomorphogenic and photoperiodic effects. Photomorphogenic effects are the responses of various plant parts to the various portions of the spectrum (quality of light). In general the blue (430–470 mμ), the red (650–700 mμ), and the far-red (735 mμ) portions have been most carefully studied (review Figure 54). These portions of the spectrum either inhibit or promote the growth of oat coleoptiles, stem elongation, leaf expansion, hypocotyl growth, straightening of the plumular hook, and root initiation. Red light inhibits hypocotyl growth, but it accelerates or stimulates straightening of the plumular hook and leaf expansion. The far-red reverses the red stimulation effects. Stem elongation is sometimes inhibited by red light, while in other circumstances red light increases stem elongation. Blue light effects on stem growth are similar to that of red light. In soybean, blue light inhibits stem growth, whereas red light stimulates it (Figure 104). Simi-

Figure 104 The effects of equal intensities of white fluorescent, incandescent, and water-filtered incandescent radiation on stem elongation of Biloxi soybeans. (*From Withrow, A.P. and Withrow, R.B. Plant Physiol. 22:494–513, 1947.*)

Figure 105 Buckwheat plants grown in various artificial light sources as compared with sunlight. (A) Left to right, sun, neon lamp, incandescent. (B) Left to right, sun, sodium vapor, incandescent. (C) Left to right, sun, mercury vapor, incandescent. *(From Crocker, William.* Growth of Plants. *Reinhold Publishing Corp., 1948.)*

lar results were obtained with buckwheat plants (Figure 105). However, other studies with oat, pea, bean, and barley internode growth have shown that red light inhibits stem elongation. These variations in results are not fully understood, but they strongly suggest a control of auxin activation or auxin destruction by means of a photoreaction. Since the active portion of the spectrum (part of spectrum that affects a photochemical process) is at 660 mμ, it would suggest a pigment in plant cells which absorbs energy at this wavelength. It should be pointed out that this active portion of the spectrum is similar for promoting lettuce seed germination and, as we shall see shortly, for photoinduction regulation of flowering. Likewise, the far-red reversal is the same.

Such studies as these, plus comparison of plants grown in darkness and in light, have led to several erroneous ideas. One such concept is that light inhibits growth. This is not true. Careful studies have shown that growth is about equal in the light and dark for stem elongation in oat seedlings (66). Another fallacious notion is that light retards growth of stems and leaves under natural conditions during the daylight hours. Ultraviolet light is said to be responsible for this inhibition of growth. Actually the earth's atmosphere permits only a small portion of ultraviolet and infrared radiation to reach the earth's surface (Figure 106).

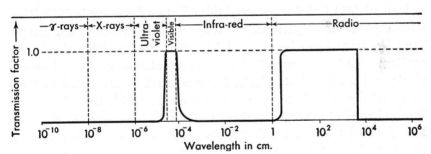

Figure 106   The transmission coefficient of the earth's atmosphere for electromagnetic waves of different lengths. *(From Odum, E.P. Fundamentals of Ecology. W.B. Saunders Co., 1953.)*

Furthermore, data from studies by Thut and Loomis (67) show that full summer sunlight did not inhibit growth of corn and other plants. Instead light increased growth by increasing photosynthesis and temperature (Figure 107). Growth during daylight hours was retarded only when excessive transpiration caused internal water deficits. Growth in open habitats may be controlled by water deficits within the plant.

Length of day affects the growth and development of plants. Garner

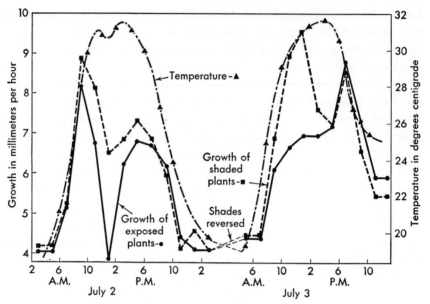

Figure 107   Height growth of corn plants as affected by light intensity, temperature, and relative humidity. Available soil moisture was probably near a pF. of 2.7 in these experiments. *(From Thut, H.F. and W.E. Loomis,* Plant Physiology. *19:117–130, 1944.)*

and Allard (47) first demonstrated this effect on flowering in 1920. They introduced the term photoperiodism for plant responses to day length. Plants in general can be grouped into three photoperiodic classes, according to their requirements for flowering: short-day plants, long-day plants, and indeterminate plants. Later research demonstrated that the photoperiodic flowering response was concerned with the initiation of floral primordia in the bud meristems. Research in the past 15 years has been directed toward an understanding of how photoperiodism controls the shift in meristematic activity from the differentiation of vegetative primordia to that of floral primordia. This is the primary step in the development of reproductive structures. Photoperiodism can also affect growth of macroscopic flower buds and their subsequent development into mature flowers or inflorescences. The discussion here will be concerned mainly with floral initiation.

Short-day plants generally require light periods of less than 12 to 15 hours, while long-day plants generally require light periods of 12 hours or more to induce floral initiation. Indeterminate plants are those in which floral initiation is independent of photoperiodism. Some examples of each of these three classes are presented in Table 34. More recently Garner and Allard have proposed a fourth category, intermediate

Table 34 Examples of species of plants sensitive to photoperiods for flower initiation. *(From Leopold, A. C. Quart. Rev. Biol. 26:247–263. 1951.)*

SPECIES		INVESTIGATOR AND WHEN ESTABLISHED
LONG-DAY PLANTS		
Plants specifically requiring long days:		
Anethum graveolens, L.	dill	Hamner & Naylor, 1939
Baeria chrysostoma, Fish & Meyer		Sivori & Went, 1944
Beta vulgaris, L.	sugar beet	Stout, 1945
Hordeum vulgare, L.	Wintex barley	Borthwick et al, 1942
Hyoscyamus niger, L.	black henbane	Melchers, 1936
Papaver somniferum, L.	opium poppy	Khlebnikova, 1941
Plantago lanceolata, L.	plantain	Snyder, 1948
Rudbeckia bicolor, Nutt.	coneflower	Murneek, 1940
Silphium trifoliatum, L.	rosinweed	Allard & Garner, 1940
Spinacea oleracea, L.	spinach	Garner & Allard, 1920
Plants promoted by long days:		
Allium cepa, L.	onion (line "74")	Scully et al, 1945
Centaurea cyanus, L.	cornflower	Funke, 1948
Lactuca sativa, L.	lettuce	Bremer, 1931
Linum usitatissimum, L.	flax	Nuttonson, 1948
Parthenium argentatum, Gray	guayule	Whitehead & Mitchell, 1943
Phleum pratense, L.	timothy	Hamner & Naylor, 1939
Poa pratensis, L.	bluegrass	Peterson & Loomis, 1949
Ricinus communis, L.	castor bean	Scully & Domingo, 1947
Solanum tuberosum, L.	McCormick potato	Werner, 1941
Triticum aestivum, L.	Marquis wheat	Garner & Allard, 1923
SHORT-DAY PLANTS		
Plants specifically requiring short days:		
Amaranthus caudatus, L.	milme	Fuller, 1949
Ambrosia artemisiifolia, L.	ragweed	Garner & Allard, 1920
Chrysanthemum morifolium, Ram.		Cajlachjan, 1936
Euchlaena mexicana, Schrad.	Chalco teosinte	Emerson, 1924
Euphorbia pulcherrima, Willd	poinsettia	Garner & Allard, 1923
Glycine max, Merr.	Biloxi soybean	Garner & Allard, 1920
Kalanchoe blossfeldiana, Poellnitz.		Harder & v. Witsch, 1940
Nicotiana tabacum, L.	Maryland mammoth tobacco	Garner & Allard, 1920
Perilla frutescens, var. *nankinensis,* Bailey		Cajlachjan, 1936
Xanthium pennsylvanicum, Wallr.	cocklebur	Hamner & Bonner, 1938
Plants promoted by short days:		
Ananas comosus, Merr.	pineapple	van Overbeek, 1946
Coffea arabica, L.	coffee	Franco, 1941
Cosmos bipinnatus, Cav.		Garner & Allard, 1923
Fragaria chiloensis, Duchesne	strawberry	Murneek, 1948
Glycine max, Merr.	Mandarin soybean	Garner & Allard, 1920
Gossypium hirsutum, L.	cotton	Sen, 1944
Oryza sativa, L.	rice	Sircar, 1948
Primula malacoides, Franch.	primrose	Post, 1936
Saccharum officinarum, L.	sugar cane	Yusuff & Dutt, 1945
Salvia splendens, Ker.	scarlet sage	Withrow & Biebel, 1936

plants, which flower on photoperiods of 12 to 14 hours, but not on longer or shorter photoperiods.

Before further discussion of photoperiodism, it should be pointed out that certain stages or phases of growth follow in an orderly sequence in plants. These stages of growth were first clearly demonstrated by Klebs in 1918. He showed that a vegetative phase must precede floral initiation, and he called this the ripe-to-flower stage. The ripe-to-flower stage may be reached when an annual has produced a certain number of leaves, whereas in fruit trees it is usually reached only after several years of vegetative growth. When the ripe-to-flowering condition is completed, stage two, floral initiation, occurs which is then followed by stage three, flower bud development and opening. One of the most interesting questions to be answered in plant physiology is why the ripe-to-flower stage is so variable and what is the nature of the process involved. Gardner and Loomis (46) have listed the three phases of flowering as induction of the flowering condition, initiation and early growth of the inflorescences, and complete development of the flowers. A different photoperiod may be required for each phase and, as will be shown later, a combination of photoperiods and temperature may be necessary for complete flowering.

Photoperiodism, as first explained and as the name denotes, was thought to mean that flowering was the result of certain durations of light hours or day-length. From studies on the cocklebur plant, a short-day species, this early concept has been modified and more precise knowledge has been gained regarding the nature of floral initiation. Some of this information can best be summarized in a series of diagrams. First, if a cocklebur plant has its leaves removed, exposure to a short-day photoinduction cycle will not cause floral initiation (Figure 108). If only one leaf is exposed, however, floral initiation will occur. The inference is that some process must originate in the leaves to set into motion floral initiation in the bud meristem. Branched cockleburs, as shown in Figure 109, can be made to flower by the translocation of a chemical substance from the leaves to the branch of the leafless shoot. Furthermore, grafting experiments showed that the chemical substance could move across graft unions (Figure 110). It is now accepted that a process originating in leaves which are exposed to the proper photoinduction cycle will cause the formation of a flowering hormone called florigen. The florigen is then translocated via the phloem to the bud meristem.

Other grafting experiments have enabled plant physiologists to establish that florigen is the same chemical substance in all species of

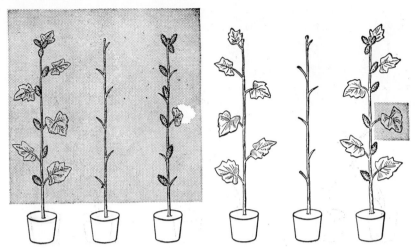

Figure 108 Relationship between photoinduction and leaf in causing floral initiation in the cocklebur. Note, one leaf if exposed to proper induction will cause floral initiation. *(From drawing by Eric Mose.* Scientific American *186:49–57, 1952.)*

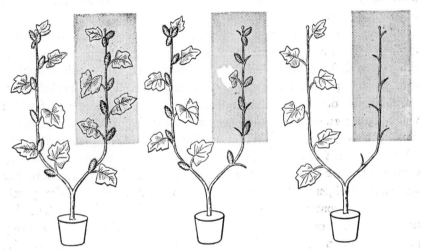

Figure 109 Translocation of florigen from photoinduced branch to non-photoinduced branch in the cocklebur shows florigen has origin in leaf. *(From drawing by Eric Mose.* Scientific American *186:49–57, 1952.)*

plants thus far investigated. Thus if a long-day plant is exposed to long-day photoinduction cycles, florigen will be synthesized. Then if a leaf is grafted to a short-day plant which has not been photoinduced, the short-day plant will flower. Likewise, a short-day plant leaf photoinduced can have its florigen transmitted by grafting to a non-photoinduced long-day

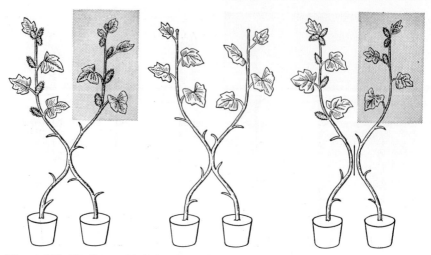

Figure 110 Grafting of photoinduced branch to a non-photoinduced branch of cocklebur shows that florigen can be translocated across a graft. *(From drawing by Eric Mose.* Scientific American *186:49–57, 1952.)*

plant. As yet the chemical nature of florigen is unknown and all attempts to isolate the floral initiation chemical stimulus have failed.

It has now been established by research on photoperiodism that the process causing the formation of florigen in leaves is not only the result of a definite light period, but also it must be combined with a definite dark period. For short-day plants, a definite dark period is required. If this dark period is interrupted by light of low intensity, florigen will not be formed. On the other hand, long-day plants also require a definite light period, but an interruption of the dark period does not inhibit florigen formation. Therefore, with long-day plants, a short day exposure followed by a dark period interrupted by light of low intensity will cause florigen synthesis. The distinctive feature of short-day plants is that a long continuous dark period is essential for flowering. The distinctive feature of long-day plants is that long night periods entirely prevent flowering but long nights interrupted by light, even briefly, cause the inhibitive effect of the night to be lost and the plants flower. This can be summarized by the diagrams of Figure 111. Consequently, it would seem that night length is the critical factor in flowering, and that a more logical terminology would designate these long-night and short-night plants.

From the above statements, one could infer that floral initiation is controlled by the length of the dark period, and that light does not play a role in floral initiation. The evidence does not support this concept.

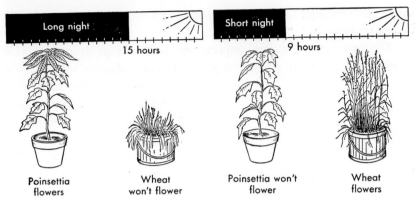

Figure 111 The effect of length of dark period on the flowering of poinsettia and wheat. (*From* U.S.D.A. Agriculture Research *1:3–6. 1953.*)

It is true that in long-day plants, long nights inhibit flowering, but is a short dark period necessary? The answer is that many long-day plants will actually flower best under conditions of continuous light. Therefore, a dark period is not a requirement for flowering in long-day plants. With short-day plants, an uninterrupted dark period is a requirement for flowering, but short-day plants also must have a light period prior to and following the uninterrupted dark period. Thus both classes of flowering plants require light for flowering.

Neither the exact role of light nor that of dark is clearly understood at the present. However, sufficient experimental data are available to show that light is necessary for the synthesis of a photosynthate-derived substrate which is used at some stage in florigen synthesis. In short-day plants, light beyond a certain duration or during the dark period causes an inhibitory effect on florigen synthesis, whereas with long-day plants the additional light promotes florigen synthesis. The first light reaction in florigen synthesis is dependent on high-light intensity, while the second one occurs at low light intensity. The low-light intensity effect is thus a photoreaction probably involving some plant pigment. The use of various wavelengths of light has shown that this photoreaction is activated by red-light (Figure 112). This is the same action spectrum that was previously discussed for photomorphogenic responses and lettuce seed germination. The pigment involved in these photoreactions has not been isolated, but it has been postulated to be a porphyrin compound of the protochlorophyll type. The low light intensity required is 100 foot candles for 1 minute or 0.1 foot candles for 9 hours. The photosynthate-substrate requirement on the other hand is proportional to the light intensity and time and is illustrated by data on soybeans in Figure 113.

The complete light-dark requirement is known as inductive cycle. Cocklebur, a short-day plant, requires only one inductive cycle for the maximum number of flowers, but all other plants studied so far require more than one inductive cycle. The number of inductive cycles varies in different species of plants and may require several weeks or several days. This relationship is brought out by the data on soybeans in Figure 114.

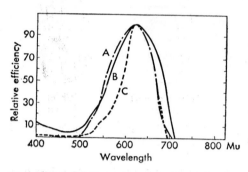

Figure 112 Action spectrum for photoinduction of long nights effect in flowering of (A) Barley, (B) Soybean, and (C) Cocklebur. *(From Leopold, A.C. Quarterly Review of Biology. 26:247–263, 1951.)*

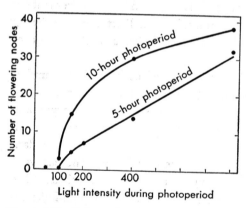

Figure 113 Relationship between light intensity during light period and number of flowers initiated in the short-day plant soybean. *(From Leopold, A.C. Quarterly Review of Biology. 26:247–263, 1951.)*

Temperature affects both the light and dark period reactions in florigen synthesis. The optimum temperature may be different for each period but, in general, the dark reaction is most sensitive. Soybeans will not respond to inductive cycles if night temperature is below 70°F. Night temperatures above 70°F. will inhibit flowering in some species, such as poinsettia. Depending on temperature, other plants such as henbane can flower either under short- or long-day conditions (Figure 115).

Our present knowledge does not permit a formulation of the exact mechanism of photoperiodism. It is known that the florigen synthesis occurs in actively growing leaves and that the florigen is translocated to bud meristems. Furthermore, if the florigen is to cause floral primordia initiation, the meristem must be in an active state of growth. Florigen synthesis is dependent on two interrelated processes,—one initiated in light (A) and for short-day plants completed in the dark (B). A and B give rise to C, that is, the flowering hormone. The B portion of florigen synthesis in long-day plants is completed when light of low intensity occurs for a certain number of hours, if the dark period is short, in continuous light, and in an interrupted dark period. Several theories have been advanced to explain the above sequences. One hypothesis is based on the effect of auxin on flowering. For short-day plants, an application of auxin to the photoinduced leaves causes an inhibition of florigen and thus prevents floral primordia initiation in the bud meristem, but stimulates vegetative primordia initiation. This is, then, an auxin-florigen balance concept. Other evidence to support this hypothesis is that an application of an anti-auxin compound will substitute for a photoinduction cycle. The effect of auxin applications to long-day plants is not inhibitory. On the contrary, some investigations support a stimulatory effect. The evidence is not yet sufficient to apply the auxin-florigen balance theory to long-day plants. Other theories discount the role of auxin in floral initiation and explain florigen synthesis as being inhibited or completed by sequences of light and dark. For a more complete treatment of photoperiodism and how the present information has accumulated by many carefully planned experiments, the

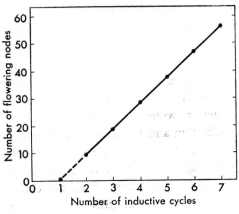

Figure 114 Relationship between number of photoinduction cycles and number of flowers initiated in the short-day plant soybean. (*From Leopold, A.C. Quarterly Review of Biology. 26:247–263, 1951.*)

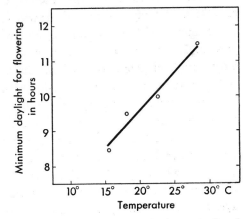

Figure 115 Modification of photoperiodic effect on flowering of henbane by temperature. (*From Leopold, A.C. Quarterly Review of Biology. 26:247–263, 1951.*)

reader is referred to the many excellent reviews available (50, 52, 54, 55, 56).

An older concept about flowering was that flowering came about as a result of a certain critical balance of carbohydrates and nitrogen in the plant. This balance was supposed to be controlled by means of nitrogen fertilizer applications. Too much soil nitrogen was thought to stimulate vegetative growth and inhibit flowering. This concept is completely erroneous, and substantial evidence now shows floral initiation cannot be caused by a manipulation of the C/N ratio. It should be kept in mind, however, that among other things, the development and growth of the flower buds are dependent on nitrogen as is true for the growth of any plant part.

Whereas floral initiation is a florigen-initiated process, development of the flower buds is a growth process dependent upon adequate auxin, minerals, water, and photosynthate. After development of the flower, pollination and fertilization must occur for seed and fruit growth. Pollination and fertilization result in the initiation of seed growth and, with seed growth, auxin synthesis occurs in the growing embryo. The synthesized auxin diffuses from the embryo into the ovulary tissue and is necessary for fruit growth except in parthenocarpic fruits. Without embryo growth, auxin is not synthesized and fruit growth will not occur. Furthermore, the embryo auxin diffusing down the phloem tissue of the fruit stalk prevents abscission. Any factor which limits this sequence will cause small fruit growth and fruit drop. The abscission of flowers, however, is the result of other factors and will be taken up during the discussion of temperature and growth correlations.

Photoperiod affects vegetative growth as well as reproductive growth. Height growth of short day plants is generally restricted by short days and promoted by long days. Long-day plants develop only as leaf rosettes during short photoperiods. The development of tubers, fleshy roots, and bulbs is markedly influenced by the length of the photoperiod. Tubers of potato and Jerusalem artichoke and fleshy roots of beets and radish form abundantly during short days. Onion bulbs on the other hand develop best under long-day photoperiods. The runners of the strawberry plant develop during long days while short days are inhibiting. The shorter days of autumn promote leaf-fall (asbscission layer formation in the petiole) and dormancy in the buds of some species of woody perennials.

In Chapters 9 and 14 we have shown how certain wave lengths of radiation cause a diversity of photochemical reactions in higher plants. These photochemical reactions cause chlorophyll synthesis, photosynthesis, phototropism, photomorphogenesis, germination of light sensitive seed, and photoperiodism. A summary is presented in Table 34-A.

Table 34-A The principal photochemical reactions of higher plants. (*Modified from Withrow, R. B. and W. H. Klein. Unpublished table. 1957.*)

PHOTO-PROCESS	REACTION OR RESPONSE	PRODUCTS	SITE OF ACTION	PRINCIPAL MAXIMA OF ACTION SPECTRUM mμ
Chlorophyll synthesis	Reduction of proto-chlorophyll	Chlorophyll *a* and *b*	Chloro-plasts	445—blue 650—red
Photo-synthesis	Dissociation of H_2O into 2[H] and O, reduction of CO_2	Unknown reductant [H] phosphoglycer-ote, trioses, hexoses	Chloro-plasts	435—blue 675—red
Photo-oxidation	Phototropism Protoplasmic viscosity Photorecovery	Oxidized auxin, auxin system and/or other cellular components	Flavins or carote-noids	440 to 480—blue
Red reac-tions	Seed germination Seedling and young shoot growth Photoperiodism	Biochemistry un-known	Possibly a tetrapyr-role	Forward, 660—red Reversal, 710 and 730—far red

Artificial Light and Plant Growth.

Artificial light assumes importance when plants are grown within controlled-environment rooms in plant physiology research, and for certain floricultural crops. As pointed out previously, photosynthesis, morphogenic reactions, and photoperiodic responses are all activated by the visible spectrum or portions thereof. All evidence leads to the conclusion that optimum plant growth is best in full sunlight which includes all the visible spectrum with an intensity of 10,000 foot candles. To duplicate sunlight with artificial visible radiation has been a difficult problem.

Incandescent-filament, fluorescent, mercury arc, carbon arc, sodium vapor, and neon lamps have been tried as sources of artificial light for plant growth on many species of plants. In general plants under a single source of artificial light have shown poor growth. The reason for this is best explained by examining the spectral energy distribution of various sources of artificial light. This information is summarized in Table 35. It is apparent that none of these approaches sunlight. Growth of some species has been successful with combinations of fluorescent and incandescent-filament radiation. Such controlled-environment rooms are expensive to operate, however, and require temperature controls. A combination of fluorescent and incandescent-filament radiation has provided satisfactory light quality but not sufficient intensity. A summary of the more complete data on artificial radiation-plant growth studies is presented in Table 36. Maximum intensity of light attained would seem to be not more than 1,200 foot candles. This is satisfactory for some species, but sufficient information is not available to infer that many species will complete their life cycles in artificial sources of radiation.

The growth of floricultural crops under sources of artificial radiation alone has been practical for only a limited number of species. However, many greenhouses use supplemental artificial light with successful results. The main use is to control flowering, and for this purpose low light intensities are sufficient. Since the action spectrum for the low light intensity reaction in photoperiodism is from the red portion of the spectrum, incandescent-filament lights are best suited for this purpose. Extension of day length by artificial light is now unnecessary, however, since the same purpose can be accomplished by irradiating the plants in the middle of the dark period for 15 minutes with incandescent-filament lights of sufficient intensity to emit 100 foot candles at the leaf surface. For a more detailed discussion, the student is referred to the articles of Crocker (43) and to Parker and Borthwick (58).

The Effects of Ionizing Radiation on Plant Growth.

The ionizing radiations are the alpha, beta, gamma, X-ray, proton, and neutron radiations. These ionizing radiations are now available from many sources; this enables their use in studying their effect on plant growth. The effects of X-rays upon plants and animals have been studied for many years. It was recognized early in this century that X-rays could induce changes in the chromosomes of nuclei. These genetic changes resulted in mutations, and X-rays have been invaluable tools in the science of genetics. However, with the initiation of the atomic energy period and with new sources of ionizing radiations and the release of such radiation by atomic and hydrogen explosions, the entire field of radiobiology has assumed great importance. Genetic studies had already established what would happen to the nuclear material of plant cells exposed to nuclear explosion, but it also became necessary to take into account that physiological changes would likewise occur. Radiation damage of a physiological nature has been more thoroughly investigated and is better understood in animals than in plants.

Ionizing radiations affect plant cells only if there is an energy interchange between these particles and the cells through which they pass. In the case of beta, gamma, and X-ray particles, all members give up

Table 35 Radiation and spectral energy distribution from various sources of artificial light. (*From data of the General Electric Co., Engineering Lamp Div.*)

	ULTRA-VIOLET	VIOLET BLUE	GREEN YELLOW	ORANGE RED	INFRA RED	IN-TENSITY	LAMP WATTS IN THE VISIBLE
	per cent	*per cent*	*per cent*	*per cent*	*per cent*	*foot candle*	*per cent*
Sunlight	5.0	28.0	28.0	44.0	55.0	10,000.0	. . .
Sodium lamp 180W	0.02	0.00	98.00	1.8	. . .	929.0	12.2
Hg-Arc, 400W	1.10	0.96	98.00	1.0	. . .	1,394.0	11.0
Fluorescent 40 W							
Cool White	0.75	4.3	81.0	14.0	. . .	204.0	19.0
Blue	1.30	18.0	80.0	2.8	. . .	121.0	21.9
Green	0.40	2.7	96.0	0.9	. . .	306.0	19.6
Pink	0.24	8.0	56.0	44.0	. . .	111.0	14.3
Gold	. . .	0.0	80.0	20.0	. . .	176.0	12.0
Red	. . .	0.0	12.0	88.0	. . .	9.2	2.5
Filament lamps							
40 Watts	. . .	2.9	72.0	25.0	76.0	43.2	7.2
100 Watts	. . .	3.1	72.0	24.5	80.0	150.0	9.8
500 Watts	. . .	3.3	73.0	24.0	79.0	919.0	12.0
1000 Watts	. . .	3.5	73.0	23.5	81.0	1,997.0	12.5

The header groups: "Distribution" spans the five spectral columns, and within that "Visible" spans Violet Blue, Green Yellow, Orange Red.

their energy to the molecules of the cell via the passage of fast electrons. The result is ionization of the molecules, which causes a chemical change. Alpha particles and neutrons cause a similar electronic excitation. The excitation or ionization of a molecule in a living cell occurs only when a radiation particle and a molecule collide, which is a chance encounter. Only a few of all the molecules of the cell are ionized. How do such small chemical changes cause so much damage to living cells? The answer to this question is a matter of opinion or theory at present. The most promising theory is based on the abundance of water in a physiologically active cell, which is much more susceptible to radiation damage than is a dormant cell of low water and high solute content. Ionizing radiation decomposes water, and some of the OH radicals combine to form H_2O_2 which is an oxidizing agent. The hydrogen peroxide disrupts the metabolism of the cell by oxidizing certain enzymes to an inactive form. The general response of plants to ionizing radiation is indicated by various kinds of abnormal growth such as inhibition of meristematic activity and cell elongation, with a reduction in growth in proportion to dosage of radiation. Many kinds of growth responses result, such as destruction of apical dominance with accompanying lateral bud growth, abnormal

Table 36 A summary of results by various investigators on growth of plants in controlled-environment rooms.

AUTHOR	REFERENCE	SOURCE OF ENERGY	LIGHT READING AT	LIGHT INTENSITY *f c*	SPECIES OF PLANT	LENGTH OF LIGHT PERIOD *hrs.*	TEMPERATURE DAY °C	TEMPERATURE NIGHT °C
Parker and Borthwick	Plant Physiol. 25:86–91. 1950.	fluorescent and incandescent	18″ from source	1,000.0	soybean	16	26.7	21.1
Camus and Went	Amer. Jour. Bot. 39:521–528. 1952.	fluorescent and incandescent	stem apex	250.0 to 1,200.0	tobacco	8	varied	varied
Withrow and Withrow	Plant Physiol. 22:494–513. 1947.	fluorescent and incandescent	at surface of pot	800.0	soybeans spinach tomato	15 15 15	20–25 20–25 20–25	20–25 20–25 20–25
Went	Amer. Jour. Bot. 31:135–150. 1944.	fluorescent and incandescent	stem apex	450.0	tomato	8	varied	varied
Crocker	Growth of Plants. Reinhold. New York. 1948.	mercury-vapor and incandescent	unknown	900.0	many species	5 to 24	26–20	26–20

leaf growth, fasciation, changes in leaf pigments, and delay in flowering. These effects suggest that auxin metabolism is affected by ionizing radiations. The effect of X-ray irradiation on the growth of tomato plants is shown in Figure 116.

Figure 116   Tomato plants 42 days after X-irradiation. Growth is somewhat retarded at 2,000 r and decreases with higher dosages until it is completely retarded at 24,000 r. (*From Gunckel, J.E. and Sparrow, A.H. Abnormal and Pathological Plant Growth. Brookhaven Symposia in Biology No. 6, 1954. U.S. Dept. of Commerce.*)

One of the most interesting ideas that has emerged from radiation studies on plants has been the speculation that low dosages of ionizing radiation from radioactive isotopes would stimulate plant growth. Biddulph (39) in a recent review of this concept has concluded that no stimulation of growth occurs as a result of radiation.

This brief summary is intended only to introduce the subject of ionizing radiation. For a more complete summary of information, the article by Kornberg (49) and the books by Lea (51) and Nickson (57) should be consulted.

Temperature.

The bioprocesses of living cells, including growth, occur within rather narrow limits of temperature. Cellular metabolic activity, generally speaking, ceases at 0°C. or at 40°C. However, living tissue can survive at temperatures as high as 50°C. and as low as within a few degrees of absolute zero if the cells are in a state of inactivity such as in dry seeds and spores.

The tolerance of living cells to temperature extremes is closely related to the amount of water in the cells and to the physicochemical condition of the protoplasm. Injury to cells from temperatures above 40°C. is due to the irreversible inactivation of the enzymes. Since enzymes are primarily protein molecules, inactivation is caused by protein denaturation. Injury to cells from temperatures below 0°C. is due to the formation of ice crystals in the cells. Irrespective of cause, tolerance to temperature extremes is at an optimum when the cells have low moisture contents.

Injury and death to cells at temperatures above 0°C. but below 8°C. are not due to a direct effect of low temperature but to the indirect effect of temperature on water absorption by roots. Under these conditions the above ground plant parts lose water by transpiration, but because of slow diffusion of water into the roots, the tissues suffer from a water deficit. This condition results in injury to or death of the cells by desiccation.

Injury or death of living plant cells usually results at temperatures below 0°C. if the cells are in an active state of growth. The mechanism that causes injury or death is directly related to what happens in cells when ice crystal formation occurs. One type of damage comes about as a result of ice crystal formation in the cell walls. Ice crystals in the cell walls cause a diffusion of water from the protoplasm into the cell walls. Thus plasmolysis occurs and the cells die of desiccation or salting-out of protoplasmic proteins. The second type of injury is a result of ice crystal formation in the protoplasm itself, and causes physical damage to the proteins. The protein molecules are thought to become disorganized and are unable to recover their normal orientation.

It is well known that plants can tolerate temperatures below 0°C. Many perennials survive such temperatures in the colder climates of the world. This survival is due to the fact that the protoplasm in their living tissues is resistant to ice crystal formation. Before these tissues become resistant or hardened, a certain exposure to temperatures above 0°C. is necessary. This hardening period requirement usually must extend for several days. The response to low temperature by hardening of the protoplasm is not characteristic of all species, however, and it is genetic in nature. Since cold tolerance is genetic, plant breeders have been able to select cold tolerant varieties for many agronomic and horticultural crops. The exact physiological nature of hardening of protoplasm has not been elucidated. Hardening has been shown to be related to the physicochemical condition of the proteins, and more recently by Siminovitch and Briggs (59) to the starch content of cells. These workers demonstrated that cells with high starch content were more susceptible to freezing injury than were cells with low starch content.

As already mentioned, the tissues of living cells of some species of higher plants are not damaged by temperatures below the freezing point of water. Before these cells are resistant to freezing damage, they enter into a physiological state known as hardening. Hardening is induced by subjecting the plant to night temperatures of 0° to 5°C. for a period of several days. Plant cells that are in a state of hardiness have their cellular water contents lowered, sugar concentrations increased, and their osmotic pressures raised. Such cells have increased permeability to water, decreased structural viscosity of cytoplasm, increased hydrophily of the protoplasmic colloids, and reduced liability to coagulation.

Response of a plant species to low temperature induction by hardening is an inherited characteristic. Temperate zone species such as dogwood, tulip tree, red cedar, maple, and beech are hardy while such subtropical trees as acacia, royal poinciana, jack tree, camphor tree, and eucalyptus cannot be hardened. The fruit trees apple, plum, and cherry are hardy species while pear, peach, and apricot are less hardy. Citrus and persimmon cannot be hardened. Vegetable crops that can be hardened are cabbage, asparagus, carrot, radish, turnip, and peas. Beans, corn, tomato, cucumber, pepper, and squash are examples of vegetable crops that cannot be hardened. In general, temperate zone species have the property of hardiness while subtropical and tropical species do not. Many ornamentals are grown in northern climates only with special precautions such as pruning the plant back and covering with a deep mulch.

Before considering how temperature affects the rate of plant growth, we must first know how any bioprocess is affected by temperature. Most of the processes in living plant cells are the result of a series of chemical reactions, but research has shown that the velocity of a bioprocess is governed by the rate of the slowest reaction. The velocity of a chemical process is related to temperature according to van't Hoff's law which states that a rise of 10°C. will double the speed of a chemical reaction:

$$\text{Temperature coefficient } (Q_{10}) = \frac{\text{velocity at } (T° + 10°)}{\text{velocity at } T°}$$

The temperature coefficient is frequently expressed by the symbol of Q_{10}. Bioprocesses are catalyzed by enzymes. Therefore, the application of van't Hoff's law in living cells is to that of enzyme systems. Certain values obtained for enzyme systems are given in Table 37. These data show that van't Hoff's law is applicable to bioprocesses only within the temperature ranges of 0°–30°C. Above 30°C. the ratio drops off rapidly from 2 to nearly 1. The reason that van't Hoff's law is not followed at temperatures above 30°C. is because the rate of enzyme inactivation increases at a more rapid rate than does the temperature effect on the velocity of the bioprocess. For some enzyme systems, inactivation occurs at lower temperatures than 30°C. Moreover, other enzyme systems do

Table 37　The Q_{10} for certain enzyme systems. *(From Gortner, R. A., R. A. Gortner, Jr., and W. A. Gortner. Outlines of Biochemistry. John Wiley and Sons, Inc. 1949.)*

ENZYME	TEMPERATURE	Q_{10}
	°C	
Steapsin	0–10	1.50
	10–20	1.34
	20–30	1.26
Pepsin	0–10	2.60
	10–20	2.00
	30–40	1.60
	40–50	1.40
Trypsin	21–31	5.30
	31–39	5.30
Invertase	25–35	1.61
Emulsin	20–30	2.62

not double their reaction velocities for each 10°C. change because of the presence of enzyme inhibitors. An example is given by the data on starch hydrolysis in Table 38. These data show a greater loss of starch at 0°C. with an accompanying increase in per cent sucrose. In general, however, most bioprocesses follow the van't Hoff law between 0°C. and 25°C., but at temperatures above 25°C. the data must be carefully interpreted with attention given to the effect of time. For example, the rate of a bioprocess may double between 20°C. and 30°C. for a period of 2 hours, but if continued for 4 hours, the rate will decrease.

Table 38　Changes in sugar and sugar derivatives in potatoes stored at various temperatures. *(From Arreguin, B. and J. Bonner. Plant Physiol. 24:720. 1949.)*

SUBSTANCE	INITIAL AMOUNT	AMOUNT IN PER CENT DRY WT. AFTER 2 WEEKS AT			
		0°C.	9°C.	16°C.	25°C.
Starch	67.00	61.00	65.00	63.00	64.00
Sucrose	1.07	6.65	1.25	0.75	0.84

　　Examination of experimental data on the effect of temperature on growth shows that growth may be treated as an enzymatically catalyzed process. The effects of temperature on the rates of growth of lupine, corn, and watermelon are shown in Figure 117. From the lupine and corn growth curves, one can see that rates of growth increase with temperature to certain optimums and then decline. Sufficient data were not available to show this relationship for watermelon. These data indicate also that opti-

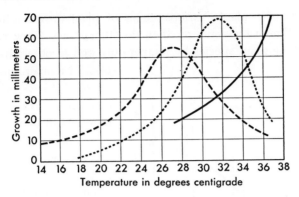

Figure 117 Effect of various temperatures on the growth of Lupine (long-dashed line), Corn (short-dashed line), and Watermelon (solid line). *(From drawing by Sara Love.* Scientific American *191:64–83, 1954.)*

mum temperatures for growth vary with species. Interpretation of the effect of temperature on growth rates, then, must be viewed with the same caution as was mentioned before for other enzyme-catalyzed processes. This is brought out clearly by the data on the growth of *Lepidium* roots (Figure 118). These data show a higher optimum temperature at 3.5 hours than at 7 and 14 hours.

In the discussion of the mechanism of the growth process (review pages 193–196), it was stated that growth is a chemical rather than a physical process. Further proof that growth is a chemical process can be obtained from the effect of temperature on the growth of corn roots at 15°C. and 25°C. (Figure 119). The rates of cell elonga-

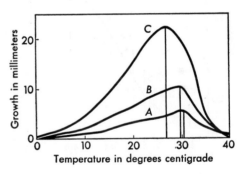

Figure 118 Relation of time to temperature effect on the growth of *Lepidium* roots. Growth after (A) 3.5 hours, (B) 7 hours, and (C) 14 hours. *(From Stiles, Walter.* An Introduction to the Principles of Plant Physiology, *2nd ed. Methuen and Co., Ltd., 1950.)*

tion for cortical cells within each of the first five 1 mm. segments of the corn radicle that were grown at 15°C. and 25°C. showed the temperature coefficient (Q_{10}) to be in the order of 2 to 4 for a rise of 10°C.

In many species of plants, the effects of temperature on total plant growth are more complex than is indicated by the growth responses of certain parts of a plant. Various stages of plant growth often require different optimum temperatures than do other stages. Flowering is controlled in some plant species by temperature and in others by combinations of temperature and photoperiod. Flowering in celery, cabbage, onions, carrots, turnips, and strawberries will not occur unless the plants are first exposed for several weeks to cool days. The studies by Thompson (55), however, do not indicate whether the response is caused by cool nights, cool days, or a combination of cool days and nights. The data in Table 39 illustrate the requirement of cool temperature to induce flowering in celery. Flowering in most species of biennials occurs only if cool temperatures follow the first growing season. Biennials placed in a warm greenhouse during the winter following the first growing season usually remain vegetative and do not flower.

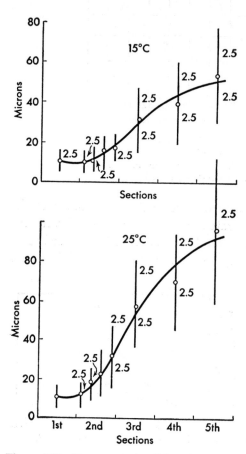

Figure 119 Mean cortical cell lengths of five 1-mm. segments of maize root tips grown at 15° C. and 25° C. The vertical lines indicate 2.5 standard deviations either side of the mean. (*From Baldovinos, Gabriel.* Growth and Differentiation in Plants. *Iowa State College Press, 1953.*)

In hyacinth, tulip, narcissus, iris, and other bulbous plants, various stages of growth occur only under specific temperature treatments (Table 40). Each stage of growth occurs in a sequence of temperature environments and suggests a cyclic growth of plants in relation to temperature. In bulbous species of plants, the nature of the cyclic growth is on an annual scale. However, F. W. Went, by means of elaborate controlled-environment chambers has demonstrated that similar temperature cycles

Table 39 Effect of exposure to relatively low temperature for 15 and 30 days on subsequent development of seedstalks of celery under three ranges of temperature. *(From Thompson, H. C. Growth and Differentiation in Plants. Iowa State College Press. 1953.)*

PRELIMINARY TREATMENT	NUMBER OF PLANTS	PERCENTAGE OF SEEDSTALKS ON DATES GIVEN			
		MARCH 20	APRIL 3	APRIL 25	MAY 8
In Medium-Temperature House (60°–70°F.)					
Check, 60°–70°F.	20	0.00	0.00	0.00	0.00
15 days 50°–60°F.	20	0.00	0.00	65.00	100.00
30 days 50°–60°F.	20	0.00	0.00	65.00	100.00
15 days 40°–50°F.	20	0.00	85.00	100.00	100.00
30 days 40°–50°F.	20	25.00	45.00	100.00	100.00
30 days 70°–80°F.	20	0.00	0.00	0.00	0.00
In Cool House (50°–60°F.)					
Check, 60°–70°F.	20	0.00	0.00	100.00	100.00
15 days 50°–60°F.	20	5.00	65.00	100.00	100.00
30 days 50°–60°F.	20	10.00	60.00	100.00	100.00
15 days 40°–50°F.	20	88.00	100.00	100.00	100.00
30 days 40°–50°F.	20	80.00	100.00	100.00	100.00
In Warm House (70°–80°F.)					
Check, 60°–70°F.	10	0.00	0.00	0.00	0.00
15 days 40°–50°F.	10	0.00	0.00	0.00	0.00
30 days 40°–50°F.	10	0.00	0.00	0.00	0.00

Table 40 Temperature requirement for various stages of growth for several species of plants. *(From Went, F. W. Ann. Rev. Plant Physiol. 1953.)*

	LEAF INITIATION	OPTIMUM TEMPERATURE FOR		
		FLOWER INITIATION	BUD DEVELOPMENT	VEGETATIVE GROWTH
	°C.	°C.	°C.	°C.
Hyacinth	34	25	13	22
Tulip	20	20	9	23
Iris	13	9	15	15
Camellia	..	30	10	..

on a daily basis are required for optimum growth at various stages for tomato, chili pepper, tobacco, and other plants. The growth and reproductive responses of plants to annual and diurnal cycles of temperature is called thermoperiodism.

Diurnal thermoperiodicity studies of tomato showed that optimum stem elongation did not occur in a constant temperature environment but required a temperature environment of 26.5°C. for the day and 20°C. for the night (Figure 120). The night temperature of 20°C. was best for early vegetative growth, but it decreased to 15°C. as the tomato reached maturity. Not only was the rate of stem elongation controlled by diurnal

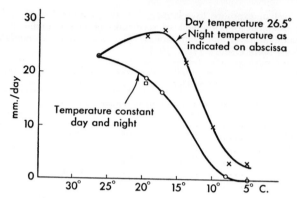

Figure 120 Relation between stem growth of tomato and variations in night temperature. *(From Went, F.W. American Journal of Botany. 31:135–150, 1944.)*

thermoperiodicity, but fruit set did not occur unless night temperatures were less than 25°C. Maximum fruit set occurred after tomato plants were exposed to 5 successive nights of 15°C. temperatures. Studies with chili peppers showed a thermoperiodic response similar to that of tomato.

In tomato and chili pepper thermoperiodic responses there is no direct experimental evidence to indicate that thermoperiodism can be a cause of florigen synthesis or of floral primordial initiation. Rather, the effect appears to be on the development of the flower buds and fruit set. Experiments with tobacco plants by Camus and Went (41), however, have given some indirect evidence that thermoperiodism may affect floral primordial initiation. In studies with such plants as chili pepper, tomato, and California poppy, Went also showed that certain night temperatures were required for each stage of vegetative and reproductive growth (Figure 121).

Another effect of temperature on flowering is the requirement of a low temperature induction period by winter varieties of cereals. Temperature induction of flowering in winter cereals is not a florigen-induced synthesis in the leaves, rather it is the result of biochemical changes in bud meristems. This temperature induction occurs at temperatures slightly above freezing and can be effective in bud meristems during germination or during vegetative growth. Experimentally this induction can cause flowering if moistened seeds, prior to germination, are placed at 3°C. for several days. This cold induction of flowering in winter cereals (and other plants) is called vernalization. Development of the flower buds, however, does not occur during the cool, short days of the winter, but

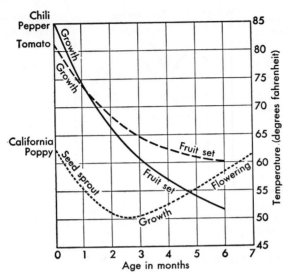

Figure 121 Optimum night temperatures for various stages in the growth and development of three annual plants are shown to differ with age and kind of plant. *(From drawing by Sara Love. Scientific American 196 (No. 6):82–99, 1957.)*

only during long days and warm temperatures. The vernalization of bud meristems causes the formation of a floral primordial initiation chemical stimulus which can be transmitted to a non-induced plant by bud grafts. Whether this chemical stimulus is the same as florigen which is synthesized in photoinduced leaves remains a question which must be answered by future research.

Gardner and Loomis (46) have shown that certain species of grasses will not complete reproductive growth unless they are exposed to certain sequences of temperature and photoperiodic inductions. Kentucky bluegrass and orchard grass will not initiate floral primordia unless preceded by short days and cool temperatures. This is revealed by an examination of the data in Table 41. Floral initiation, however, occurs under long days and warm temperatures, and the complete development of the flowers follows in long days and warm temperatures, plus optimum growing conditions provided by adequate soil moisture, nitrogen, and photosynthate. The entire sequence of reproductive growth requirements is summarized in Figure 122. Many native American grasses and grasses indigenous to southern latitudes flower without low temperatures and short photoperiods.

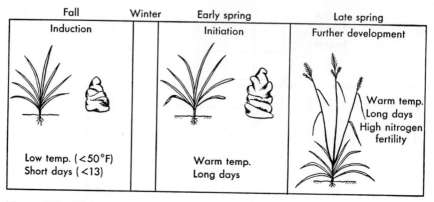

Figure 122   Diagrammatic representation of the effects of temperature and photo-period on flowering in orchard grass. *(From Gardner, F.P. and Loomis, W.E.* Plant Physiology. *28:201–217, 1953.)*

Table 41   Number of flowering heads produced by four grasses after induction under different temperatures and photoperiods from October 9 to December 22, 1950. Flowers developed in a warm greenhouse under 18-hour photoperiod after December 22. *(Data are panicles on four pots.) (From Gardner, F. P. and W. E. Loomis.* Plant Physiol. *28:201–217. 1953.)*

TYPE OF GRASS	STRAIN OR VARIETY	LENGTH OF PHOTOPERIOD DURING INDUCTION, IN HOURS									
		9	11	12	12.5	13	13.5	14	16	18	N
		Cold greenhouse									
Orchard grass	OG-126	34	33	38	17	1	0	0	0	0	18
	OG-144	32	36	45	8	8	1	3	0	0	14
	OG- 14	35	23	28	14	6	0	4	0	0	13
	Total	101	92	111	39	15	1	7	0	0	45
Kentucky bluegrass	Commercial	26	41	33	14	8	5	3	0	0	51
		Warm greenhouse									
Orchard grass	OG-126	0	0	0	0	0	0	0	0	0	0
	OG-144	0	0	0	0	0	0	0	0	0	1
	OG- 14	0	3	0	0	0	0	0	0	0	0
	Total	0	3	0	0	0	0	0	0	0	1
Kentucky bluegrass	Commercial	0	0	0	0	0	0	0	0	0	0

Other Environmental Factors.

Light and temperature affect the growth process directly at the cellular level as well as controlling the reproductive developmental proc-ess. However, water, essential minerals, gases such as oxygen and carbon dioxide, and other external factors can retard growth when any one of them is limiting. As already explained, a deficit of water can restrict growth (review the data presented in Figure 17 and Figure 107). The discussion of mineral nutrition (Chapter 6) has pointed out that the lack of any one of the essential minerals retards growth (review Figure 24), and that without the essential minerals, many bioprocesses do not function. Abundant data may be found in the plant science literature which relates the required amount of a particular essential mineral to yield, but scarcely any data are available which relate various phases of the growth process to any particular essential mineral. The data in Figure 123 and Figure 124 illustrate the basic principle of the relation of con-

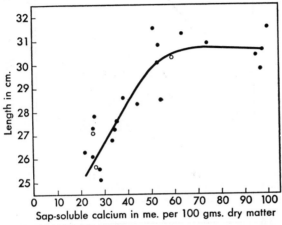

Figure 123   Relationship between soluble calcium in leaves and total stem growth of guayule plants. (*From Covil, Bruce J. Plant Physiology. 23:286–308, 1948.*)

centration of an essential mineral and total growth. This principle indicates that increasing the concentration of any given mineral beyond a certain level will not cause a further increase in plant growth. However, this principle does not always hold true for all essential minerals in relation to the growth of all plant meristems. For example, the total stem length of guayule plants was shown to be little affected by potassium concentration. On the other hand, the growth in diameter of guayule plants (cambial growth) was closely related to potassium concentration (Figure 125).

The effect of oxygen concentration on the daily rate of elongation of cotton roots is shown by the data in Figure 126 which show that too much or too little oxygen can retard cotton growth. A sharp reduction in root growth occurred when the oxygen level was decreased to 5 per cent and below or increased to 90 per cent and 100 per cent. Cotton roots which were grown at oxygen levels of 21 per cent were not retarded by concentrations of carbon dioxide as high as 45 per cent, but 60 per cent carbon dioxide inhibited root growth completely. Some recent studies

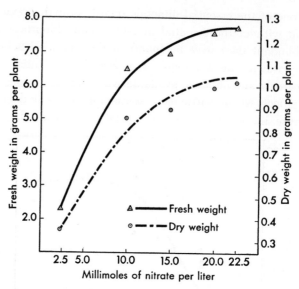

Figure 124   Relationship between nitrate concentrations in nutrient solution and fresh and dry weights of oat plants after 84 days of growth. *(From Langston, Ruble. Plant Physiology. 26:115–122, 1951.)*

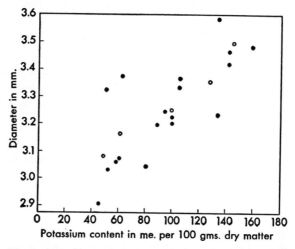

Figure 125   Relationship between total potassium in entire plant and total stem diameter of guayule plants. *(From Covil, Bruce J. Plant Physiology. 23:286–308, 1948.)*

have indicated that stem elongation occurs at a more rapid rate at low oxygen concentrations (less than the normal 20 per cent of air) because auxin destruction by indoleacetic acid oxidase is inhibited.

The normal constituents of the atmosphere do not have unfavorable

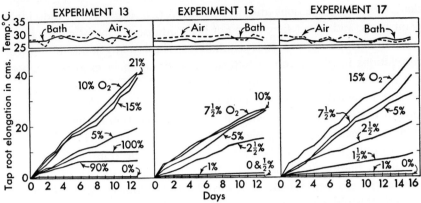

Figure 126 Effect of various concentrations of oxygen on the daily primary root growth of cotton plants. (*From Leonard, O.A. and Pinckard, J.A. Plant Physiology. 21:18–36, 1946.*)

effects on plant growth. However, certain industrial gases and products of the oxidation of gasoline vapors and other hydrocarbons that are released into the atmosphere are toxic to plants. These toxic substances are usually found in areas that are near smelters and in large cities. The toxic gases from smelters are either sulfur dioxide or hydrogen fluoride. These gases in low concentrations of 0.1 to 2.0 parts per million cause leaf injury. The leaf injury symptoms are watery spots, dead brown areas, and chlorosis. Other industrial gases that were shown to be toxic are hydrogen chloride, chlorine, and ammonia. The leakage of illuminating gas will cause epinasty growth responses in plants and is due to the presence of ethylene in the illuminating gas. In certain large cities such as Los Angeles the gasoline vapors and other hydrocarbons are oxidized to peroxides and ozonides of the hydrocarbons, and these products are toxic to plants. The phytotoxins are produced only under certain meteorological conditions that cause what is commonly known as smog. Effects on plants are a leaf-spotting that is called silver leaf. Sulfur dioxide, hydrogen fluoride, smog, etc., if present in toxic quantities, not only cause leaf injury but also a reduction in plant growth. The decreased growth rate is thought to be caused indirectly by a reduction in the rate of photosynthesis that results from a loss of photosynthetic tissue in the necrotic areas of the leaves.

GROWTH CORRELATIONS

In the beginning of this chapter it was pointed out that all the plant parts play an interrelated role in the growth process. The interrelationships among plant parts as well as among cells are called growth correlations. Growth correlations are more involved than is growth of individual plant parts, and as yet they have not been intensively investigated. However, sufficient information is available to show many kinds of growth correlations in plants and to indicate how these affect crop production.

Before discussing growth correlations, we should summarize our present knowledge of solute transport in the phloem. Many kinds of growth correlations are dependent upon translocation of inorganic and organic molecules from one plant part to another, chiefly via the phloem. For example, florigen synthesized in leaves must be translocated to bud meristems before floral primordia initiation will occur. At present the kind of mechanism which is involved in the translocation of solutes through the phloem is unknown. Theoretically, three mechanisms have been postulated, but first let us mention some known facts about phloem translocation. Movement of solutes from leaves either to shoot or to root growing and storage tissues always occurs in the phloem. The mature sieve tubes are the phloem structures through which solutes are principally translocated. Therefore, any explanation of the nature of phloem transport must be compatible with the anatomical characteristics of sieve tubes. Mature sieve tubes have only a thin parietal layer of cytoplasm enclosing a large lumen almost devoid of cytoplasmic contents. The cytoplasm is continuous from one sieve tube to another by means of strands (plasmodesms) which traverse the sieve plates. Opinions differ as to the level of the metabolic activity and the physical condition of the sieve tube cytoplasm. One concept views the cytoplasm as fluid at a high metabolic level and as undergoing cyclosis or streaming. Crafts (42), however, states that cytological evidence shows that the cytoplasm of the sieve tubes is not in a fluid state, but rather that it is tough and elastic with a low level of metabolic activity, and that it does not undergo cyclosis. In this regard, certain facts must be kept in mind. Movement through the sieve tubes does not occur unless these structures are living. Rate of solute movement is rapid and often in large amounts. Two kinds of solute molecules may move in opposite directions at the same time in the phloem. However, it is not known whether this bidirectional movement occurs in the same or different sieve tubes. Many solute molecules move in the phloem only in one direction (polarity), e.g., auxin from apical buds downward and sugar from the leaves. Some kinds of molecules are translocated only when food molecules are moving and always in the same direction. Examples of such translocation are those of viruses and plant growth regulators.

The three theoretical mechanisms which attempt to explain phloem transport are: 1. mass flow; 2. protoplasmic streaming (cyclosis); and 3. activated diffusion. The mass flow hypothesis is based on a mass movement of water and solute molecules from regions of high turgor pressure to regions of low turgor pressure. According to this hypothesis the sieve tube cytoplasm plays a passive role. On the contrary the protoplasmic streaming hypothesis postulates that the cytoplasm plays an active role in solute movement via the phloem, and that it constitutes the only feasible explanation of the large amounts and high rates of solute transport. The activated diffusion hypothesis does not include cyclosis, but it surmises rather an unknown role of the cytoplasm in speeding up the movement of solute molecules, each kind of molecule moving according to its own diffusion gradient independent of the other. None of the three theories completely explains the known facts of phloem translocation.

Other interesting data obtained from phloem translocation studies have shown diurnal fluctuations in solute transport. Sugar translocation from corn leaves is at a maximum in the late afternoon, while sugar translocation from tomato leaves is at a maximum during the night. The reasons for the differences in time of maximum translocation of sugar in corn and tomato are unknown, but they may be related to temperature effects on the translocation process. An attempt to settle the question of effect of temperature on translocation has produced only obscure and conflicting data. If the rate of translocation of a solute molecule were doubled for a change of 10°C., then considerable evidence would be available to support the protoplasmic streaming hypothesis. However, as already mentioned, no clear cut data reproducible by two independent investigators are available. For a recent review of the phloem translocation problem and literature citations on many of the above statements, the student is referred to Crafts (42) and Arisz (37).

Many growth correlations are the result of competition among plant parts and/or cells for available photosynthate. Others are interrelationships of growth among plant parts. An example of the competitive type of correlation is the channeling of available photosynthate to growing reproductive organs, which results in a cessation of vegetative growth. This is brought out by the data of Eaton on cotton plants as shown in Table 42. A comparison of the weights of leaves, stems, and roots of the deflorated and of the fruiting branches removed with those of the vegetative parts of the check (no reproductive parts removed) brings out the reduction in vegetative growth by reproductive growth. The effect of one plant part on the growth of another plant part is shown by the data in Figures 127, 128, 129.

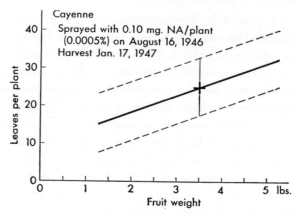

Figure 127 Growth correlation between number of leaves and fruit weight per pineapple plant. The broken line is the standard error of estimate. *(From Van Overbeek, J.* Plant Growth Substances. *University of Wisconsin Press, 1951.)*

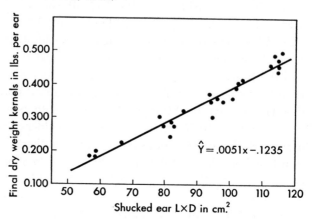

Figure 128 Correlation between kernel weight per ear and ear weight of corn. *(From Shaw, R.H. and Loomis, W.E.* Plant Physiology. *25:225–243, 1950.)*

Table 42 Effect of fruiting on vegetative growth of cotton. *(From Loomis, W. E.* Growth and Differentiation. Iowa State College Press. 1953.)

| | Green weight in grams | | | | | |
TREATMENT	LEAVES	STEMS	ROOTS	FRUITS	TOTAL	ROOT/TOP × 100
Check	90	102	80	230	502	16
Deflorated	186	298	237	19	740	32
Fruiting branches removed	197	357	326	0	880	37

Loomis (55) has proposed the growth-differentiation balance concept for explaining the use of available photosynthate by plant cells. Available photosynthate is used in the synthesis of more cells when the

REGRESSION OF WEIGHTS OF MAIZE EARS
ON STALK DIAMETER-1941

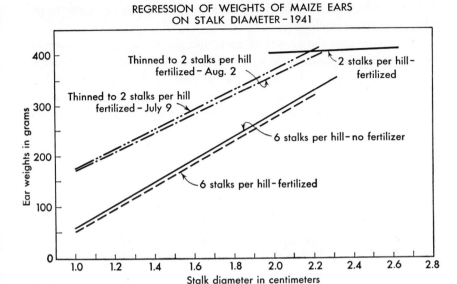

Figure 129 Growth correlation between ear weight and stalk diameter of corn plants as affected by number of stalks per hill and fertilizer. (*From Shaw, R.H. and Loomis, W.E. Plant Physiology. 25:225–243, 1950.*)

environmental factors, including available water, temperature, essential minerals, and light, are at an optimum. Cellulose and lignin as well as certain cellular inclusions, such as alkaloids and saponins, are synthesized in large quantities when available water is low. Water deficits in plants cause cessation of growth. Under such conditions, available photosynthate is used for synthesis. However, some products, such as flavor in fruits, are synthesized in environments of cool nights. Flavor products thus accumulate when growth is limited by low temperature. Under most natural habitats, growth and differentiation tend to balance each other, and the kind of plant form is one of neither extremely short nor long internodes, nor extremely thick nor thin leaves. Low light intensity or optimum available water causes a poorly differentiated plant having long internodes and thin, well expanded leaves, while high temperatures and a low available water supply lead to the opposite kind of plant form. The growth-differentiation balance concept is very useful in crop management. Many examples can be cited, but one need remember only the basic principles and apply them to a particular crop production problem. For leafy vegetable production, an environment which induces optimum growth is desirable, while for best fruit flavor a cool night temperature is required. Southern pines produce large yields of turpentine because of long growing seasons followed by an optimum environment for synthesis of resin. The same kind of environmental sequence in the tropics is best for rubber production.

Correlations in the growth of roots and shoot are primarily competitive for available photosynthate. Essential minerals and available water, if either is deficient, will result in decline of shoot growth and translocation of available photosynthate to the roots. High available moisture and essential minerals, however, will increase shoot growth greatly over root growth. This correlation is illustrated by the data in Table 43.

Table 43   Growth of shoots and roots of tomato with varying water and nitrogen levels. (*From Loomis, W. E. Growth and Differentiation. Iowa State College Press. 1953.*)

MOISTURE	NITROGEN	WT. OF SHOOTS	WT. OF ROOTS	ROOTS/TOP × 100
		gm.	gm.	
Optimum	Optimum	224	43	19.2
Low	Optimum	137	42	30.7
Optimum	Low	93	46	49.5
Low	Low	73	40	55.4

Removal of plant tops either by clipping at too frequent intervals or by overgrazing will reduce available photosynthate and retard root growth. Many practical applications can be made on the root/shoot ratio correlation. Abundant soil moisture from frequent irrigation or excessive rainfall will cause excessive shoot growth and little root growth. If a drought follows, such plants will show desiccation injury more quickly than plants growing under occasional periods of low soil moisture. Greenhouse plants and nursery stock are often grown under high moisture and fertilizer treatments. As a result, such plants cannot tolerate suboptimum environments. Cutting back of tops prior to transplanting nursery stock only makes the situation worse. Removal of tops reduces the leaf area and results in less photosynthate for root growth.

Some growth correlations are determined by naturally occurring auxin. Perhaps all growth correlations which involve food competition are partially controlled by auxin. Apical dominance and cambial growth are specific examples of growth correlations which are auxin controlled. In apical dominance, auxin which diffuses from the growing apical bud or from leaves causes an inhibition of growth of lateral buds. Removal of the apical bud brings about a partial removal of inhibition of lateral bud growth, that is, it may lead to the growth of lateral buds into branches, but in some species the expanded leaf at the same position on the node as the lateral bud must also be removed to achieve this same effect. The downward diffusion through the phloem of auxin which inhibits lateral bud growth causes cambial growth initiation. Cambial growth will stop below a girdle which has severed the phloem tissue. As pointed out earlier, with the exception of parthenocarpic fruits, growth of fruit is correlated with auxin which diffuses from the growing embryo in the seed. This correlation is shown by the data in Table 44 which relates fruit size and weight to number of seeds.

Table 44 Correlation between size and fruit weight to number of seeds. (*From Heinicke, A. J. Cornell Agr. Exp. Sta. Bull. No. 393. 1917.*)

NO. OF SEED	FRUIT DIAM.	FRUIT WT.
	mm.	*gm.*
1	8.0	2.98
2	10.5	3.27
3	11.9	3.60
4	13.2	4.84
5	14.6	5.47
6	16.8	6.53

A recently discovered correlation effect of auxin is its influence on abscission. Research has shown that abscission is controlled by the auxin gradient across the abscission zone. This auxin gradient is determined by the concentration of auxin in the leaf or fruit (distal region) and the concentration of auxin in the stem (proximal region). The proximal auxin level is increased by growing fruits and young leaves. Thus, young leaves increase the auxin proximal to old leaves which have low auxin levels, and this combination sets up a gradient across the abscission zone that will result in abscission. Abscission also results if no gradient is present. In other words a high distal-low proximal auxin gradient results in no abscission. This auxin correlation may be better understood by reference to the diagrams in Figure 130. Fruits which are already set and growing will increase the proximal auxin level to young fruit and the resulting gradient across the fruit stalk abscission zone will cause the young fruit to absciss. Abscission which is a result of a lack of gradient is a normal response of leaves that have their auxin levels lowered by insects and diseases, by the low temperatures and short days of the autumn season, and by senescence. It is interesting that a sudden drop in temperature to below freezing will not cause the leaf abscission response in some species of plants. As a result the leaves remain on such plants. For a recent review on the physiology of abscission, the student is referred to Addicott and Lynch (36).

The initiation of reproductive growth in plants causes many changes in the mineral nutritional pattern. As already pointed out, not only are

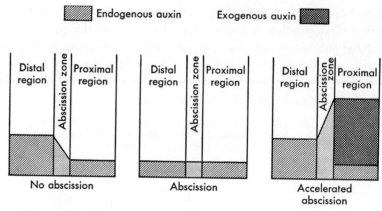

Figure 130   Relation of auxin gradient across the abscission zone to causing abscission of plant parts. Endogenous refers to auxin synthesized within the plant while exogenous is applied auxin. Distal means auxin present in the leaf, fruit, and other parts while proximal refers to auxin in the stem. *(From Addicott, F.T. and Lynch, R.S. Annual Review of Plant Physiology. 6:211–233, 1955.)*

root and vegetative shoot growth commonly stopped by growth of reproductive parts, but mineral absorption is also slowed down and the developing fruits must obtain many of their essential minerals from the leaves. This is particularly true of nitrogen, phosphorus, sulfur, potassium, and magnesium. In a recent review on the exportation of minerals from leaves to fruit, Williams (71) cites data which show a loss of from 60 to 80 per cent of the nitrogen, phosphorus, and sulfur of leaves to the growing fruits for such plants as corn and wheat. Thus, growing fruits cause an outward translocation from leaves resulting from protein hydrolysis in the leaves. Protein hydrolysis changes the entire leaf cellular metabolism from a state of active metabolism to one of low metabolic activity, and the final result is a state of senescence in the leaves. A similar pattern is followed in the growth of seedlings. The rapidly growing leaves and stem cause a translocation of minerals from cotyledons to the shoot.

15.
PLANT REACTIONS TO STIMULI

We are often inclined to think of plants as being stationary and without noticeable sensitivity or movement. Nevertheless, some lower plants are motile and can swim about in water just as freely and as rapidly as small animals. The movements or reactions of the larger, more complex plants, however, are limited chiefly to the bending, twisting, or elongation of certain organs or to specific parts of organs.

Although seed plants are commonly fixed in the soil and are not motile in the sense that higher animals are, the organs of such plants do display movements. Perhaps the most spectacular superficial evidences are the movements manifested by the opening and closing of flowers and the changing positions of the supporting flower stalks. But stems, leaves, and roots also show changes in position or in direction of growth which vary in character and extent with different plants and with the effect of various internal and external factors or stimuli.

In general plant movements, or orientation phenomena, are induced either by external agencies, such as light, temperature, gravity, and mechanical contact, which exert an influence upon cell materials and products in such a way as to effect changes in the rate of growth (often a difference in growth rate on opposite sides of a plant organ); or by changes in turgor in certain cells or tissues. Consequently, two classes of movements of living organs of higher plants are generally recognized. One of these classes includes all growth reactions, or growth curvatures, characterized by the fact that the orientation reached is determined by growth. Such growth is irreversible, but it may be modified by later growth in another direction. Movements of the other class, caused by significant changes in the turgor of certain cells or in the turgidity of supporting tissues, result only in the plant part concerned temporarily assuming a new position. In the latter class a full recovery of turgidity (involving a reversible change) restores the part to approximately its previous position.

Sometimes the term irritability is used to explain plant movements. Such a term should not be construed to mean that plants have structures comparable with the nervous system of higher animals and that a stimulus is received by a particular organ, transmitted to a "brain," which then directs a specific response. Satisfactory evidence has never been presented to prove this concept. On the contrary most, if not all, of the so-called "plant reactions to stimuli" can now be described in terms of turgor and growth. It is perhaps correct to refer to any change, be that internal or external, which activates a series of processes in a plant as a stimulus. Likewise it is probably correct to say that the processes activated or retarded by the changed condition constitute a response on the part of the plant. But it must be kept in mind that the so-called "stimulus" may be beneficial or harmful to the plant; and it may consist of a change in only one factor which influences a plant's behavior, or it may be the result of a combination of factors of varying intensity and effect. Similarly the "response" of the plant may be definitely detrimental to it, and the reaction usually results from the interplay of several processes. Certainly there is nothing to indicate that the plant's reaction constitutes an act of intelligence. Therefore, to say that the capacity to respond to a stimulus is irritability, and that this capacity is one of the fundamental characteristics of living protoplasm, is of little help in the interpretation of plant behavior.

Likewise during the early studies other terms, such as nutations, nastic movements (hyponasty and epinasty), tropisms (phototropisms, geotropisms, etc.), and "sleep movements" were coined because of inadequate knowledge of cause and effect relationships in certain types of plant movements. Although as previously indicated, most, if not all, plant movements may be explained by growth or turgor, such terms as those just mentioned, if handled cautiously, may still be used to designate the end result or visible effects. But they in no way explain the basic cause or intervening steps in such reactions. Here is a case where it is perhaps better to use several words in describing a phenomenon rather than indulging the habit of trying to reduce such activities to one catchy, but frequently, obscure term. Since these terms are often encountered in the literature, however, a brief explanation of each will be given.

Nutation is the term applied to the phenomenon in which a growing stem tip does not extend in a straight line; rather it moves or twists in a somewhat irregular spiral as it grows in length. In other words nutations result from unequal growth rates. The effects are perhaps best accounted for by assuming that successively around the stem each vertical segment grows for an interval at an accelerated rate. The extent of nutation is generally related to the rapidity of growth, and undoubtedly results from the interrelationships of auxin and external factors, especially contact or mechanical shock as is seen in the development of many twining plants and tendrils.

Nastic growth movements are especially characteristic of dorsi-ventral organs; that is, organs such as leaves and flower petals which have distinct upper and lower surfaces. The factors, such as temperature and light which induce the movement, may act on all parts of the organ and from all directions, or they may act chiefly on one side. In a growing shoot, the early development of a leaf in the bud is characterized by greater growth on the morphologically lower or under side so that for a time the leaf remains appressed against the stem tip. Such accelerated growth on the under side is called hyponasty. Later in development, more rapid growth in the upper cell layers of the leaf tends to dispose the leaf at a greater angle to the direction of growth of the stem tip, as seen in the later stages of bud unfolding. The more rapid growth of the upper cell layers is known as epinasty. The movements of floral parts, moreover, often result from inequalities of growth on opposite sides. For example, the opening of the sepals and petals of a tulip is due to a greater growth on their inner or upper side. In the evening or as the light wanes, these flower parts "close up," indicating that growth is greater on their outer sides. In such plants it is logical to assume that light, and perhaps temperature, affects either the distribution or potency of auxin which, in turn, regulates the growth behavior.

Tropism is the general term used to designate the visible effects of unequal growth of tissues of cylindrical organs such as stems, leaf petioles, and roots. One of the most familiar of these is observed when plants placed in a window, or in some other position where they receive unequal illumination, bend toward the light. The phenomenon is called positive phototropism. It is usually explained by assuming that the auxin tends to move toward the shaded side, or that the influence of the auxin on the more brilliantly lighted side of the growing stem tip is reduced, and thus growth on that side is retarded. Simultaneously, growth on the opposite or shaded side of the stem tip continues unrestrictedly, or it may even be accelerated. Hence a greater growth occurs on the less brightly lighted side which causes the stem to bend toward the light. This growth reaction to light is most pronounced in the region of cell elongation.

Another familiar example of tropism is seen in the tendency of most primary stems to grow upward and of primary roots to grow downward. If a rapidly developing seedling is placed in a horizontal position, the stem tip usually turns upward and the primary root downward. The same reactions occur when a seed germinates. Regardless of the position in which a seed is planted, the stem will grow away from the earth and the primary root will grow into the soil. This growth reaction is considered to be due to the influence of gravity and is called geotropism. Apparently gravity deflects the auxin to the under or lower side of a plant axis which is not vertical to the surface of the earth. Therefore, the auxin tends to accumulate on the side toward the pull of gravity. The excess auxin apparently stimulates the growth of stem cells on the underside, thus bringing about an unequal growth rate which results in the stem assuming a perpendicular position (negative geotropism). On the contrary the excess of auxin on the under side of the root exerts an opposite effect to that in the stem; that is, the growth of the root on the underside is retarded. Hence the more rapid growth of the cells on the upper side of the root causes the root to turn downward (positive geotropism).

Leaf mosaics are due primarily to the unequal growth of petioles and stems which results in these organs twisting and frequently displaying the leaf blades to maximum illumination. Young developing leaf blades apparently assimilate greater amounts of auxin when shaded. Therefore, if a developing leaf is partly covered by another leaf, the blade of the young leaf produces more auxin on the shaded side. The auxin moves back directly into that portion of the petiole on the same side as the shaded portion of the leaf blade. This causes the petiole on that side to grow more rapidly causing it to twist or bend and thus change the position of the blade. This orientation phenomenon may continue until the upper surface of the leaf blade is evenly illuminated or until growth of the leaf has stopped. Climbing vines on walls and trees at the edge of dense forests often display leaf mosaics.

Other tropisms, such as hydrotropic, chemotropic and thigmotropic movements, are explained on the basis of the major environmental factor which appears to influence the growth behavior.

Turgor movements result from changes in water (turgor) pressure within cells or groups of cells in certain organs of some plants. We have already seen that when the concentration (diffusion pressure) of water surrounding a plant cell is higher than the concentration of the water within the vacuole, the water will osmose into the cell, thus causing an increase in cell turgor which results in additional pressure on the cell walls. The opposite occurs when the greater diffusion pressure of water is within the vacuole of the cell; that is, water will osmose out of the cell, turgor decreases, and in extreme cases plasmolysis followed by death may result. When all the cells of a plant organ, such as a leaf, flower or stem, become distended, they press against each other with the result that the whole plant structure bcomes rigid or turgid. Conversely, when turgor is reduced in all the cells, their pressure against each other diminishes and the plant becomes flaccid or wilts. The irregular shapes of parenchymatous cells may usually be attributed to the pressure exerted upon them by adjoining cells.

Movements result when the cells on one side of an organ, such as a pulvinus, lose or gain turgidity more than those on the opposite side. Included in the movements arising as a result of changes in turgor are the so-called "sleep movements" of the leaves of species of beans, peas, clover, alfalfa, oxalis, and other plants; the very rapid movements of the leaves and petioles of the sensitive plant (*Mimosa pudica*) when struck or when the light intensity is materially reduced; and the turgor movements of sensitive stigmas (*Torenia*, catalpa, trumpet-creeper) and sensitive stamens (*Centaurea*, barberry). Needless to say "sleep movements" of plants bear no relation to the sleep of animals.

Highlights of plant growth may be summarized as follows:

1. For convenience in discussing the physiology of growth, growth may be considered as cell division plus cell elongation, or as an irreversible increase in the size of the plant.

2. The rate of growth of a plant or organ varies with age, being initially slow, later more rapid, and finally less rapid or completely ceases. Thus, the increase in plant size or mass with time follows an S-shaped or sigmoid curve.

3. Dormancy occurs in buds, seed, bulbs, tubers and corms. Certain physiological changes occur in cells which cause them to enter a state of dormancy. Other physiological changes must then take place in dormant cells before dormancy is broken. Initiation of these other physiological changes in breaking dormancy is brought about by temperature and chemicals.

4. Plant growth is regulated by minute quantities of chemicals called plant growth regulators. Naturally occurring plant growth regulators are indoleacetic acid, vitamins, and certain unknown compounds. Indoleacetic acid regulates a multiplicity of growth reactions in plants, but its principal role is in cell elongation. Many synthetic compounds cause growth responses in plants. These have been used in agriculture to inhibit flower and fruit abscission, to promote flowering, to hasten or delay fruit ripening, to accelerate rooting of cuttings, to prevent sprouting in tubers and bulbs, and as herbicides.

5. The elongation phase of growth is dependent on an optimum level

of indoleacetic acid which acts in some manner as a coenzyme in cell wall synthesis and other bioprocesses associated with growth.

6. Light mainly affects growth indirectly by its control of the rate of photosynthesis. The direct effects of light on plant growth are morphogenic and photoperiodic. Photoperiodic requirements for flowering in plants require an uninterrupted dark period of 12 to 15 hours for short-day plants. A light period of 12 to 15 hours, interruption of the dark period with light, or continuous light will all cause flowering in long-day plants. Indeterminate plants will flower under either short-day or long-day photoperiods. In some species of plants, the photoperiodic requirement may be modified by temperature.

7. The rate of plant growth is regulated by temperature in the same manner as is any enzymatically controlled chemical reaction. Within certain ranges, a temperature change of 10°C. will double the rate of growth. This usually occurs in the range of 0° to 30°C. Temperature regulates the rate of vegetative growth and flowering in some species of plants due to certain combinations of day and night temperatures. This is known as thermoperiodism. The phenomenon of flowering in winter cereal crops, biennials, and other species which occurs as a result of treatment of the bud meristems with cool temperatures is known as vernalization. Temperatures above 35°C. cause injury and death to cells as a result of an irreversible inactivation of the cellular enzymes, while temperatures below freezing cause ice crystal formation that results in cell desiccation and disorganization of the protoplasm.

8. Growth is influenced by other environmental causes such as water, minerals, oxygen, carbon dioxide, and biotic factors.

9. Plant growth is the result of many interrelationships among various plant parts. These interrelationships are called growth correlations. Growth correlations are due to food competition and/or auxin effects. Some examples of growth correlations are the relations of reproductive growth to vegetative growth, of root to shoot growth, of leaf area to size of fruits, of auxin inhibition of lateral bud growth, of auxin activation of cambial growth, and of auxin gradients in the abscission zone.

10. In retrospect plant growth is the result of complex interactions among plant parts and/or cellular processes all of which are controlled by genetic and environmental factors.

REFERENCES

1. Meyer, B. S. and D. B. Anderson. Plant Physiology, 2nd ed. New York: D. Van Nostrand Company. 1952.
2. Ahlgren, H. L. Fundamental Principles Versus Facts in Crops Instruction. Agronomy Journal 43: 367–370. 1951.
3. Bonner, James and Arthur W. Galston. Principles of Plant Physiology. San Francisco, Calif.: W. H. Freeman and Company. 1952.
4. Sharp, L. W. Fundamentals of Cytology, New York: McGraw-Hill Book Company, Inc. 1943.
5. Sayre, J. D. Physiology of Stomata of *Rumex patienta*. Ohio Jour. Sci. 26: 233–266. 1926.
6. Crafts, A. S., H. B. Currier, and C. R. Stocking. Water in the Physiology of Plants. Waltham, Mass.: Chronica Botanica Co. 1949.
7. Kramer, P. J. Plant and Soil Water Relationships. New York: McGraw-Hill Book Company, Inc. 1949.
8. Maximov, N. A. The Plant in Relation to Water. London: George Allen and Unwin, Ltd. 1929.
9. Lundegardh, H. Absorption, Transport, and Exudation of Inorganic Ions by the Roots. Ark. Bot. 32A: 1–139. 1945.
10. Franco, C. M. and W. E. Loomis. The Absorption of Phosphorus and Iron from Nutrient Solutions. Plant Physiol. 22:627–634. 1947.
11. Hoagland, D. R. and D. I. Arnon. The Water-Culture Method for Growing Plants Without Soil. Calif. Agr. Exp. Sta. Circular 347. 1950.
12. Hambridge, G., Editor. 2nd ed. Hunger Signs in Crops. Washington, D. C.: Judd and Detweiler. 1949.
13. Hoagland, D. R. Lectures on the Inorganic Nutrition of Plants. Waltham, Mass.: Chronica Botanica Co. 1944.
14. Stiles, W. Trace Elements in Plants and Animals. New York: The Macmillan Co. 1946.
15. Truog, E., Editor. Mineral Nutrition of Plants. Madison, Wis.: University of Wisconsin Press. 1951.
16. Wallace, T. A., et al. Trace Elements in Plant Physiology. Waltham, Mass.: Chronica Botanica Co. 1951.
17. Jenny, Hans. Factors of Soil Formation. New York: McGraw-Hill Book Company, Inc. 1941.

18. Dittmer, H. J. A Quantitative Study of the Roots and Root Hairs of a Winter Rye Plant. Amer. Jour. Bot. 24:417–420. 1937.

19. Fuller, Harry J. and Oswald Tippo. College Botany. New York: Henry Holt and Company. 1949.

20. Baver, L. D. Soil Physics. 2nd ed. New York: John Wiley & Sons, Inc. 1948.

21. Lyon, T. L. and H. O. Buckman. The Nature and Properties of Soils. 4th ed. New York: The Macmillan Co. 1943.

22. Russell, E. W. Soil Conditions and Plant Growth. 8th ed. London: Longmans-Green. 1950.

23. Thorne, D. W. and H. B. Peterson. Irrigated Soils. Philadelphia: The Blakiston Co. 1949.

24. Weaver, John E. Root Development of Field Crops. New York: McGraw-Hill Book Company, Inc. 1926.

25. Weaver, John E. and W. E. Bruner. Root Development of Vegetable Crops. New York: McGraw-Hill Book Company, Inc. 1927.

26. Loomis, Walter E. Photosynthesis—The Major Enzymatic Process. Amer. Assoc. Cereal Chem. Trans. 9:48–52. 1951.

27. Loomis, Walter E. and James Franck. Photosynthesis in Plants. Ames, Iowa: Iowa State College Press. 1949.

28. Rabinowitch, E. I. Photosynthesis and Related Processes. Vols. I, II. New York: Interscience Publishers, Inc. 1945, 1951.

29. Carbon Dioxide Fixation and Photosynthesis. Symposia of the Society for Experimental Biology. No. 5. New York: Academic Press, Inc. 1951.

30. Baldwin, Ernest. Dynamic Aspects of Biochemistry. 2nd ed. Cambridge: Cambridge University Press. 1952.

31. Bonner, James. Plant Biochemistry. New York: Academic Press, Inc. 1950.

32. Claypool, L. I. and F. W. Allen. The Influence of Temperature and Oxygen Level on Respiration and Ripening of Wickson Plums. Hilgardia 21:129–160. 1951.

33. Stiles, Walter and William Leach. Respiration in Plants. 3rd ed. London: Methuen and Co. 1952.

34. Summer, James B. and Fred G. Somers. Chemistry and Methods of Enzymes. 3rd ed. New York: Academic Press, Inc. 1953.

35. Thomas, Meirion. Plant Physiology. 3rd ed. London: Churchill Ltd. 1947.

36. Addicott, F. T. and R. S. Lynch. Physiology of Abscission. Ann. Rev. Plant Physiol. 6:211–238. 1955.

37. Arisz, W. H. Transport of Organic Compounds. Ann. Rev. Plant Physiol. 3:109–130. 1952.

38. Audus, L. J. Plant Growth Substances. New York: Interscience Publishers, Inc. 1953.

39. Biddulph, Orlin. Studies of Mineral Nutrition by Use of Tracers. Bot. Rev. 21:251–295. 1955.

40. Bonner, J. and R. S. Bandurski. Studies of the Physiology, Pharmacology, and Biochemistry of the Auxins. Ann. Rev. Plant Physiol. 3:59–86. 1952.

41. Camus, C. C. and F. W. Went. The Thermoperiodicity of Three Varieties of *Nicotiana tabacum*. Amer. Jour. Bot. 39:521–527. 1952.

42. Crafts, A. S. Movement of Assimilates, Viruses, Growth Regulators and Chemical Indicators in Plants. Bot. Rev. 17:203–284. 1951.

43. Crocker, William. Growth of Plants. New York: Reinhold Publishing Corp. 1948.
44. Frey-Wyssling, A. Growth of Plant Cell Walls. In Symposia of the Society for Experimental Biology. No. 6. New York: Academic Press, Inc. 1952.
45. Galston, A. W. and L. Y. Dalberg. The Adaptive Formation and Physiological Significance of Indoleacetic Acid Oxidase. Amer Jour. Bot. 41:373–380. 1954.
46. Gardner, F. P. and W. E. Loomis. Floral Induction and Development in Orchard Grass. Plant Physiol. 28:201–217. 1953.
47. Garner, W. W. and H. A. Allard. Effect of Length of Day on Plant Growth. Jour. Agr. Res. 18:553–606. 1920.
48. Koepfli, J. B., K. V. Thimann, and F. W. Went. Phytohormones: Structure and Physiological Activity. Biol. Chem. Jour. 122:763–780. 1938.
49. Kornberg, H. A. Biochemical Effects of Ionizing Radiations. Oregon State College: Biology Colloquium. 1949.
50. Lang, A. Physiology of Flowering. Ann. Rev. Plant Physiol. 3:265–306. 1952.
51. Lea, D. E. Actions of Radiations on Living Cells. New York: The Macmillan Co. 1947.
52. Leopold, A. C. Photoperiodism in Plants. Quart. Rev. Biol. 26:247–263. 1951.
53. Leopold, A. C. Auxins and Plant Growth. Berkeley: University of California Press. 1955.
54. Liverman, J. L. The Physiology of Flowering. Ann. Rev. Plant Physiol. 6:177–210. 1955.
55. Loomis, W. E. Growth and Differentiation in Plants. Ames, Iowa: Iowa State College Press. 1953.
56. Murneek, A. E. and R. O. Whyte. Vernalization and Photoperiodism. Waltham, Mass.: Chronica Botanica Co. 1948.
57. Mickson, J. J. Symposium on Radiobiology, The Basic Aspects of Radiation Effects on Living Systems. New York: John Wiley and Sons, Inc. 1952.
58. Parker, M. W. and H. A. Borthwick. Influence of Light on Plant Growth. Ann. Rev. Plant Physiol. 1:43–58. 1950.
59. Siminovitch, D. and D. R. Briggs. Studies on the Chemistry of the Living Bark of the Black Locust in Relation to its Frost Hardiness VII. A Possible Direct Effect of Starch on the Susceptibility of Plants to Freezing Injury. Plant Physiol. 29:331–336. 1954.
60. Skoog, Folke. Plant Growth Substances. Madison, Wisconsin: University of Wisconsin Press. 1951.
61. Skoog, Folke. Chemical Regulation of Growth in Plants. In Dynamics of Growth Processes. Princeton: Princeton University Press. 1954.
62. Smith et al. A Textbook of General Botany. 5th ed. New York: The Macmillan Co. 1953.
63. Steward, F. C., R. H. Wetmore, J. F. Thompson, and J. P. Nitsh. A Quantitative Chromatographic Study of Nitrogenous Components of Shoot Apices. Amer. Jour. Bot. 41:123–134. 1954.
64. Thimann, K. V. The Action of Hormones in Plants and Invertebrates. New York: Academic Press, Inc. 1952.

65. Thimann, K. V. Growth in Plant Tissues. Amer. Sci. 42:589–606. 1954.

66. Thomson, Betty F. The Effect of Light on Cell Division and Elongation. Amer. Jour. Bot. 41:326–332. 1954.

67. Thut, H. F. and W. E. Loomis. Relation of Light to Growth of Plants. Plant Physiol. 19:117–130. 1944.

68. Tukey, H. B. Plant Regulators. New York: John Wiley and Sons, Inc. 1954.

69. Van Overbeek et al. Nomenclature of Chemical Regulators. Plant Physiol. 29:307–308. 1954.

70. Went, F. W. Physical Factors Affecting Growth in Plants. In Dynamics of Growth Processes. Princeton, New Jersey: Princeton University Press. 1954.

71. Williams, R. F. Redistribution of Mineral Elements During Development. Ann. Rev. Physiol. 6:25–42. 1955.

INDEX

(Page numbers in italics refer to illustrations)

Abscission, 32, 242, 265, *266*
Absorption, mineral, factors affecting, 66–68
  primary, 65
  secondary (ionic exchange), 65, 66
  water absorption related to, 62–63
  water, 45*ff*., 56, 57, 62–63
   active, 45–47, 51, 62
   passive, 47, 48, 50, 62, 63
Accumulation of food, in storage organs, 180–83
Acetic acid, 150
Acetone, chlorophyll extracted in, 120
Addicott, F. T., 265
Adenine, 209, 225
Adenosine formation, and respiration, 149
Adsorption, 17
  in germination, 6
Aeration, 75, 112, 113, 115
Afterripening, 197, 198, 199 (table)
Alcohol solution, 15
  chlorophyll extracted in, 120
Alfalfa, 3, 58
  root system of, *108*
  "sleep movements" of, 271
Algae, chlorophyll contents of, 121
  cultured for photosynthetic studies, 140, *141*, 142
  future use of, in photosynthesis, 127
  glycogen in, 162
Alkaloids, 179
Allard, H. A., 234
Allen, F. W., 154
Alpha particle, 244, 245
Aluminum, in soil, 91, 113, 176

American Society of Plant Physiologists, 200
Amino acids, 169, 170
  synthesis of, 148, 167, 168–69, 171
Ammonia, 168, 170, 176, 259
Ammonium sulfate, 168
Amylase, 55, 146 (table), 160, 163
Amylopectin, 160, 161
Amyloplast, 30, 161
Amylose, 160, 161
Anaerobes, obligate, 146
Anderson, 86
Angiosperm seeds and seedlings, *4*
Anion(s), defined, 14
  minerals as, 62
  in soil, 92, 95
Antagonism, related to permeability, 66
Anthers, 7
Anthocyanins, 173, 174, 175, 176
Anti-auxins, 200, 207, 241
Antibiotics, 179
Apex, of root, 101, 103, 113
Arisz, W. H., 261
Arnon, 68
Artificial light, and plant growth, 243–44
Assay methods, auxin, 201–2, *204–5*
Assimilation, 7, 8, 59, 60, 144, 171–83
  defined, 171
  products of, 172, 173–80
Atom(s), nucleus of, 10, 12, 13
  weight of, 10, 11 (table), 12
Atomic numbers, 11 (table)
Atomic weights, 10, 11 (table), 12
Audus, L. J., 222

Autoradiography, 13
Auxin synergists, 207
Auxins, 200, 203, 207, 222, 223, 224, 225, 226, 270
  bioassay methods for analyzing, 201–2, 204–5
  bound, 203, 206
  distribution of, in bean seedling, 203 (table)
    in oat coleoptile, 203 (table)
  flowering affected by, 241
  free, 203
  growth correlations controlled by, 264, 265
  synthesis of, 203, 206
  as "trigger agents," 226
Avena tests, auxin, 202, 204–5
Azotobacter, 78

Bacteria, anaerobic, 146
  glycogen in, 162
  green sulfur, photosynthesis of, 138
  and light absorption by carotenoids, 121
  nitrogen-fixing, 78, 167
  root rot caused by, 115
  symbiotic, 78
Balata, 178
Bamboo, 195
Bandurski, R. S., 213
Bark, 106, 192
Barley, and radioactive tracer studies, 65, 66
  water absorption in, 62, 63
Bean, 3
  growth pattern of, 194
  hypocotyl of, 3
  proteins in, 170
  seed of, 4
  seed leaves of, 3
  seedling of, 4
    auxin distribution in, 203 (table)
    2,4-D applied to, 219
  "sleep movements" of, 271
Belladonna, 180
Beta radiation, 244
Biddulph, Orlin, 247
Biennials, 252
Bioassay methods, auxin, 201–2, 204–5
Biosyntheses, plant, 160–83
Bipolar tip growth, 223
Blackman, 135, 229
Blue lupine, effects of aeration on, 112
Bonner, J., 213
Boron, deficiency of, 76 (table), 77 (table)
  essential for plant growth, 71, 72 (table)

Boron (Cont.):
  toxic in high concentration, 113
Borthwick, H. A., 244
Boysen-Jensen, 201
Briggs, D. R., 248
Brownian movement, 22
Buckwheat, 232, 233
Buds, dormancy in, 198–99
Bulbous plants, 252
"Burning," 40

Calcium, in cell wall, 36
  deficiency of, 76 (table), 77
  essential for plant growth, 71, 72 (table)
  non-mobility of, 70
Calcium pectate, 32
Calcium superphosphate, 168
Callose, 32, 34, 36
Cambium, 69, 105, 107
  cork, 106, 185, 190–92
  vascular, 187–90, 192
Camus, C. C., 254
Capillarity, 17, 18, 90, 91
Carbohydrates, 117, 125, 162
  accumulation of, 181 (table), 182, 183
  in chlorophyll synthesis, 122
  and fat synthesis, 164, 165
  in photosynthesis, 136
  See also Glucose; Starch; Sugar
Carbon, atomic weight of, 11 (table), 12
  in chlorophyll synthesis, 122
  as constituent of plant tissue, 71
  essential for plant growth, 71, 72 (table)
  fixation by photosynthesis, 126, 127
  radioactive, 136, 138, 140, 143
Carbon cycle, 131, 132
Carbon dioxide, concentration of, and photosynthesis, 128, 129, 130–32
  and root growth, 257
  as constituent of plant tissue, 71
  diffused into chloroplasts of chlorenchyma, 7
  in guard cells, 55
  and passage through stomates, 134
  and photosynthetic equation, 136, 137, 138
  in respiration, 149, 150, 151, 152, 154, 156
    fixation of, 148
  and root growth, 257
Carbon dioxide acceptor, 149
Carbon-nitrogen ratio, and floral initiation, 242
  in plant materials, 96
Carboxylase, 146 (table), 147
Carboxylation, 148

Carotene, 120, 121 (table), 175
Carotenoids, 120, 121, 122, 124, 174, 175
Carrot, food accumulated by, 183
    root system of, *108*
    as source of vitamin A, 175
Casein, 167
Castor bean, cell from endosperm of, *182*
Cation(s), defined, 14
    minerals as, 62, 64
    in soil, 91–92, 95
Caulocaline, 207
Celery, seedstalks exposed to low temperature, 253 (table)
Cell(s), bioprocesses affected by temperature, 247–50
    cork, *29*, 32, 35, 106, 190, *191*, 192
    epidermal, walls of, *29*, 32, 35, 55
    flaccid, 39
    guard, *47*, 50, 54, 55
    ice crystals in, 248
    meristematic, 62, 65, 101, 102, 103
    mesophyll, *47*, *49*, 50, 52, 133, 134, 175
    parenchyma, 48, 101, 104, 105, 106, 107, 161, 192
    parts of, 24–36
    phloem, 187, 189, 190
    root absorption, 47, 63
    turgid, 39
    wood, walls of, *29*, 32, 34
    xylem, 35, 47, 187, 189, 190
Cell differentiation, *4*, 6, 7, 101, 103, 104, 172, 185–86
Cell division, *4*, 6, 7, 30, 69, 101, 102, 104, 172, 185, 201, 225
Cell elongation, *4*, 6, 7, 62, 68, 69, 101, 102, 103, 185, 201, 202, 223, 224, 225, 226, 270
Cell sap, of vacuole, 30, 31, 42
Cell wall, *29*, 31–36, 223, 224, 227
Cellulase, 34, 146 (table)
Cellulose, 17, *29*, 32, 33–34
Centaurea, 271
Cereals, winter, 254
Chelates, 74–75
Chemotropic movement, 270
Chicle, 178
Chlorenchyma, 7, 133, 161, 175
Chlorine, atomic weight of, 11 (table), 13
    essential for plant growth, 71, 72 (table)
    toxicity as industrial gas, 259
Chloroform, chlorophyll extracted in, 120
Chlorophyll, 120, 121, 128, 129, 174, 175
    light absorbed by 123–24
    synthesis of, factors in, 122
    in seedling, 7, 8

Chloroplasts, 7, 29, *47*, 120, 121, 123, 124, 125, 133, 134, 135, 161, 162, 174, 175
Chlorosis, 122, 123, 259
Chondriosomes, *25*, 30
Chromatin, *25*, 30
Chromatography, paper, 138, 140, *143*
Chromonemata, 30
Chromoplasts, 29, 175
Chromosomes, 30, 170
Chrysanthemum morifolium, terminal meristem of, *188*
Citric acid cycle, Krebs, 148, 150
Clay soil, 23, 84, *85*, 88, *90*, 93, 95, 96
Claypool, L. I., 154
Clostridium, 78
Clover, 3, 371
Coagulation, 22, 23, 27
Cocklebur, inductive cycle in, 240
    translocation of florigen in, 236, 237, 238
Coleoptiles, oat, *see* Oat, coleoptiles of
Coleus, terminal bud of, *187*
Colloidal suspension, 19, 20
Colloidal systems, types of, 21 (table)
Compensation point, 157
Compound(s), 9, 10
    and equivalent weight in solution, 15
Continuous phase, of colloidal supsension, 19
Copper, as catalyst in chlorophyll synthesis, 122
    deficiency of, 76 (table), *77* (table)
    essential for plant growth, 71, 72 (table)
Cork cambium, 106, 185, 190–92
Cork cell, *29*, 32, 35, 106, 190, *191*, 192
Corn, effects of aeration on, 112, *113*
    glucose produced by, 126
    growth of, *194*, *234*
        correlations in, *262*, *263*
        effects of temperature on, 250, *251*
    as long-day plant, 119
    minerals translocated from leaves of, 266
    proteins in, 170
    rainfall required for, 48
    root system of, *109*
    seed and seedling of, *4*
    translocation of sugar from leaves of, 261
    zein of, 167
Cortex, 103, 104, *105*, 106, *107*
Cotton, 129, 130 (table)
    boll growth of, and light intensity, 230
    root growth of, 257, *259*
    vegetative growth of, effect of fruiting on, 261, 262 (table)

Cotyledons, of beans, 3
Crafts, A. S., 260, 261
Critical light intensity, 129
Crocker, William, 196, 244
Cross root growth inhibition test, 202, 204–5
Crystal lattice structure, in soil, 93, 94
Cutin, 32, 34, 35–36, 53, 133, 163, 172, 220
Cuttings, growth regulator for rooting of, 213, 214, 216–17
Cyclosis, 27, 261
Cystine, 167
Cytoplasm, 6, 25, 26–28, 42, 69, 260, 261

Dalberg, L. Y., 206
Darwin, 201
Dehydrogenase, 146 (table), 147
Desiccation, 49, 56, 57, 87, 248
Deuterium, 12
Dextrin, 162
Dicot, germination of, 4
  herbaceous stem of, 188
  root of, 104–6
    secondary growth in, 107
Differentially permeable membrane, 39, 41, 42
Differentiation, cell, 4, 6, 7, 101, 103, 104, 172, 185–86
Diffusion, 37ff., 69, 261
Diffusion pressure, 37, 38, 39, 40, 41, 42, 55, 270, 271
Diffusion pressure deficit, 40, 42–48 passim, 50, 51, 57
Digitalis, 180
Diseases, 133
  caused by mineral deficiencies, 77 (table)
Dispersed phase, of colloidal suspension, 19
Dittmer, H. J., 98, 108
Diurnal thermoperiodicity, 253–54
Dormancy, 8, 196, 197, 198, 199, 200
Drought resistance, 57–58, 61
Dry weight, of oat plant, and nitrate concentrations, 258
  and protein nitrogen of cells, 226
  in storage organs, 181 (table)
Dynamic equilibrium, 18, 37, 42

Earth, the, composition of crust of, 92 (table)
Eaton, 261
Edlefsen, 86
Elaioplasts, 30
Electrons, 10, 245
  weight of, 12, 13

Elements, atomic numbers of, 10, 11 (table)
  atomic weights of, 11 (table)
  and equivalent weight in solution, 15
  essential, for plant growth, 70–73
    sources of, 78–79
  symbols of, 11 (table)
  trace, see Trace elements
  See also Minerals
Embryo, 6, 7, 197, 198, 242
Embryo sac, 7
Emulsifiers, 20
Emulsions, 19, 20, 21
Endodermis, of root, 103, 104, 105, 106, 107
Endosperm, 7
Enzymes, 6, 227, 245
  in fat digestion and synthesis, 164, 166
  list of, 146 (table)
  in photosynthesis, 129, 134–35, 136
  in protein digestion and synthesis, 170, 171
  in starch digestion, 163
  in starch synthesis, 160, 161
  Q, 160
  in respiration, 144, 145, 146, 147, 148, 149
  and van't Hoff's law, 249–50
Ephedrine, 180
Epicotyl, 3, 198
Epicotyl tip, 6, 7
Epidermal cells, walls of, 29, 32, 35, 55
Epidermis, of leaf, 47, 54, 107, 133, 134
  of root, 103, 104, 105, 106
Epinastic response, 217, 218, 259, 269
Equivalent weight, in solution, 15
Erosion, soil, 79
  prevented by roots, 101
Essential oils, 178
Ether, chlorophyll extracted in, 120
Ethylene, and epinastic response, 259
Etiolation, 122
Exudation, 46, 51 (table)

Fats, 117, 163, 164
  accumulation of, 181 (table), 183
  digestion of, 164, 165, 166
  synthesis of, 7, 8, 163, 164, 165, 166
Fatty acids, 148, 164, 165, 166
Fertilization, 242
Fertilizer, 117, 242
  foliar application of, 70
  nitrate salts in, 167–68
Flaccid cell, 39
Flocculation, 23
Floral initiation, 236, 238, 241, 242, 255, 260
Florida pine, 127

Florigen, 236, 237, 239, 240, 241, 254, 255, 260
Foliar application, of fertilizer, 70
Foods, accumulation in plants, 180–83
 defined, 100, 117
 distinguished from assimilation products, 172–73
 synthesized by green plants, 100, 117
Frey-Wyssling, 223
Fruits, as food storage organs, 181 (table), 183
 seedless (parthenocarpic), 213, 214, 215, 216
 size and weight of, and number of seeds (table), 265
Fuller, Harry J., 100
Fungi, antibiotics assimilated by, 179
 food accumulated by, 182
 gibberellins synthesized by, 209
 glycogen in, 162
 parasitic, pectic compounds digested by, 32
 root rot caused by, 115

Galston, A. W., 206
Gamma radiation, 244
Gardner, F. P., 275
Garner, W. W., 233, 234, 236
Gas exchange technique, measurement by, of photospnthesis, 138–40
 of respiration, 151
Gelation, 19, 27
Gels, 19, 20, 27, 58
Genes, 170, 184
Geotropism, 270
Germination, 6–8
Gibberellins, 209
Gliadin, 167
Glucose, amounts synthesized by plants, 126 (table)
 and starch digestion, 163
 starch synthesized from, 163
 See also Carbohydrates; Sugar
Glucosides, 180
Glutamic acid, 150, 225
Glycerol, 164, 165, 166
Glycocol, 167
Glycogen, 162, 163
Glycolysis, 146, 148, 149
Granum, defined, 120
Grasses, effects of temperature and photo-period on flowering of, 256 (table)
 floral initiation of, 255
 glucosides produced by, 180
 root systems of, 108, 109, 111, 115
Greenhouse, 89, 129, 244, 264
Growth, and artificial light, 243–44
 and auxins, *see* Auxins

Growth (*Cont.*):
 bipolar tip, 223
 cambial, 257, 258, 264, 265
 in controlled-environment rooms, 246 (table)
 correlations in, 259–66
 defined, 184–85, 186
 dynamics of, 193–227
 elements essential for, 70–73
 as enzymatically catalyzed process, 250
 by expansion, 2
 floral initiation stage of, 236, 238
 and gibberellins, 209–11
 hormones as factor in, 194
 and ionizing radiation, 244–47
 and light, 228–43
 mechanism of, 222–27
 and mineral nutrition, 67, 79–80, 113, 115, 256–57, 264
 molecular requirements for, 211
 nature of, 222–27
 nutrient solutions for, 73–75
 patterns of, 193–96
 processes involved in, 6–8
 regulators of, 200–13
  agricultural applications of, 213–22
 ripe-to-flower stage of, 236
 root, *see* Roots (root systems), growth of
 of seedlings, 266
 shoot, 60
 and temperature, 247–59
 top, 60
 and traumatic acid, 209
 and water deficits, 58, 196, 233, 256, 263
 in weight, 2
Growth-differentiation balance, 262, 263
Guard cell, 47, 50, 54, 55
Guayule plant, 257, 258
Gums, 58, 176, 177
Gustafson, 213
Gutta-percha, 178
Guttation (exudation), 46, 51 (table)

Hardening, of protoplasm, 248, 249
"Hard-pan," 84, 99
Helium, 10, 11 (table), 12
Hemicellulose, 29, 32, 34, 36
Hemlock, 180
Henbane, 240, 241
Herbicides, 217–22
Hexose, 146, 149, 151
Hill reaction, 135, 136
Hoagland, 69, 73
Hooke, Robert, 24
Hormones, 115, 194, 200, 201
Humus, 71

Hydathodes, 46
Hydration, 19, 48
Hydrocarbons, toxic to plants, 259
Hydrocyanic acid, 180
Hydrogen, atomic number of, 10, 11 (table), 12
  atomic weight of, 11 (table), 12
  in chlorophyll synthesis, 122
  as constituent of plant tissue, 71
  essential for plant growth, 71, 72 (table)
  heavy, 12, 13
  in photosynthetic equation, 136, 137, 138
Hydrogen acceptor, 135, 136
Hydrogen chloride, toxic to plants, 259
Hydrogen fluoride, leaf injury caused by, 259
Hydrogen-ion concentration, 68
Hydrophilic sols, 19, 21, 23
Hydrophobic sols, 19, 20, 21, 22, 23
Hydroponics, 75
Hydrotropic movement, 270
Hygroscopic moisture, 86, 88 (table), 89
Hypocotyl, 3, 198, 231
Hypocotyl tip, 7
Hyponasty, 269

Ice crystal formation, in cell walls, 248
Imbibition, 6, 8, 38–39
Imbibition pressure, 39
Inclusions, within cell, 31
Indoleacetic acid, 115, 201, 203 (table), 206, 207, 213, 222
Indoleacetonitrile, 206
Indolebutyric acid, 213, 215
Inductive cycle, 240, 241
Infrared radiation, 233
Insects, leaf surface reduced by, 133
Intercellular space, 47, 133
Interfacial adsorption, 17
Interfacial tension, 18
Interionic effect, 66, 68
Internal vapor pressure, 52
Inulin, 162
  in cells of dandelion root, 182
Iodine, radioactive, 13
Iodine solution, 17
Ion(s), 14
  and mineral nutrition, 62, 63, 64, 65, 66, 67, 68, 70
  mobile, 70
  in nutrient solutions, 74
  translocation of, 63, 69, 70
Ionic accumulation, 63, 64, 65, 66, 67, 68
Ionic exchange, 65, 66
Ionizing radiation, growth affected by, 244–47

Iron, atomic weight of, 11 (table), 12
  as catalyst in chlorophyll synthesis, 122
  in cell wall, 36
  chelated, 74
  deficiency of, 76 (table), 77 (table)
  essential for plant growth, 71, 72 (table)
Isotopes, radioactive, 13, 62, 247

Kaolin group, of crystal lattice, 93, 94
Ketoglutaric acid, 150
Klebs, 236
Knop, 71, 73
Koepfli, J. B., 211
Kornberg, H. A., 247
Krebs cycle, 147, 148, 149, 150

Lamella, middle, 29, 32, 33, 34
Latex, 59, 172, 177–78
Lea, D. E., 247
Leaching, 79
Lead, atomic number of, 10, 11 (table)
Leaf, autumnal coloration of, 174
  chlorophyll content of, 121
  cucumber, growth pattern of, 194, 195
  as food storage organ, 181 (table), 183
  gases injurious to, 259
  green light absorbed by, 124
  minerals translocated from, 266
  mosaics, 270
  potato, see Potato, leaf of
  seed, of bean, 3
  "sleep movements" of, 271
  spot disease of, 133, 259
  sugar translocation from, 261
  symptoms of injury to, 259
  temperature of, 52
Legumes, and nitrogen cycle, 4, 78, 115
Leopold, A. C., 202, 222
Lepidium root, 251
Lespedeza, 58
Lettuce, root system of, 110
Leucoplasts, 28, 161
Light, absorbed by chlorophyll, 123–24
  artificial, and plant growth, 243–44
  blue, effects on growth, 231
  in chlorophyll synthesis, 122, 128
  far-red, effects on growth, 231, 233
  growth affected by, 228–44
  intensity of, critical, 129
  and photoperiod, 119, 120, 129
  in photosynthesis, 128–30, 135, 136, 137
  red, effects on growth, 231, 244
    and florigen synthesis, 239
  wave length of, 118, 119
Lignin, 32, 34–35, 172
Lipase, 146 (table), 164

Lipids, 163
Loblolly pine, 129, 130 (table)
Lodging of small grains, 1, 2, 3
Long-day plants, 119, 234, 235 (table),
 237, 238, 239, 241, 242
Loomis, W. E., 233, 236, 255, 262
 quoted, 171–72, 186
Lynch, R. S., 265
Lysine, 167, 225

Macronutrients, 71, 72 (table)
Macropore space, in soil, 87, 89
Magnesium, in chlorophyll synthesis, 122
 deficiency of, 76 (table), 77
 essential for plant growth, 71, 72
 (table)
 translocated from leaves, 266
Manganese, as catalyst in chlorophyll synthesis, 122
 deficiency of, 67, 76 (table), 77
 (table)
 essential for plant growth, 71, 72 (table)
Manometer, 138, *139*
Mass-flow mechanism, 69, 261
Membrane, differentially permeable, 39,
 41, 42
 nuclear, *25*, 30, 39
 plasma, *25*, 28, 39
 vacuolar, *25*, 28, 39, 66
Mercury, atomic weight of, 11 (table), 12
Meristem, 186–93, 196, 203
 intercalary, 193
 lateral, 187–90, 192
 terminal, 186–87, *188*, 190, 192
Meristematic cell, 62, 65, 101, 102, 103
Mesophyll cell, 47, *49*, 50, 52, 125, 133,
 134, 175
Metabolism, function of essential elements
 in, 72 (table), 73, 113
 ionic accumulation controlled by, 64,
 66, 68
 and respiration, 150
Methanol, chlorophyll extracted in, 120
Micelles, 19, 20, 33, 38
Microfibrils, 223
Micronutrients, *see* Trace elements
Micropores, of soil, 17, 87, 89
Middle lamella, *29*, 32, 33, 34
Milliequivalent, defined, 15
Mimosa pudica, 271
Mineral nutrition, 62–81
 and growth, 67, 79–80, 113, 115
 and ions, 62, 63, 64, 65, 66, 67, 68, 70
 mechanisms of, 64–66
 and roots, 64, 100, 113, 115
Mineralization, of soil, 97
Minerals, in cell wall, 32, 34, 36
 deficiency of, symptoms of, 75–77

Minerals (*Cont.*):
 food made from, by green plants, 100,
 117
 and growth, 67, 79–80, 113, 115, 256–
 57, 264
 in soil, 62, 84, 86, 91, 92, 93, 96, 97,
 113
 sources of, 78–79
 See also Elements
Mitochondria (chondriosomes), *25*, 30
Molal solution, 15
Molar solution, 15
Molecule(s), adhesion of, 16, 17
 and adsorption, 17
 aggregates of, in colloidal suspensions,
 19, 20
 in emulsions, 20, 21
 and Brownian movement, 22
 and capillarity, 17, 18
 chlorophyll, 120, 122
 cohesion of, 16, 17
 defined, 9–10
 in dynamic equilibrium, 18, 38
 ionization of, 245
 motion of, 16, 17, 22
 and osmosis, 6, 39, 40, 41, 42
 protein, 22, 23, 145, 169, 170, 171, 248
 size of, 16
 in solution, 14, 15
 and surface tension, 18
Molybdenum, 71, 72 (table)
Monocot, germination of, *4*
Montmorillonite group, of crystal lattice,
 93, *94*
Mosaics, leaf, 270
Mosses, chlorophyll contents of, 121
Movements, plant, 267–71
Mucilages, 58, 176, 177
Mustard seed, and respiratory intensity,
 156 (table)
Mutations, created by radioactive isotopes,
 13

Naphthaleneacetic acid, 215, 217
Nastic movement, 269
Nematodes, 115
Neutrons, 12, 13, 244, 245
Nickson, J. J., 247
Nicotinic acid, for root growth, 115, 207,
 213
Nitrates, 78
Nitrogen, in amino acid synthesis, 171
 in atmosphere, 167
 in chlorophyll synthesis, 122
 deficiency of, 75, 76 (table), 77
 essential for plant growth, 71, 72
 (table), 113, 242
 in legumes, 4, 78, 115

Nitrogen (*Cont.*):
  in protein synthesis, 167, 168
  in soil, 3, 4, 84, 92, 167
  translocated from leaves, 266
Nitrogen cycle, 78–79, 115
Normal solution, 15
Nuclear membrane, 25, 30
Nuclear proteins, 30
Nuclear sap, 25, 30
Nucleic acid, 31
Nucleolus, 25, 30–31
Nucleus of atom, 10, 12, 13
Nucleus of plant cell, 30–31
Nutation, 268–69
Nutrient solution, 73–75
Nutrition, mineral, *see* Mineral nutrition

Oak, red, 129, 130 (table)
Oat, coleoptiles of, auxin distribution in,
    203 (table)
  Avena tests on, 202
  growth affected by light, 231, 233
  effect of 2, 4-D on, 220, *221*
  fresh and dry weights, in relation to
    nitrate concentrations, *258*
Oils, 117, 163, 164, 165
  accumulation of, *182*
Orientation phenomena, 267*ff.*
Osmosis, 6, 7, 8, 39–40, 51, 54, 271
Osmotic pressure, 40, 41, 42, 43, 44, 45,
    57
Ovary, 7
Oxaloacetate, 148
Oxidation-reduction process, 165, 169
Oxygen, atomic weight of, 11 (table), 12
  in chlorophyll synthesis, 122
  as constituent of plant tissue, 71
  effect of, on absorption of radioactive
    potassium, 65
  essential for plant growth, 71, 72
    (table)
  and photosynthesis, 125, 133, 136, 137
  respiration affected by, 154, *156*
  in root growth, as limiting factor, 113,
    257, *259*
  and saturated soils, 114

Paper chromatography, 138, 140, *143*
Parenchyma cell, 48, 101, 104, 105, 106,
    107, 161, 192
Parker, M. W., 244
Parthenocarpic (seedless) fruit, 213, 214,
    215, *216*, 242
Pea, 3, 195, *197*, 271
Peanut, effect of aeration on, *112*
Pectic compounds, 29, 32, 33, 58
Pectin, 32, 33
Peptide bonds, 169

Perennials, growth of, 195
  in low temperatures, 248
Pericycle, *105*, 106, *107*
Periwinkle, leaf of, *47*
pF, of soil moisture, 88, 89 (table)
pH, anthocyanin color related to, 176
  and breaking of dormancy, 197–98
  and mineral absorption, 68
  in nutrient solutions, 74
  in soils, 95, 96, 114
  in starch digestion, 161
Philodendron, 129, 130 (table)
Phloem, 69, 70, 103, 105, 106, *107*, 187,
    189, 190, 260, 261
Phosphate bonds, high-energy, 148, 149,
    150
Phosphoglyceric acid, 137, 149
Phosphorus, 168
  deficiency of, 75, 76 (table), 77
  essential for plant growth, 71, 72
    (table), 113
  in protein synthesis, 167, 168, 169, 171
  in soil, 84, 96, 167
  translocated from leaves, 266
Phosphorylase, 146, 160
Photodecomposition, of water, 135, 136
Photoinduction, 233, 236, 237, *240*, 241
Photomorphogenic effect, 231
Photons, 118, 119, 129
Photoperiod, 119, 120, 129, 199, 236, 242,
    256
Photoperiodic effect, 231, 234, 236, 240,
    241, 242, 244
Photosynthate, defined, 229
Photosynthesis, 7, 8, 48, 49, 114, 117, 120,
    121, 125
  and carbon dioxide concentration, 128,
    129, 130–32
  in chloroplasts, 134
  dark reaction in, 135, 136, *137*
  efficiency of, 126–28
  enzymes in, 129, 134–35, 136
  equation for, 136
  light intensity in, 129, 130 (table)
  light reaction in, 135, 136, *137*
  magnitude of, 126
  measurement of, 138–42
  mechanism of, 135–38
  and oxygen, 125
  rate of, 130 (table)
    factors in, 128, 131, 132, 133, 134
    in potato leaves, 132, *155*
    reduced, 58, 59, 133
  respiration related to, *155*, 157
  starch synthesis different from, 162
  and temperature, 132–33
Photosynthesis in Plants, 137
Phototropism, 206, 269

Phyllocaline, 207
Phytohormones, 200
Phytotoxins, 259
Pigments, 173–76
Pine, Florida, 127
  loblolly, 129, 130 (table)
Pineapple, growth correlations of, 262
Pistil, 7
Plasma membrane, 25, 28, 39
Plasmodesms, 25, 28, 29, 69, 260
Plasmolysis, 39–40, 43, 49, 248, 271
Plastids, 28–30, 161, 163
Plumule (epicotyl tip), 6, 7
Poinsettia, 239, 240
Poisons, as assimilation products, 180
Polarization, in cytoplasm, 27
Pollen, 7
Pollen tube, 7
Pollination, 7, 242
Potassium, in cambial growth, 257, 258
  deficiency of, 75, 76 (table), 77
  essential for plant growth, 71, 72
    (table), 113
  radioactive, 65
  in soil, 91
  translocated from leaves, 266
Potassium sulfate, radioactive, 66
Potato, food accumulated by, 182, 183
  leaf of, and rate of photosynthesis, 132,
    155
  and rate of respiration, 155
  size affected by rate of respiration, 158
Precipitation reaction, between elec-
    trolytes, 23
Proplastids, 28
Proteins, 117
  accumulation of, 181 (table), 182, 183
  digestion of (hydrolysis), 170, 171, 266
  emulsions of, 20
  nuclear, 30
  synthesis of, 7, 8, 167, 169, 170, 171
Protons, 12, 13, 244
Protopectin, 32, 33
Protoplasm, 13, 14, 17, 100
  coagulation of, 23
  as colloidal system, 23
  fats and oils in, 164
  gels in, 20
  hardening of, 248, 249
  hereditary structures of, 170
  of nucleus, 30
  physicochemical nature of, 24–26
  protein content of, 23
  sols in, 20
  Tyndall phenomenon in study of, 22
Protoplast, 25, 26–31
Purple three-awn grass, root system of,
    109, 110

Pyridoxine, for root growth, 115, 207
Pyruvate, and respiration, 148
Pyruvic acid, 146, 147, 150

Q-enzymes, 160
Quiescence, 196, 198

Radiant energy, 118–19
Radiation, ionizing, growth affected by,
    244–47
Radical, defined, 14
Radicle, 7, 198
Radioactive isotopes, 13, 62, 247
Radioactive tracer studies, 62, 63, 64, 65,
    66, 69, 75, 136, 137
Ranunculus, 104–6
Red oak, 129, 130 (table)
Refrigeration, of fruits and vegetables,
    156–57
Regions of root tip, 101–4
Regulators, of growth, 200–222
Resins, 172, 176, 177, 180
Respiration, 6, 7, 8, 144, 227
  aerobic, 146, 147, 148, 151, 154
  anaerobic, 146, 147, 154
  enzymes in, 144, 145, 146, 147, 148,
    149
  ionic accumulation related to, 65
  measurement of, 150–51
  mechanism of, 145–50
  photosyntheses related to, 155, 157
  rate of, and changes in concentration
    of carbohydrates, 152
    factors affecting, 150–56
    at night, 157–58
    and oxygen concentration, 156
    of plant organs, 152 (table)
    of plant species, 151 (table)
    potato affected by, 155, 158
    and temperature, 153, 155, 157, 158
    and time effect, 153, 154
  research on, applied to agricultural
    problems, 156–58
Respiratory quotient, 151
Retting process, 32
Rhizobium, 78
Rhizocaline, 207
Rice, proteins in, 170
Ripe-to-flower stage, of growth, 236
Root cap, 101, 102
Root hairs, 101, 103, 104, 106, 115, 116
    (table)
Root pressure, 46
Root rot, 115
Root tip, 101–4, 113
Roots (root systems), absorption cells of,
    47, 63
  aromatic substances obtained from, 101

Roots (*Cont.*):
  characteristics of, 106–12
  cotton, 257, 259
  dicot, older, 106
    young, 104–6
  dry weight yield of, 112 (table)
  dyes obtained from, 101
  economic importance of, 100–101
  erosion prevented by, 101
  fibrous, 108
  five major capacities of, 100
  food accumulated by, *182*, 183
  food for, translocation of, 114–15
  as food storage organs, 181 (table),
    183
  growth of, 60, 100, 201
    correlated with shoot growth, 264
    factors affecting, 112–15, 257, *259*
  lateral, 98, 99, 106, 109
  length of, 110 (table), 113
  medicinal value of, 101
  and mineral nutrition, 64, 100, 113,
    115
  organisms destructive to, 115
  pharmaceutical use of, 101
  positive geotropism in, 270
  primary, 7, 99, 106
  secondary, 7, 99, *101*, 106
  semi-fibrous, 107–8, *109*, *110*
  as soil-binders, 101
  tap, 106–7, *108*
  tertiary, 7
  water movement into, 45*ff*.
  See also Soil(s)
Round worms, 115
Rubber, 178

Sachs, 71
Salt, table (NaCl), in solution, 14, 15
Sambucus canadensis, stem of, *191*
Sandy soil, 84, 85, 88, *90*, 96
Sap, nuclear, 25, 30
Saturated solution, 15
Seed coats, 6, 36
Seed leaves, of bean, 3
Seedless (parthenocarpic) fruit, 213, 214,
  215, *216*, 242
Seedlings, bean, *see* Bean, seedling of
  chlorophyll synthesis in, 7, 8
  corn, *4*
  growth of, 266
  shoot of, 7
Seeds, corn, *4*
  dormancy in, 196–97
  embryos in, 6, 7
  fat produced in, 165
  as food storage organs, 181 (table)
  and imbibition, 6, 8, 38–39

Seeds (*Cont.*):
  moisture removed from, 157
  storage of, 157, 158 (table), 198
"Shade plants," 129
Shive, 73
Shoot, 7, 60, 114–15, 264
Short-day plants, 119, 234, 235 (table),
  237, 238, 239, 240, 241, 242
Sieve tubes, 260
Silica, in cell wall, 36
  in soil, 91
Silt, in soil, 84, 85, 86, *90*, 96
Silver, atomic weight of, 11 (table), 12
Silver leaf, 259
Siminovitch, D., 248
Skoog, Folke, 209, 225
Slade, 217
"Sleep movements," 271
Smith et al, 190
Smog, 259
Sodium, in soil, 113
Sodium chloride (NaCl), in solution, 14,
  15
Soil(s), aeration of, 112, 113, 115
  arid, 91, 93 (table)
  clay, 23, 84, 85, 88, *90*, 93, 95, 96
  crumb structure of, 84, 86, 88
  crystal lattice structure in, 93, *94*
  defined, 82
  erosion of, 79
    prevented by roots, 101
  horizons of, 82, 83 (table), 84, 109
  humid, 91, 93 (table)
  micropores of, 17, 87, 89
  mineralization of, 97
  minerals in, 62, 84, 86, 91, 92, 93, 96,
    97, 113
  nitrogen content of, 3, 4, 84, 92, 167
  organic matter in, 84, 85, 86, 88, 89,
    91, 96, 97
  origin of, 82
  parent materials of, 82, 83 (table), 91,
    96
  pH of, 95, 96, 114
  properties of, 84–97
  sandy, 84, 85, 88, *90*, 96
  silt in, 84, 85, 86, *90*, 96
  temperatures of, 114
  texture of, 84, 88, 113
  See also Roots (root systems)
Soil aggregation, 86
Soil moisture, 113
  equilibrium points of, 86
  retention points of, 88 (table)
  and tensions, 88 (table)
  transpiration affected by, 51, 53, 59
Soil profile, 82
Soil solution, 15, 42, 44, 84

Solar radiation, and efficiency of photo-synthesis, 127
  transpiration affected by, 51
Solation, 19, 27
Sols, 19, 20, 21, 22, 23, 27
Solutions, 14–16
  concentration of, 15–16
  Hoagland's, 73, 74
  nutrients, 73–75
  osmotic pressure of, 41, 42
  types of, 16
Soybean, 170, 231, 240
Spectrum, of radiant energy, 118, 119, 124, 231, 233, 244, 245 (table)
Split pea test, auxin, 202, 204–5
Squash, growth of, 195, 196
Starch, accumulation of, 161, 182
  commercial products made from, 162
  digestion of, 160, 161, 162, 163
  in guard cells, 55
  synthesis of, 7, 8, 160, 161, 162, 163
  See also Carbohydrates
Stele, 104, 105
Stems, elongation of, affected by light, 229, 231, 233
  controlled by diurnal thermoperiod-icity, 253–54
  as food storage organs, 181 (table), 183
  negative geotropism in, 270
Stigma, 7
Stomates, 47, 50, 51, 52, 55, 56, 133
  carbon dioxide passage through, 134
  closure of, and photosynthesis, 133
  number of, in common leaves, 54 (table)
  transpiration through, 53
Stratification, 198
Style, 7
Suberin, 32, 34, 35, 163, 172, 192
Substomatal cavities, of leaves, 49, 50
Sugar, made by green plants, 117, 126, 129, 144
  and respiration, 149, 157
  starch synthesized from, 161
  translocation of, 261
  See also Carbohydrates; Glucose
Sulfur, 168
  in amino acid synthesis, 171
  deficiency of, 76 (table)
  in essential oils, 178
  for plant growth, 71, 72 (table)
  in protein synthesis, 167, 168
  in soil, 84, 167
  translocated from leaves, 266
Sulfur dioxide, leaf injury caused by, 259
Sun, as source of radiant energy, 118
"Sun plants," 129

Sunflower, stem of, 193
Surface tension, 18

Tannins, 32, 34, 36, 177
Tap root, 106–7, 108
Temperature, and afterripening, 198, 199
  bioprocesses of cells affected by, 247–50
  and bulbous plans, 252
  in chlorophyll synthesis, 122, 133
  flowering controlled by, 252, 256
  and growth, 247–59
  low, celery seedstalks exposed to, 253 (table)
    and hardening, 248, 249
  night, for early vegetative growth, 253, 255
    and flowering, 240
  in photosynthesis, 132–33
  respiration affected by, 153, 155, 157, 158
  of soil, and root growth, 114
  in starch digestion, 161
  van't Hoff's law related to, 249–50
Terpenes, 178
Thermoperiodism, 253, 254
Thiamin, 115, 207
Thigmotropic movement, 270
Thimann, K. V., 201, 211, 222, 224
Thompson, 252
Thut, H. F., 233
Tippo, Oswald, 100
Tobacco, mineral deficiencies in, 77
  as short-day plant, 119
Tomato, and aeration, 112
  as day-neutral plant, 120
  epinastic response of, 218
  growth correlations of, 264 (table)
  and light intensity, 229, 230
  parthenocarpic, 216
  root growth of, 264 (table)
    B-vitamins for, 207, 208
  stem elongation of, 229
  thermoperiodic responses of, 253–54
  translocation of sugar from leaves of, 261
  X-irradiation of, 247
Toremia, 271
Trace elements (micronutrients), 71, 72 (table)
  deficiencies of, 76 (table), 77 (table)
  toxic in high concentrations, 113
Tracheids, 105
Translocation, 6, 7, 8, 49, 60, 63, 69, 70, 217
  of florigen in cocklebur, 236, 237, 238
  of food for roots, 114–15

Translocation (*Cont.*):
  of phloem, 260, 261
  of sugar, 261
Transpiration, 7, 8, 46, 47, 48, 49, 50, 51, 63
  cuticular, 53, 56
  factors affecting, 51–54
  and soil moisture, 51, 53, 59
  and solar radiation, 51
  stomatal, 53, 56
  and wind velocity, 51, 52–53
Transpiration pull, 48, 51, 63
Transpiration stream, 69
Traumatic acid, 209, 213
Trees, growth patterns of, 195, *197*
  and hardening, 249
  lateral root development of, *98*, 109
Tropism, 269–70
Tryptophane, 167
Turgor, 6, 31, 267, 268, 271
Turgor movement, 270, 271
Turgor pressure, 39, 40, 42, 43, 44, 54, 55, 261, 270
Tyndall phenomenon, 21–22

Ultramicroscope, 22
Ultraviolet radiation, 119, 233, 245 (table)
Uranium, atomic weight of, 11 (table), 12

Vacuolar membrane, 25, 28, 39, 66
Vacuoles, 6, 25, 30, 31, 69
  and diffusion pressure deficit, 42, 50
  ionic accumulation in, 63, 64, 65, 66
Van Helmont, 229
van Niel, 138
van't Hoff's law, 249, 250
Vapor pressure, internal, 52
Vapor pressure gradient, 50, 52, 56
Vegetable crops, and hardening, 249
Vernalization, 254, 255
Vitamin A, 175
Vitamins, for root growth, 207, *208*, 213
  translocation of, 115
Volume molar solution, 15
Volume percentage solution, 15

Wall pressure, 43
Water, absorption of, 45*ff*., 56, 57, 62–63
  in chlorophyll synthesis, 122–23

Water (*Cont.*):
  in cytoplasm, 27
  deficits of, effects of, 58–60, 196, 233, 256, 263
  diffusion of, 37*ff*.
  and imbibition, 6, 38–39
  and osmosis, 6, 7, 39–40, 51, 271
  photodecomposition of, 135, 136
  in photosynthesis, rate of, 133
  relations to plants, 37–61
  and transpiration, 7, 48, 49, 51, 62
Water table, 89, 90, 91, 92, 93, 99
Weeds, control of, 217, 219
Weight molar solution, 15
Went, F. W., 201, 211, 229, 252, 254
Western wheat grass, root system of, 109, *110*
Wheat, flowering of, and dark period, *239*
  food accumulated by, *182*
  gliadin of, 167
  minerals translocated from leaves of, 266
  proteins in, 170
  toxic reactions to 2, 4-D, 219, *220*
Williams, R. F., 266
Wilting, 49, 56, 86, 87, 88, 89, 90 (table), 133
Wind velocity, transpiration affected by, 51, 52–53
Wood cells, walls of, *29*, 32, 34
Wound growth regulator, 209

Xanthophyll, 120, 121 (table)
Xylem, 17, 43, 46, 47, 48, 50, 51, 63, 103, 189
  phloem separated from, 69
  primary, 104, 105, 106, *107*
  secondary, 106, *107*, 187
X-rays, 244, 247

Yeast, respiratory reaction in, 146
Yield, defined, 185

Zein, 167
Zinc, as catalyst in chlorophyll synthesis, 122
  deficiency of, 76 (table)
  essential for plant growth, 71, 72 (table)
Zygote, 7